Prod No.	P99951
Date	11.09.19
Supplier	Artron

T.P.S	270 x 210mm (portrait)
Extent	224pp total in 4/4 (cmyk)
	157gsm NPI matt art paper throughout
Bellyband	1c (K) on 130gsm Yulong P. (back/vertical, sealed with round st.)
PLC	4/0 (cmyk) on 128gsm Chinese OJI gloss art paper
	with matt lamination 1 side only
Label	1c (K) on 130gsm Yulong pure + die-cut with rounded corners
Binding	Quaterbound, first and second lined, square backed with stiff spine inlay, cased-in with 2mm greyboards. PLC quarterbound using black JHT real cloth, blocked on spine using white matt foil. Debossed panel on front with printed label stuck in position.
Ends	1/1 (solid black) + sealer varnish on 140gsm offset + sealer 2s
HT bands	plain black.

Lesage
Brodeur

Lesage
Brodeur

Patrick Mauriès

Thames & Hudson

La broderie est à la robe ce que la femme, selon Madame Necker, est à l'art de la conversation : « comme ces duvets qu'on introduit dans les caisses de porcelaines : on compte ces duvets pour rien et tout se briserait sans eux. » Elle est l'ornement qui vient donner corps à la ligne ; elle est la lumière, l'éclat – si vifs qu'on les voit sans les voir ; elle est de l'ordre de la trace, du sillage, de la persistance visuelle, tout en étant méticuleusement, minutieusement pensée, pesée, dessinée, exécutée.

La mode est depuis la fin du xixe siècle, et Charles Frederick Worth, affaire de noms. Connaît-on pour autant un seul nom de brodeur? Ils ne comptent qu'au rang des (petites) mains anonymes sans lesquelles la robe ne serait pourtant pas, mais qui restent seuls à le savoir. Ils ont longtemps été considérés comme de simples «fournisseurs» auxquels était réservée une entrée secondaire et discrète; qualificatif que François Lesage retourna ironiquement, le transformant en un titre de gloire, lui qui fut le premier à affirmer avec force, dans la seconde moitié du xxe siècle, la présence, l'identité, le nom, la «griffe» du brodeur comme tel. Non que certains n'aient eu avant lui conscience aiguë de la valeur, de la puissance créatrice de ce qui est autant un art qu'une technique: il revient à Charles-Germain de Saint-Aubin, aîné d'une fratrie d'artistes virtuoses de l'ornement minuscule, d'avoir publié dès 1770 un célèbre *L'Art du brodeur* qui formule, illustre, codifie les différents aspects d'un métier immémorial, et exalte la conscience de sa valeur, comme le faisaient certains traités de l'art de peindre dès le xvie siècle.

La volonté d'être moins un interprète qu'un *interlocuteur* des différents créateurs avec lesquels il fut amené à travailler, l'intelligence des situations, la présentation de collections d'accessoires brodés en nom propre ont fini par assurer à François Lesage, deux siècles après la parution du traité de Saint-Aubin, une place à part entière au sein du Comité Colbert, qui rassemble les plus grands noms du luxe français. Il parachevait une trajectoire entamée par ses parents, Albert et Marie-Louise, et prolongée par son fils, Jean-François, qui transforme la destinée de cette maison, à travers ses multiples collaborations – de Vionnet à Schiaparelli, de Balenciaga à Saint Laurent, Christian Lacroix et Chanel –, en une histoire parallèle, une histoire en filigrane de la mode depuis la fin du xixe siècle.

Thiers, au tome 13 de son *Histoire du Consulat et de l'Empire*, fait remonter à l'hiver 1802, précisément, la renaissance du luxe en France. L'un des effets singuliers, dramatiques de la Révolution française, et de ses bouleversements, avait été la dissolution des ligues et corporations d'artisans, le hiatus dans le passage des générations, l'affaiblissement des savoir-faire. La volonté napoléonienne de renouer avec la pompe du pouvoir, les quatre millions consacrés aux cérémonies du sacre, les commandes de soieries aux manufactures lyonnaises, celles de linon (destinées à Joséphine) à Saint-Quentin, le goût des velours et des lamés opulents, les broderies rehaussant les tenues protocolaires, profitèrent, écrit Henri Baudrillart dans sa classique *Histoire du luxe*, de « tout l'élan que donne un régime monarchique qui fait de l'éclat pour ainsi dire son système ».

Les trois expositions des produits de l'industrie qui se succédèrent pour relancer l'économie et la production entre 1801 et 1806 (après celle, inaugurale, de 1798) frappèrent vivement, poursuit Baudrillart, les contemporains : « les brocarts d'or et d'argent, les satins et les velours, la broderie et la passementerie, les dentelles et les blondes étalaient partout leurs richesses. » Après une période de bouleversements et de destructions sans fin, on aspirait à nouveau au calme et à la volupté du luxe.

Divers facteurs, d'ordre sociologique, économique et technique, contribuèrent à un épanouissement progressif des dépenses somptuaires, scandé aux yeux de l'historien en trois temps : une première vague, de 1815 à 1830, de démocratisation du luxe, répondant au développement des classes moyennes et aux premières formes de reproduction mécanique (par le plaqué d'acajou, le carton pierre) qui se traduisirent par une baisse des prix. Une deuxième, entre 1830 et 1848, marquée par l'affirmation de l'imaginaire romantique, mais aussi par celle d'un éclectisme bourgeois, passant de l'imitation de l'Antiquité à celle du Moyen Âge, puis du Grand Siècle au xviiie Pompadour, « sorte de juxtaposition, poursuit Baudrillart, de toutes les époques, en dehors de toute relation avec les besoins de notre siècle ». Une troisième enfin, entre 1848 et 1872, d'expansion continue, portée par « la prospérité matérielle, la rapidité extrême des fortunes, le tourbillon qui emporte le capital vers le plaisir », culminant dans l'opulence exaltée du Second Empire, et répandue dans tous les secteurs de la société (« j'ose dire, ponctue curieusement Baudrillart, en évoquant Balzac, Chateaubriand, Dumas et Lamartine, qu'à aucune époque l'idée du luxe n'a tenu tant de place dans les œuvres et dans la vie des écrivains célèbres »).

À décorum et besoins nouveaux, fournisseurs et artisans d'exception : tandis que la cristallerie de Baccarat se réinvente en 1816, surgissent l'un après l'autre les noms les plus fameux du luxe français : Christofle en 1830, Hermès en 1837, Vuitton en 1854. S'imposent incidemment les prémisses de ce qui deviendra l'expression la plus nouvelle, et sans doute de plus longue portée, de cette culture du superflu ruineux : la haute couture, avec l'ouverture des salons de Charles Frederick Worth en 1858. Jacques

Doucet prendra les rênes du magasin familial, 21 rue de la Paix, en 1875 ; Redfern s'établit à Paris en 1881 ; Paquin, au 3 rue de la Paix, dix ans plus tard ; et les sœurs Callot, en 1895, au 24 rue Taitbout. Un périmètre s'ouvre, qui ne changera plus, jusqu'à s'intégrer dans la définition même du luxe parisien.

On peut faire de Worth le battement d'aile du papillon dont sortira Lesage. C'est que le premier des « grands couturiers » est moins un maître de la ligne – qu'il ne cherche pas à redessiner, se contentant plutôt de l'accentuer, de la souligner, partageant le corps en deux lobes autour d'une taille étranglée – qu'un virtuose de l'opulence, de l'*enrichissement* des matériaux et des textures. Il offre en cela l'expression parfaite de l'esprit de l'époque : de ce Paris du XIXe siècle dont Walter Benjamin a souligné le goût pour la superposition, la combinaison, la multiplication d'éléments et pour l'enchâssement, le gainage, le capiton, les jeux de jours et de découpes : tout un lexique conjoint au mobilier et au vêtement, dont la passementerie serait le lieu commun. Tropisme que décrit aussi Baudrillart, en le chargeant de curieuses connotations morales (« dans le groupe des fils et des tissus, que d'ornements, de dentelles, de broderies, de boutons, de franges, de nouveautés, dont je ne médis pas, mais dont l'excès ne contribue à développer ni l'épargne chez les pauvres, ni la vertu chez les riches… »).

Chenilles, pompons, soutaches, passements de soie, incrustations de velours, perles de jais, bulles de verre, fleurs enchiffonnées : à cette infinie variété d'invention, qui transforme chaque robe, de jour comme du soir, en un lourd reliquaire, s'ajoute naturellement l'usage traditionnel de la dentelle et de la broderie. « Sous l'impulsion de Worth, rapporte Palmer White dans son livre sur Lesage dont ces lignes sont tributaires, la broderie connut un tel essor que plus de quarante ateliers se développèrent presque du jour au lendemain. »

Parmi ces ateliers, celui d'un jeune brodeur, Albert Michonet, devait se distinguer par son excellence, et fournir non seulement Worth, mais la plupart des grandes maisons de ce que l'on appellerait désormais la Couture jusque dans les années 1920. C'est à ce moment, on le verra, que de la chrysalide Michonet allait surgir le papillon Lesage.

page ci-contre Michonet, fin du XIXe siècle
double page suivante Michonet, 1904

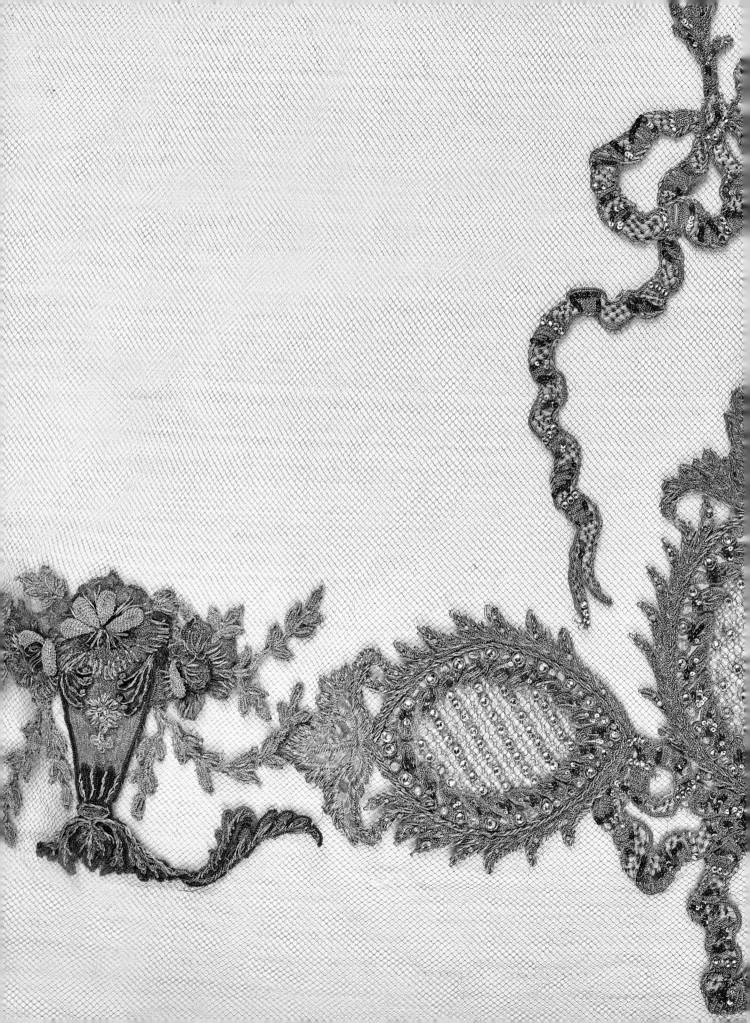

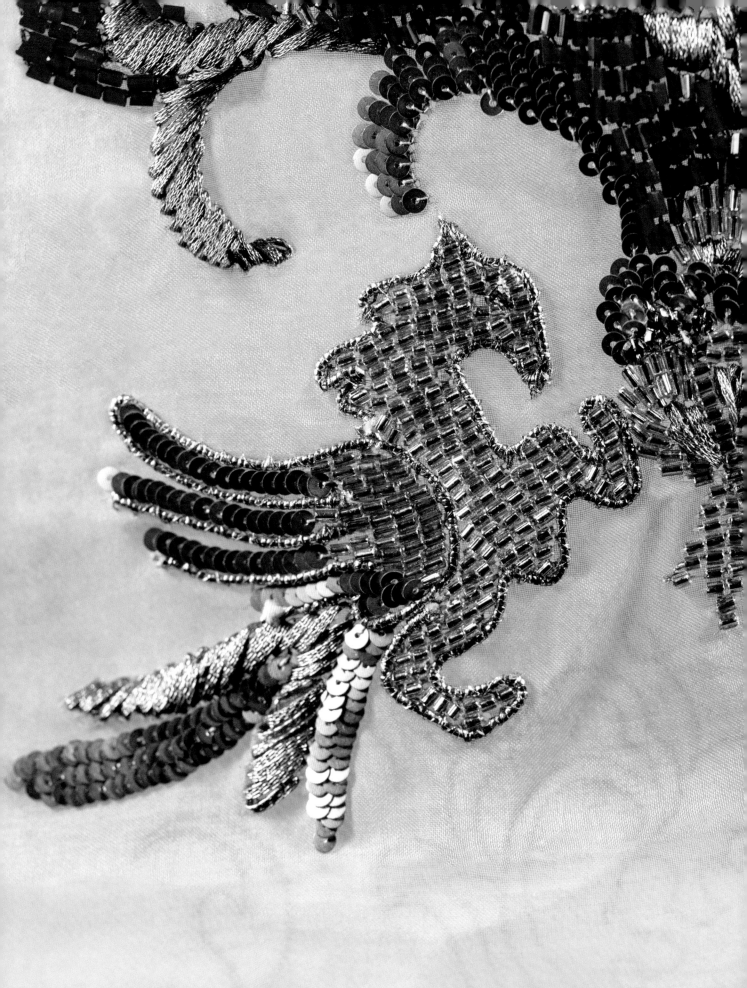

Originaires de Normandie, installés en Lorraine après la Révolution, les Lesage furent chassés de leurs terres par l'annexion allemande de 1871. Fuyant la région pour la capitale, Adèle et Gustave Lesage – les grands-parents de François – s'établirent rue Fontaine, non loin de la place Pigalle, dans un quartier populaire alors en pleine modernisation (l'arrivée du gaz de ville dans ces années-là transforma singulièrement l'arrondissement, entraînant le percement de nouvelles rues). Archiviste chez Hachette, d'une nature tranquille et réservée, Gustave se distinguait par une passion particulière, celle du dessin, qui l'amenait tous les dimanches au parc de Saint-Cloud pour y croquer sur le vif. Ce sera l'un de ses points communs avec son fils, Albert. Adèle se contentait pour sa part du rôle classique de femme au foyer.

ci-dessus Albert Lesage, Chicago, 1920
page 22 Michonet, 1921

Albert Lesage naquit en 1888. Plutôt bon élève, il mena à bien ses études (où il démontra un certain don des langues), accomplit son service militaire (qui durait alors trois ans), avant de devoir, à vingt-deux ans, trouver un emploi. Il le fit dans ce que l'on appelait une société de commissionnaires en commerce extérieur, c'est-à-dire de courtiers chargés de transmettre, de négocier et d'exécuter des ordres d'achat ou de vente pour le compte de tiers, souvent étrangers. C'était en particulier le cas des grands magasins et firmes de couture américains, qui ne suivaient pas encore le rite des expéditions bi-annuelles vers les défilés parisiens, et s'en remettaient aux commissionnaires pour faire le lien avec les fournisseurs et les maisons de mode. Tel fut le biais par lequel Albert Lesage accéda à un monde qui devait être le sien jusqu'à sa mort en 1949.

Cette trajectoire sans encombres fut brusquement interrompue, quatre ans plus tard, par la déclaration de guerre d'août 1914. Blessé au début des opérations, lors de l'offensive allemande de la Meuse, Albert fut fait prisonnier et envoyé au camp de Merseburg, au sud de la Saxe-Anhalt, où il resta plus de quatre ans parmi quelque dix mille prisonniers français. Il laissa de ces longues années de captivité de nombreux témoignages graphiques – dessins, aquarelles, caricatures – qui offrent une chronique détaillée de son quotidien – en même temps que d'innombrables variations autour d'une figure féminine imaginaire, mélange d'idéal et de mannequin de mode.

À son retour en France, début 1919, Albert Lesage reprit son ancien emploi, dont il éprouvait à présent les limites. Le hasard allait cependant le servir, sous la forme d'une amie de la famille, Simone Bouvet de Lozier, qui s'était fait un nom de modiste sur la Cinquième Avenue, et avait pour intermédiaire la société de courtage dans laquelle travaillait Albert. Impressionnée par les dessins du jeune homme, et consciente de son insatisfaction, elle se proposa de l'aider en présentant ses croquis au directeur d'un magasin de luxe de Chicago, Marshall Field and Co, autre client de la firme de commissionnaires. Quelques semaines plus tard, Lesage recevait une proposition d'embauche comme responsable et modéliste du département féminin du magasin.

Six mois à peine après son retour de la guerre – il avait trente-et-un ans –, Albert s'embarqua pour l'Amérique, ouvrant un nouveau chapitre de son existence. Si l'on en croit Palmer White (sans doute inspiré par François Lesage), le voyage fut incidemment prétexte à un nouveau jeu du hasard, qu'il ne découvrirait que quinze ans plus tard, au détour d'une conversation. Dans les étages et les classes supérieures du navire qu'avait emprunté Albert, voyageait un couple d'aristocrates, le comte William Wendt de Kerlor et sa jeune épouse, une Romaine de bonne famille, tombée sous le charme de ce qu'il est convenu d'appeler le regard magnétique de son exotique compagnon. Elle devait, des années plus tard, et après avoir repris son nom de jeune fille, jouer un rôle de premier plan dans l'histoire de la mode, et dans la destinée d'Albert Lesage.

Le séjour aux États-Unis laissa une trace profonde dans l'esprit, et l'approche, des deux futurs protagonistes. Ils se trouvèrent confrontés à une économie, une culture, une dynamique, des instruments de diffusion de la mode totalement différents de ceux qu'ils connaissaient, et ils surent ensuite mettre à profit cette expérience nouvelle. Albert devait pour sa part répondre aux attentes de clientes appartenant aussi bien à la moyenne bourgeoisie de Chicago qu'à une bonne société constituée pour une bonne part de fortunes nouvelles, issues du commerce et de l'industrie. Il s'agissait de leur fournir une formule approchée, adaptée de l'élégance parisienne. Le succès de cet entre-deux fut relatif; l'original vaut toujours mieux que la copie, fût-elle intelligente. «Quand il eut fêté ses trente-quatre ans, résume Palmer White, Albert avait amélioré son anglais, appris nombre de choses sur les méthodes de gestion à l'américaine et économisé un joli pactole. Il était temps, lui sembla-t-il, de s'en aller chercher le bonheur, la vie – ailleurs.»

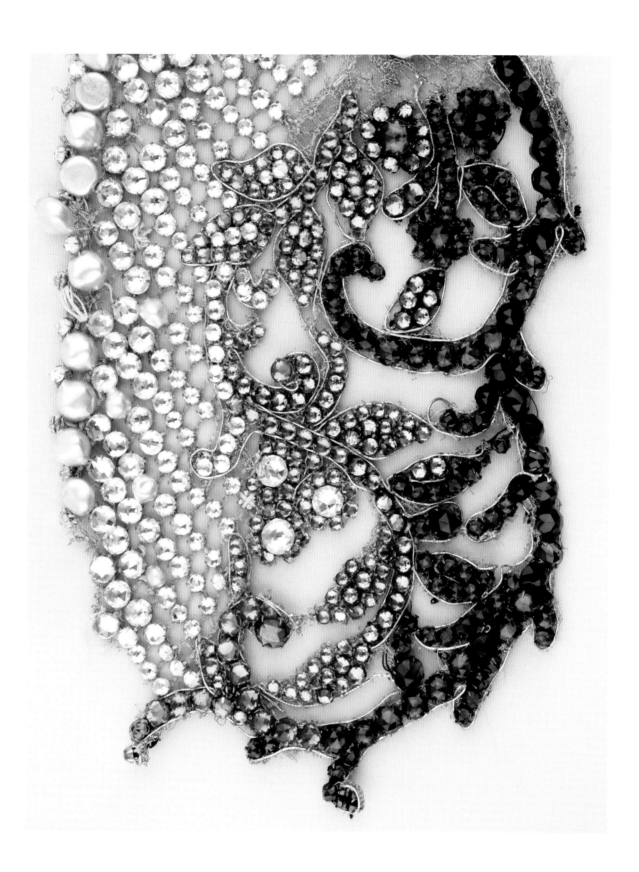

L____e Paris qu'il retrouve à son retour, en 1922, a profondément changé. La valeur d'exemple de la mode parisienne s'est affirmée, et les donneurs d'ordre américains commencent à se déplacer ou envoyer leurs acheteurs pour suivre au plus près le fil des collections, chargeant ensuite les commissionnaires de l'achat des prototypes ; se met ainsi en place le dispositif qui perdurera jusqu'à présent.

Le climat intellectuel et artistique est aussi marqué par une série de bouleversements et de ruptures : le brûlot Dada a été lancé en 1916 ; le scandale de *Parade* éclate un an plus tard ; l'orientalisme du début des Ballets Russes le cède à la provocation d'avant-garde ; Breton publie le *Manifeste du surréalisme* en 1924 ; et l'Exposition des Arts décoratifs catalyse, un an plus tard, une nouvelle sensibilité dans le domaine des arts appliqués. La quinzaine d'années précédant la Seconde Guerre mondiale sera d'une exceptionnelle richesse créative, voyant se succéder mouvements et contre-mouvements ; et ces courants, loin de se réduire à de simples théories, allaient avoir une incidence directe sur le trajet d'Albert Lesage.

Tissée de l'étoffe même du changement, la Couture a vu l'étoile de Worth pâlir face à celle de Poiret, avant que l'aura de ce dernier ne s'efface à son tour devant la litote moderniste de Chanel et Patou; la ligne s'est épurée, les matières fluidifiées, l'ornement redessiné. Des dizaines de brodeurs de la Belle Époque ne subsistent plus, écrit Palmer White, que vingt-deux ateliers, dont celui, toujours florissant, d'Albert Michonet, qui a su s'adapter et répondre aux besoins de nouvelles maisons. Seul à la tête de sa firme, et désormais âgé, il souhaiterait s'en retirer sans pour autant voir disparaître le résultat de tant d'efforts et d'inventivité. Méthodique, il a constitué une archive d'échantillons et de dessins qui constitue en soi un capital; à quoi s'ajoute la solidité financière et commerciale. Sa clientèle comprend aussi bien Paquin, Doucet, Redfern, que des figures de l'aristocratie et de la royauté. L'extrême virtuosité de ses motifs s'adapte aussi bien à la passementerie qu'au costume de théâtre dont il sait maîtriser la richesse et la nécessité de l'effet.

Conscient de l'enjeu, et fort du capital amassé lors de son passage aux États-Unis, Albert Lesage prend rendez-vous avec Michonet, dont les ateliers se trouvent alors rue Feydeau, derrière la Bibliothèque Nationale, et noue avec lui à l'automne 1922 un accord provisoire. Ils entameront leur collaboration par une période d'essai de six mois, avant de véritablement s'associer, puis de procéder à la vente dans un délai de dix-huit mois. Le contexte économique, dont les conséquences seront funestes à long terme, favorise la démarche d'Albert : la spéculation qui se déchaîne contre le franc début 1924, et qu'enflammera l'arrivée, en mai, du Cartel des Gauches, valorise de près de trois cents pour cent sa fortune en dollars au moment même où est fixée la réalisation de la vente. Qui plus est, la période d'essai se révèle concluante. Mais c'est l'une des conséquences annexes, et imprévue, de l'opération qui jouera un rôle plus décisif encore dans l'avènement de la maison Lesage. Une lointaine descendante de la famille Spencer – appelée à une autre actualité plus tard dans le siècle – et l'une des plus grandes couturières de l'histoire de la mode en sont les protagonistes inconscientes.

page ci-contre   Michonet, début du xxᵉ siècle
page 32   Michonet, fin du xixᵉ siècle

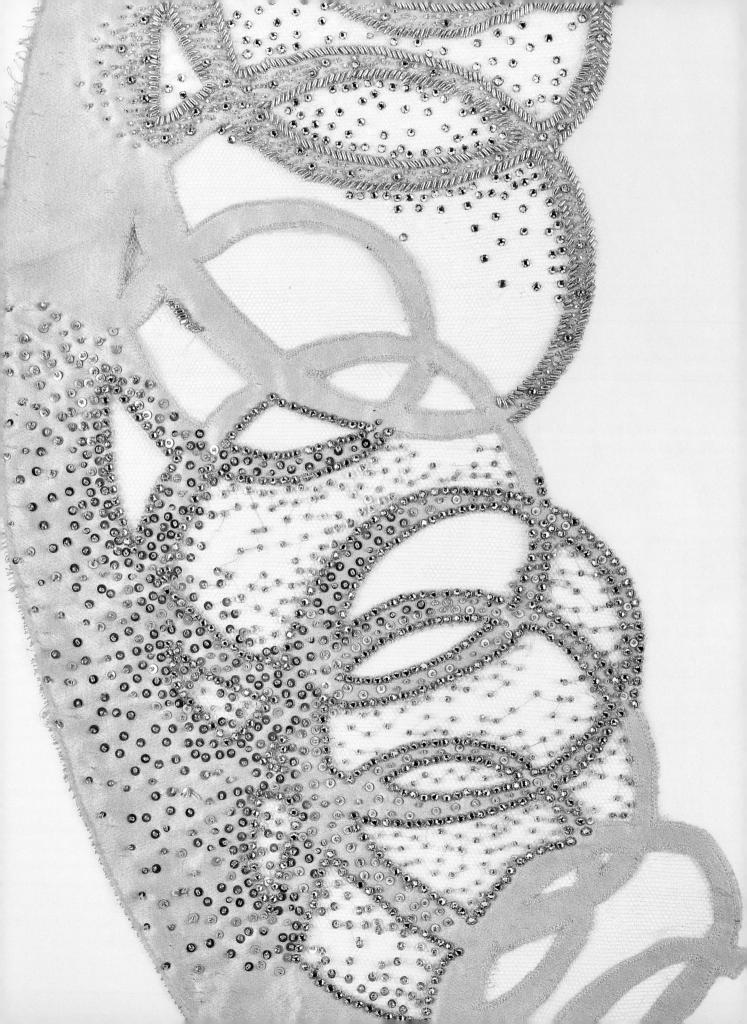

Comme plus tard Cristóbal Balenciaga et Azzedine Alaïa, Madeleine Vionnet est l'une des rares figures de l'histoire de la mode (c'est l'un de ses paradoxes) à avoir su couper, surfiler, coudre et monter un vêtement. Née en 1876 dans le Loiret, avant de suivre sa famille à Aubervilliers, dans la banlieue de Paris, elle commence son apprentissage à treize ans dans un modeste atelier de couture. Une fois acquis les rudiments du métier, elle entre comme apprentie chez le couturier Vincent, rue de la Paix à Paris, en 1890. D'une rare indépendance d'esprit pour l'époque, et alors qu'elle n'a pas encore dix-huit ans, elle traverse la Manche, où elle vit d'expédients avant de trouver une place chez une couturière de Dover Street, Kate Reily, et de se former aux techniques de coupe rigoureuses des tailleurs anglais. De retour à Paris en 1900, elle est engagée comme première d'atelier dans l'une des maisons les plus en vue du moment, les sœurs Callot, « sous les ordres, écrit Palmer White, de Madame Gerber, l'aînée des trois sœurs, une perfectionniste pour laquelle elle gardera toujours une vive estime ».

ci-dessus   Madeleine Vionnet, 1930
page 36   Vionnet, 1938

Cinq ans plus tard, c'est l'un des autres grands couturiers du moment, Jacques Doucet, qui fait appel à elle, sur les conseils d'un de ses anciens modélistes, Paul Poiret, initialement approché pour un poste qui alors ne l'intéresse pas. Impressionné par la sensibilité et le savoir-faire de la jeune femme, Doucet ne tarde pas à lui laisser une certaine latitude, et Madeleine Vionnet s'attache immédiatement à suivre le leitmotiv de son existence : la recherche de la fluidité, le goût du drapé (repris ensuite par Madame Grès), la volonté de dégager le corps de toute contrainte, à l'opposé de ce qui caractérise encore la mode du moment (volonté qui l'autorise à contester à Poiret la véritable initiative de l'abolition du corset).

Le succès de ses créations lui permet de s'émanciper, et d'ouvrir en 1912 sa première boutique, au 222 rue de Rivoli, qui connaît une réussite immédiate. Elle est contrainte de la fermer, deux ans plus tard, par l'entrée en guerre ; mais la rouvre dès la fin de celle-ci, grâce à l'appui d'un riche financier de l'époque. N'ayant pour autant jamais cessé de travailler, elle met au point en 1926 un procédé emblématique dans l'histoire de la mode : la coupe en biais dans des tissus souples et légers dont elle accentue ainsi la plasticité.

Cette innovation lui assure incidemment une place de pionnière dans un autre domaine : face aux innombrables emprunts, copies et adaptations dont sa mode fait l'objet, elle se retrouve au centre d'une cause célèbre, dont elle sort victorieuse, revendiquant le droit d'invention de ce procédé, limitant la production de ses créations, et allant jusqu'à authentifier chacun de ses modèles par son empreinte digitale. Créant près de six cents modèles par an, Vionnet, résume Palmer White, « ne cesse de jouer avec la fluidité des lignes, l'harmonie et le diaphane, éléments qui donnent à ses créations leur magie aérienne. Elle choisit alors des tissus souples : la mousseline de soie, le crêpe de Chine et le crêpe romain, spécialement créé pour elle d'après des toges antiques, privilégie les tonalités monochromes, le blanc cassé, l'ivoire, le beige, le vert pâle, utilise fort peu de couleurs soutenues, à l'exception du fameux "rouge Vionnet", du rouille, du vert foncé, et bien sûr du noir... Les points doivent demeurer invisibles... Parfois fermé par quelques agrafes ou pressions, jamais par une fermeture à glissière, le vêtement tombe en plis harmonieux ».

page 40   Vionnet, robe Petits Chevaux, 1921
page 41   Vionnet, 1937
page 42   Vionnet, robe de soirée coupée en biais, 1935
page 43   Vionnet, 1925

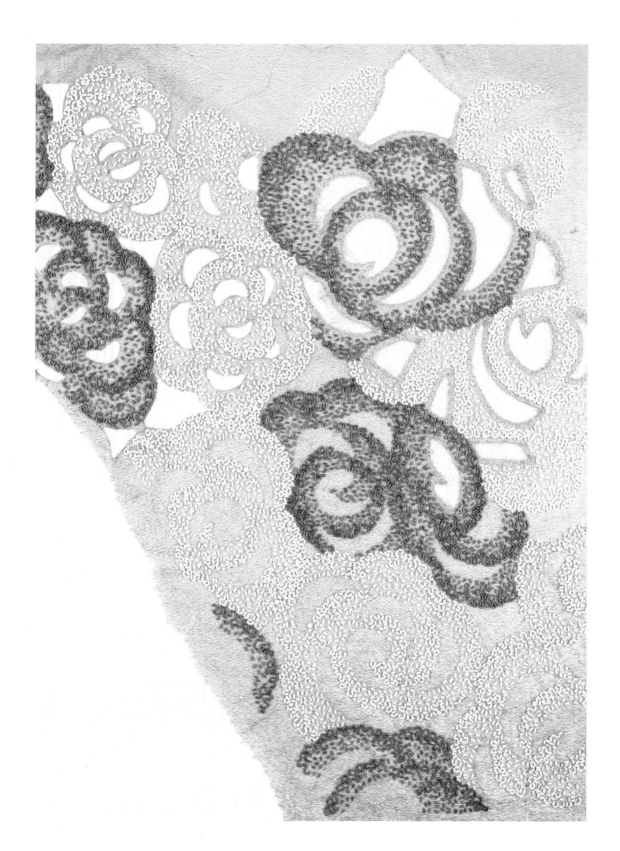

Autre motif récurrent dans ses créations : de longues guirlandes, des bouquets ou des colliers de roses viennent s'enrouler autour du corps, en contrepoint à la simplicité de la ligne. Coupées de biais dans une mousseline de soie ombrée, gansées d'une broderie au fil de soie, ces délicates fleurs de chiffon ne sont que l'un des défis que doit relever la maison Michonet pour répondre aux attentes de Madeleine Vionnet. Car c'est vers le brodeur d'excellence que la couturière s'est tournée pour concevoir et exécuter ornements et motifs adaptés à ses matériaux de prédilection. La donne a totalement changé : il est à présent essentiel de ne pas contrarier le mouvement et la légèreté d'une mousseline ou d'un crêpe coupé en biais par la charge de matériaux trop denses – perles, franges ou jais. Il faut aussi modifier le graphisme, les couleurs, les textures, les adapter à l'esprit d'une modernité dont Vionnet admire et collectionne les plus grands créateurs, de Jean Dunand (dont elle adapte les couleurs) à Pierre Chareau ou Jean-Michel Frank.

ci-dessus à gauche   matériel de ponçage
ci-dessus à droite   « petit crochet » ou lunéville
page 44   échantillon de broderie

Pareille volonté a des incidences immédiates sur les techniques d'exécution, et nous donne incidemment l'occasion d'aborder une opposition essentielle, et ignorée, de l'art du brodeur. L'aiguille à la main, enfilant perles, paillettes, strass ou sequins avant de les repiquer sur le tissu, les brodeuses ont traditionnellement coutume de coudre un élément après l'autre, qu'il s'agisse d'un strass, d'une pierre précieuse ou d'une lame de plastique, dans un long et méticuleux jeu de patience ; ce qui leur vaut la qualification, dans le jargon du métier, de « mainteuses ».

Dans la première moitié du XIXe siècle cependant, des ouvrières de Lunéville prirent l'initiative d'une nouvelle économie (de geste, de temps et donc de coût) en complétant l'aiguille d'un petit crochet, ou « lunéville », qui leur permettait de fixer paillettes ou sequins préalablement distribués sur un fil : travaillant « à l'aveugle », une main tenant le crochet, l'autre sous le métier, la brodeuse place le fil, fait glisser les paillettes sur l'endroit, et les fixe sur l'envers à l'aide du crochet. Bien plus rapide que celle des mainteuses, et initialement vouée aux gémonies par ces dernières, la technique des « lunévilleuses » permet surtout de poser avec précision les matériaux les plus fins, comme les sequins, les tubes ou les perles minuscules. La mode des robes chasubles, souvent rebrodées de perles dans les années 1920 et la nécessité de répondre à une demande toujours croissante favorisèrent un premier développement de la broderie de Lunéville ; pour revenir à Madeleine Vionnet, une telle méthode offrait à Albert Lesage un instrument parfaitement adapté aux contraintes que posait la mode de la couturière : elle permettait de déposer de subtils motifs sur les tissus fluides et fragiles – mousselines, crêpes ou souffles de soie – qui avaient sa prédilection. Elle lui fournit aussi l'occasion d'exercer son ingéniosité, et le prétexte à d'innombrables innovations. Mais il n'aurait pu le faire sans l'intervention d'une autre figure essentielle de l'histoire de la maison, que le hasard et Madeleine Vionnet conduisirent aux ateliers Michonet un jour qu'Albert s'y trouvait.

Seule sans doute l'oreille érudite et subtile du généalogiste peut-elle discerner derrière le nom de Despense l'écho assourdi de celui, si fameux en Angleterre, de Spencer. Le premier n'est pourtant que l'adaptation du second à une oreille française, à laquelle un couple de la prestigieuse famille, arrivé en France dans la suite de Marie Stuart en 1558, jugea nécessaire de procéder. Anoblis par cette dernière, et gratifiés du domaine de Railly en Bourgogne, ces Spencer se réinventèrent en comte et comtesse de Despense-Railly.

Trois siècles plus tard, Berthe de Despense-Railly, dont la fortune avait pâli, s'énamoura d'un de ses cousins, originaire de Chevannes, Paul Favot, et quitta la modeste gentilhommière de famille, après avoir épousé son prétendant, pour s'installer à Auteuil où elle prit les rênes du ménage, se chargeant en particulier de travaux de couture à domicile. Elle donna naissance en 1895 à une fille, Marie-Louise, qui hérita de sa dextérité et de son sens artistique. Une solide éducation dans ce domaine permit à cette dernière de développer très tôt le sens des formes et des couleurs, et une certaine habileté dans le trait ; si bien qu'après avoir terminé ses études secondaires, elle choisit de passer, à dix-neuf ans, le concours d'entrée à l'École Nationale des Arts Décoratifs, qu'elle réussit. Les quatre années qu'elle y passa, avant d'en sortir

ci-dessus   Marie-Louise Lesage, 1922
page 48   Michonet, début du XXᵉ siècle
double page suivante   Vionnet, 1930

diplômée, coïncidèrent avec celles de la Grande Guerre, de la mobilisation de son père et de certaines difficultés matérielles ; elle fut donc amenée, pour soutenir le foyer, à aider sa mère dans ses travaux de couture et apprit les techniques de la coupe, de l'ajustement et de la finition d'un vêtement.

La guerre et son cycle d'études terminés, se posa la question d'un emploi. De toutes les voies possibles, Marie-Louise choisit celle de la mode ; et, après avoir hésité entre les deux noms les plus en vue du moment – ceux de Paul Poiret et de Madeleine Vionnet – se présenta chez cette dernière, 222 rue de Rivoli, qui l'engagea sur le champ. Pour se distinguer des multiples homonymes dans l'atelier, elle choisit de réduire son prénom à un hiatus sonore et cristallin – « Yo » – qui devait lui rester attaché toute sa vie. Chargée de rassembler documents et sources d'inspiration pour la créatrice, elle l'assistait aussi dans la mise au point des modèles : « tout comme Poiret avant elle, résume Palmer White, et Madame Grès après elle, la célèbre couturière drapait d'abord la toile sur un mannequin miniature en bois, puis sur le mannequin vivant. L'ébauche de la toile réalisée, elle demandait à Marie-Louise de dessiner sur coton l'emplacement destiné à la broderie. »

Si le styliste d'aujourd'hui a la possibilité de donner une direction ou un thème au brodeur, ou de se fonder, à l'inverse, sur des échantillons proposés par ce dernier pour imaginer ses créations, la place de la broderie sur le vêtement était chez Vionnet pour ainsi dire strictement réservée : pensée, dessinée et mise en place ; il revenait en particulier à Marie-Louise de veiller à la bonne exécution par Michonet des motifs, à la justesse des tons et des couleurs tels qu'ils avaient été conçus sur la toile. Elle était ainsi amenée à se rendre fréquemment rue Feydeau pour y contrôler le travail des brodeuses ; et c'est au cours d'une de ces visites qu'Albert Michonet lui présenta le jeune homme avec lequel il venait de signer un contrat de partenariat qui devait l'amener à reprendre la maison. Le coup de foudre, selon White, fut immédiat ; et le mariage fut célébré quelques mois plus tard, sous les auspices bienveillants de la même Simone Bouvet de Lozier qui avait favorisé le départ d'Albert aux États-Unis, et fit le voyage de New York pour l'occasion.

Il ne pouvait être question pour Marie-Louise, toujours aussi foncièrement indépendante, d'abandonner son travail; elle ne quitta Madeleine Vionnet, qui était alors au sommet de sa gloire et dont la firme comptait autour de mille deux cents employés, que pour suivre son mari chez Michonet, et s'occuper en particulier des relations avec celle qui lui avait, la première, accordé sa confiance. En dehors même de leur relation personnelle, Marie-Louise et Albert Lesage semblaient faits pour se compléter: à lui le dessin, à elle la couleur; à elle la culture artistique et une certaine fantaisie, à lui le goût de l'entreprise et les fruits de son expérience américaine. Marie-Louise avait en outre l'avantage d'être déjà familiarisée avec les techniques de la broderie, et les méthodes de travail de l'atelier de la rue Feydeau. Mettant à profit les deux années d'intérim prévues dans l'accord de cession, Albert et Marie-Louise eurent tout le loisir d'explorer les impressionnantes archives de la maison, ses collections d'échantillons et de

en haut à gauche   François Lesage avec son frère aîné Jean-Louis et sa sœur jumelle Christiane
en haut à droite   Elisabeth, comtesse Greffulhe, dans une robe Worth, v. 1900
ci-dessus   La famille Lesage
page 54   Worth, 1944

56

modèles qui remontaient à plus d'un demi-siècle, et de partager l'expérience singulière qui était celle d'Albert Michonet.

Il fallait en même temps suivre l'esprit du temps, et accompagner la mutation du goût dont la mode de Vionnet n'était que l'un des symptômes. L'acquisition de Michonet par Lesage profite, on l'a dit, des contingences économiques de 1924; elle précède aussi d'une année seulement la véritable révolution, la cristallisation esthétique représentée par la grande Exposition des Arts décoratifs qui fonde véritablement un style nouveau. Vionnet partage, dans le domaine de l'ornement, le répertoire stylistique des artistes et des créateurs qu'elle collectionne: goût de l'aplat, des formes simples, géométriques, abstraites, organiques, de la ligne brisée souvent.

On a vu aussi combien ses techniques de coupe autant que ses matériaux de prédilection réagissaient immédiatement sur le dessin, les éléments et la texture même de la broderie. Albert et Marie-Louise doivent immédiatement innover pour répondre à cette nouvelle donne. Ils améliorent la technique du vermicelle, qui consiste à coudre au point de Lunéville un réseau sinueux de perles minuscules en un motif de plus en plus dense, exigeant une dextérité hors pair de la brodeuse; ils utilisent des perles de verre irrégulières, des semis de tubes, des fibres végétales, traitées à la vapeur et couvertes de perles. Dans leur recherche d'une délicatesse extrême, ils créent aussi une technique de dégradé qui consiste à plonger, centimètre par centimètre, dans un bain de couleur de moins en moins dense, le motif brodé, puis à le replacer sur la robe, créant ainsi un effet d'«ombré», appelé à devenir l'une des spécialités de la maison. Poussant encore le perfectionnisme, Albert, écrit Palmer White, «va jusqu'à utiliser une table de logarithmes pour calculer les proportions qu'il doit donner à ses broderies s'il veut respecter l'harmonie de la tenue»; mais il sait aussi mettre à profit incidents et contingences: «les ateliers sont encore chauffés grâce à des poêles à charbon. Un jour par une maladresse bénie, une boîte de paillettes tombe sur l'un des poêles. On s'aperçoit alors que les paillettes gonflent comme du pop-corn: c'est ainsi que sont nés les paillettes et les motifs soufflés qui ponctuent certaines des broderies de Madeleine Vionnet ou d'Elsa Schiaparelli...»

Pendant plus de quinze ans, Lesage accompagne l'irrésistible ascension de la première, qui ouvre un salon à Biarritz, s'implante sur la Cinquième Avenue, créée un institut de formation et inaugure, en 1932, avenue Montaigne, un édifice de cinq étages ne comportant pas moins de vingt-et-un ateliers, ainsi qu'une clinique et un cabinet dentaire, nouvelle marque de son attention au bien-être de ses employés. Lesage créera ainsi plus de mille cinq cents motifs pour la couturière, jusqu'à ce jour d'août 1939 où elle décide de présenter sa dernière collection, bien consciente de la catastrophe à venir. (Elle vivra encore plus de trente ans, menant une existence strictement privée sans négliger pour autant d'assurer sa trace dans l'histoire de la mode, en particulier par un legs important au Musée des Arts décoratifs.) La seule ampleur de sa collaboration avec Lesage suffit à laisser une empreinte indélébile sur l'histoire de la maison; elle ne trouvera d'équivalent, un peu plus tard, que dans le dialogue avec une autre couturière, au goût beaucoup moins retenu.

Vionnet, robe de soirée, 1929

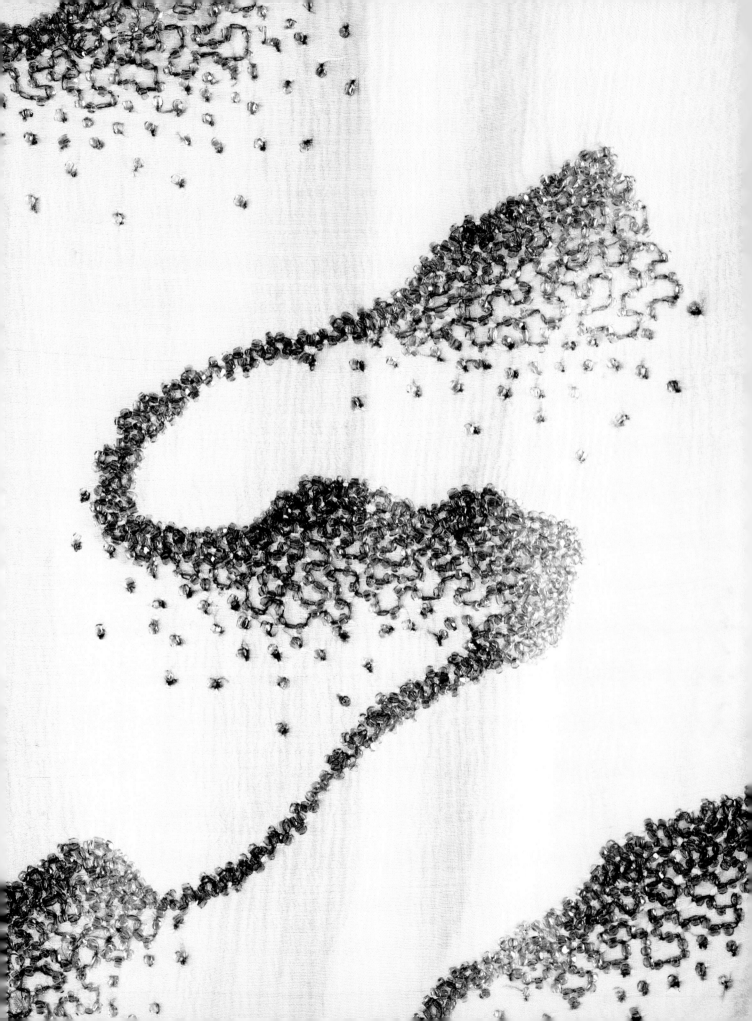

L_____ e 31 mars 1929, naît François Lesage ; il précède de quelques heures (qui suffiront à la faire naître le 1ᵉʳ avril…) sa sœur jumelle, Christiane, à laquelle il restera, dans la diversité même de leur parcours, lié toute sa vie par une indissoluble complicité. Leur frère aîné, Jean-Louis, est né cinq ans plus tôt et porte déjà, en dépit d'une santé fragile, les espoirs de la famille. Les Lesage viennent de traverser une période plutôt faste, et se sont installés à Chaville, dans un ancien pavillon qui restera le lieu de rassemblement de la famille pendant plusieurs générations.

La société Albert Lesage et Cie a, conformément au protocole prévu, absorbé Michonet en 1924 et semble promise à un avenir tranquille. Jusqu'à ce jour d'octobre 1929 où, quelques mois à peine après la naissance des jumeaux, la bourse de New York s'effondre, premier temps d'une réaction en chaîne qui va bouleverser l'économie mondiale. La mode perd d'un coup sa clientèle américaine ; les grandes maisons sont confrontées à une réduction drastique de leur chiffre d'affaires ; leurs fournisseurs – bottiers, modistes, plumassiers, maroquiniers ou fourreurs – sont les premiers à subir le contrecoup de la crise, et les brodeurs parmi eux (on parle de six mille licenciements pour les seules ouvrières de Lunéville).

Faisant preuve d'une des qualités remarquables dont héritera la maison – son inventivité, sa mobilité, sa capacité à réagir dans l'immédiat –, Albert Lesage imagine de nouvelles stratégies : allier par exemple, pour sortir des registres convenus, une broderie simplifiée à des tenues de ce que l'on n'appelle pas encore *sportswear* ; il essaie aussi, sans que l'opération soit concluante, de se lancer dans l'imprimé, qui correspond à l'esprit du temps, mais qu'il ne maîtrise pas aussi bien que les soyeux du moment, Bianchini en premier lieu. Une autre initiative, un peu plus fructueuse, consiste à utiliser les ressources de la broderie et de la passementerie pour développer une ligne d'accessoires – ceintures, sacs ou bijoux fantaisie – qui viennent relever d'une touche fantaisiste la ligne d'un vêtement ; idée somme toute naturelle que reprendra, à un demi-siècle d'écart, celui qui n'est encore qu'un nouveau-né, avec cette fois-ci un succès certain.

Albert est surtout amené à réduire son équipe, et à faire preuve de pragmatisme : « dans l'atelier Lesage, résume Palmer White, on se répartit les corvées. Le comptable se charge du ménage, Marie-Louise du courrier, Albert des courses. Dans le Paris d'avant le krach, on comptait vingt ateliers de broderie. Aujourd'hui, il n'en reste plus que dix et Albert craint de plus en plus que ce chiffre ne passe à neuf. » (La situation préfigure étrangement celle que devra affronter François Lesage à son tour lorsque la mode, portée au début des années 1980 par la vague du prêt-à-porter de luxe et par une esthétique rebelle à l'ornementation, délaissera la broderie, nouveau moment particulièrement critique, on le verra, pour la maison.)

Dans l'adversité, Albert semble malgré tout favorisé par la fortune. De même que les circonstances, et la dévaluation du franc, l'avaient servi au moment de la transaction avec Michonet, de même se voyant, en 1931, contraint de quitter la rue Feydeau à cause d'une opération immobilière, parvient-il à mettre la situation à profit : jouant de l'impatience des promoteurs, il fait monter les enchères, et profite des circonstances pour déménager l'équipe qui l'entoure, désormais réduite, au 13 rue de la Grange-Batelière, adresse qui reste aujourd'hui celle de certaines activités de la maison. Mais c'est surtout le coup de fil inopiné, en 1934, d'une véritable *dea ex machina*, l'ex-comtesse Wendt de Kerlor, qui va lui permettre de redresser la situation.

page ci-contre Vionnet, 1938
page 60 Vionnet, 1938

Depuis sa traversée commune, mais non partagée, de l'Atlantique avec Albert en 1919, Elsa Wendt de Kerlor avait en effet perdu son titre, en même temps que ses illusions sur son mari (dont la noblesse était au demeurant passablement douteuse: il s'était en fait contenté d'accoler les patronymes de ses deux parents). Partageant dans un premier temps son goût pour l'occultisme, la magie et autres vertiges théosophiques, fascinée par lui au point d'en devenir le sujet hypnotique, elle avait fini par se lasser d'une relation instable, de déménagements incessants, de visites d'huissiers et d'une vie d'expédients. Après une brève romance avec un chanteur d'opéra à la carrière prometteuse, interrompue par la mort prématurée de ce dernier, madame de Kerlor décida de reprendre son calligraphique nom de jeune fille – Schiaparelli – et de revenir en Europe en compagnie du seul bienfait que lui eût laissé son mari, sa fille, surnommée Gogo.

ci-dessus   Elsie de Wolfe (lady Mendl) portant la cape Apollon de Versailles de Schiaparelli
(collection « Astrologique »). Photographie de Cecil Beaton, fin des années 1930
page ci-contre   Schiaparelli, cape Apollon de Versailles, collection « Astrologique » 1938
page 64   Schiaparelli, collection « Cirque » 1938

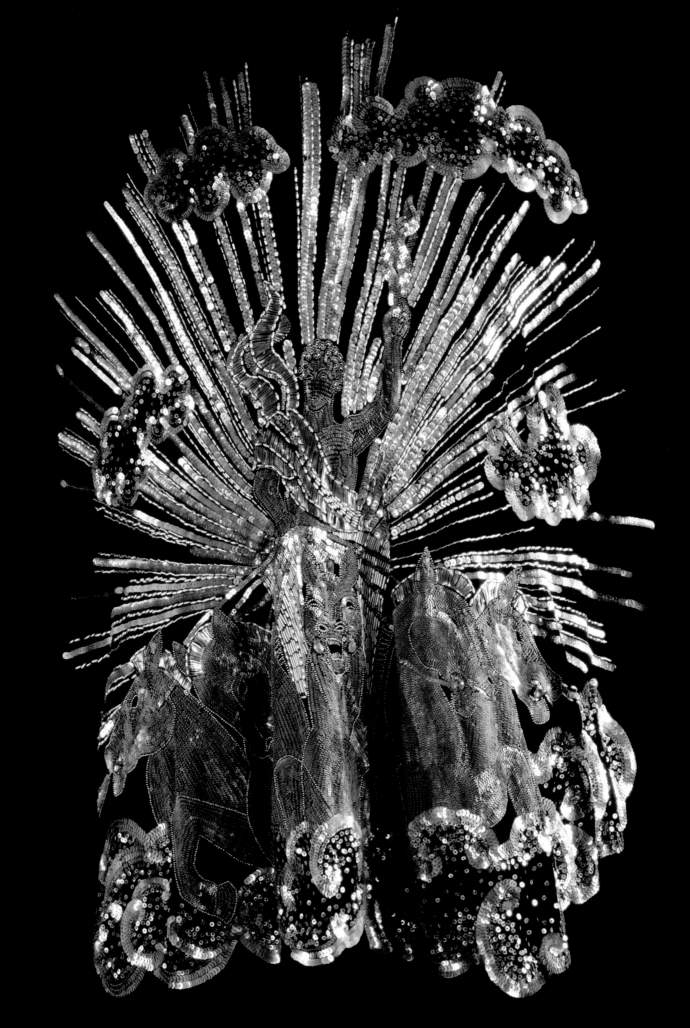

Portrait d'Elsa Schiaparelli par Christian Bérard offert à François Lesage
par Schiaparelli avant son départ pour les États-Unis en 1946

De retour à Paris en 1922, chaperonnée par une de ses amies elle aussi en voie de séparation, Gabriële Buffet-Picabia, elle fut immédiatement plongée dans le Tout-Paris littéraire et artistique de l'époque, rencontra ceux qu'il fallait rencontrer – de Tzara à Duchamp et Cocteau – et fut vue où il fallait l'être. En particulier par Paul Poiret, dont elle fréquentait le théâtre privé et qui, remarquant sa façon chic de s'habiller, lui offrit de porter gracieusement certaines de ses créations. Une robe du soir quasiment improvisée pour son amie Gabriële, qui lui valut une nouvelle fois les compliments du grand couturier, la projeta d'un coup, et sans même qu'elle s'en rendît compte, selon sa biographe Meryle Secrest, dans l'univers qui devait être le sien pendant plus de trente ans.

Son premier modèle fut un sweater à manches trois-quarts et nœud en trompe-l'œil, monté selon une technique particulière qui en assurait la tenue, et qui se distinguait de ceux de ses concurrents à la fois par sa texture et par la présence d'un motif sur ce que l'on considérait jusqu'alors comme un vêtement purement fonctionnel; il représentait, comme l'écrit Meryle Secrest, «une façon de s'habiller qui comblait le gouffre entre les styles décontracté et habillé» et connut un succès foudroyant. Il fut salué par le numéro de *Vogue* de décembre 1927 comme «un chef-d'œuvre et un triomphe en terme de mélange des couleurs». La démarche préfigurait, plus d'un demi-siècle à l'avance, celle de nombre de «designers» d'aujourd'hui, et cette première création préluda à une série d'innovations – robe sans couture, maillot de bain une pièce, «Mad cap» (un petit bonnet à deux pointes) – qui furent autant de succès commerciaux, assurèrent la fortune de la créatrice et lui permirent de créer sa propre firme, soutenue par Charles Kahn, des Galeries Lafayette, en décembre 1927.

Dans le sweater inaugural de Schiaparelli, se trouvent réunies la plupart des données de sa mode future. Elle suppose un corps féminin plutôt mince, dégagé, aux formes peu marquées (en 1932, sous l'influence en particulier de Chanel et Patou, est déjà fixée la typologie de la femme «moderne», qui est encore la nôtre).

Elle brouille les frontières entre le «jour» et le «soir», cherchant avant tout la simplicité de l'allure et la liberté du mouvement pour l'un comme pour l'autre (en ouvrant par exemple de deux grandes fentes en éventail une stricte jupe droite). Schiaparelli n'est pas une virtuose de la coupe, comme Vionnet, ni ne cherche à révolutionner la construction du vêtement. Son intervention est plutôt de l'ordre de la trouvaille, de l'*effet*, du clin d'œil, de la séduction; penchant prévisible chez cette aristocrate romaine, plutôt portée sur le baroque, que ne devaient certes pas contrarier ses amitiés (et collaborations) artistiques, de Dalí à Cocteau, Bérard et Vertès, Leonor Fini ou Picabia.

Effet paradoxal de son flair, à un moment où nombre de maisons ferment et qu'éclate la crise, le succès de la couturière, qui a étendu son empire de New York à Londres et Paris, reste éclatant, au point de lui permettre de quitter, début 1935, l'espace compté du 4 rue de la Paix, où elle s'était installée en 1927, pour un hôtel particulier de la place Vendôme de quatre-vingt-dix-huit pièces qui restera son siège historique.

page ci-contre Schiaparelli, collection « Astrologique » 1938
page 72 Schiaparelli, manteau de soirée Cocteau d'après un dessin de Jean Cocteau, 1937
page 73 Illustration de Cecil Beaton pour *Vogue* représentant le manteau de soirée Cocteau, 1937
page 74 Dessin de Jean Cocteau pour une veste de soirée Schiaparelli, 1937
page 75 Schiaparelli, veste de soirée Cocteau, 1937
page 76 Schiaparelli, chemisier du soir, collection « Astrologique », automne-hiver 1938–1939
70   *page 77* Schiaparelli, collection « païenne » 1938

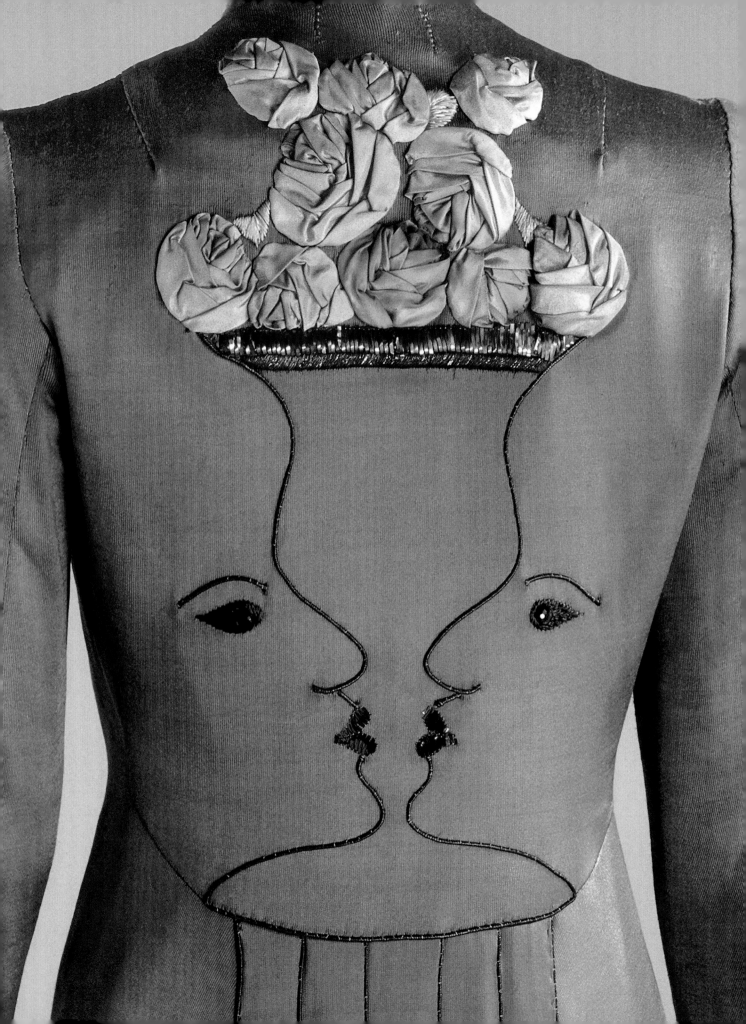

Robe de Schiaparelli - 1937.

Orné par Jean Cocteau.

Schiaparelli

A gray linen dress embroidered
with Cocteau's design — hair golden,
lips pink, eyes peacock blue,
and a blue Cellophane hand-
kerchief. Hattie Carnegie.

Chanel

White marocain twinkling with
black paillettes, a black ribbon
belt and a mad coiffure con-
cocted of ribbon, feathers and
a pailletted veil. Salon de
Couture, Bonwit Teller.

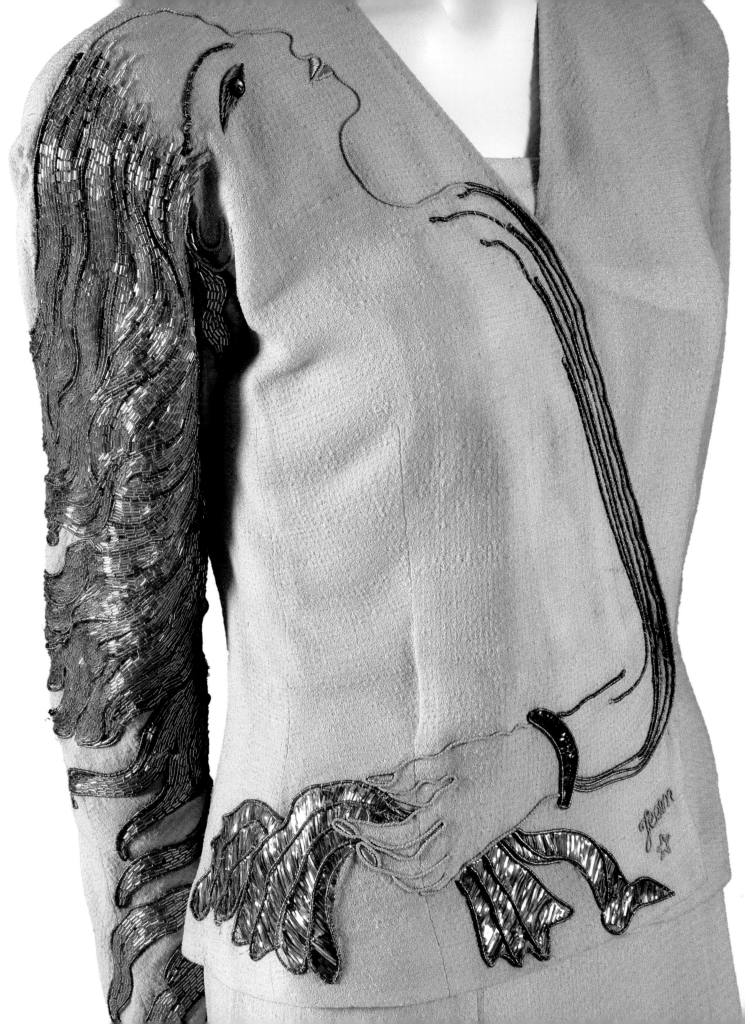

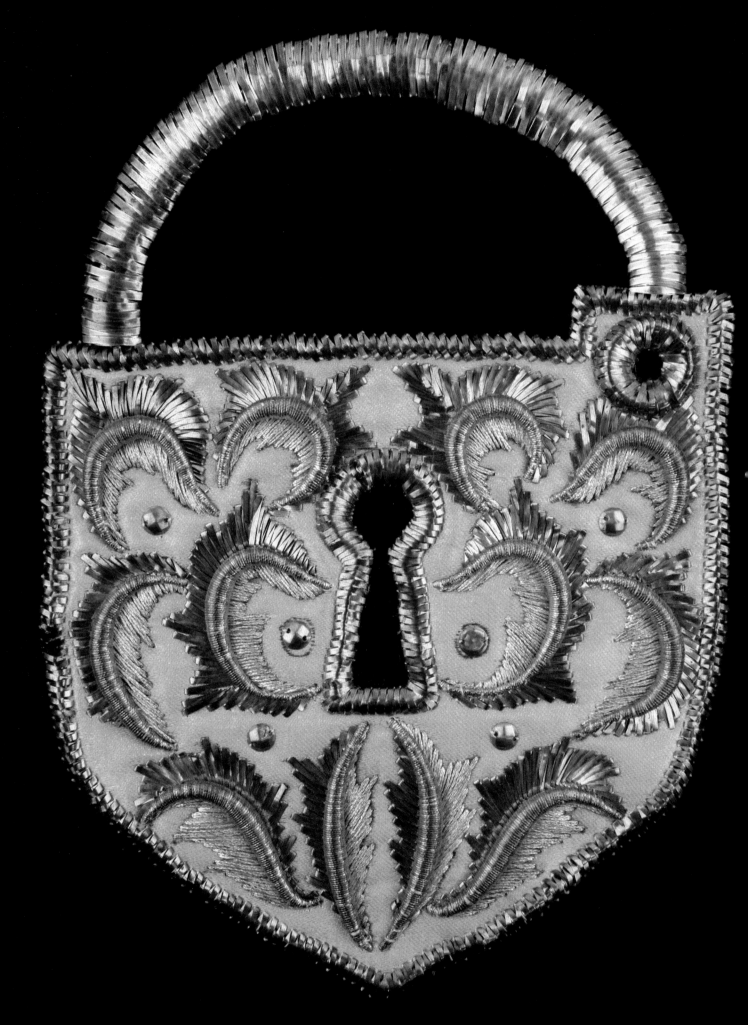

L orsque Schiaparelli se tourne vers Lesage en 1934, c'est bien sûr pour élargir son registre ornemental, qui se réduisait jusqu'alors à de la passementerie, et pour donner à sa mode le tour qui la singularisera définitivement, mais aussi, plus discrètement, pour aider l'atelier dont elle sait, par sa position dans la Chambre syndicale de la Haute Couture, les difficultés. Elle commande en manière de test à Albert et Marie-Louise une première série de ceintures brodées, somptueuses passementeries de fils d'or, ponctuées de gros cabochons en pierres semi-précieuses de corail et turquoise. Une collection de colliers fantaisie prélude ensuite aux interventions sur sa mode proprement dite – tailleurs, robes, manteaux, boléros et mythiques capes – et la relation entre la couturière et l'atelier n'ira qu'en s'approfondissant au cours d'une collaboration qui ne s'interrompra que vingt ans plus tard lorsque Schiaparelli fermera sa maison.

C'est qu'à l'imaginaire baroque, jubilatoire, ludique, décalé de la créatrice italienne, les Lesage savent répondre, comme ils l'avaient fait, à l'autre extrême, face à la volonté d'*understatement* et de discrétion de Madeleine Vionnet, par une capacité d'invention et d'expérimentation sans égale. « Pour ces créations hors pair constate Palmer White, Albert sait trouver des matériaux exceptionnels : verre soufflé de Murano afin d'inventer de petites fleurs ; imitations de pierres dures, tel le lapis-lazuli, le jade, roche de turquoise gainée de filets noirs ; pierres artificielles, galets, cabochons et bien d'autres. Il écrase des paillettes de gélatine pour leur donner l'apparence de pièces de monnaie martelées et associe, luxe s'il en est, la chenille, passementerie veloutée, au... vison ! À la demande d'Elsa Schiaparelli, il remet au goût du jour la cannetille, fil métallique torsadé. Il recourt aussi au métal pour en souligner la diversité d'emploi, fidèle en cela à l'esprit de l'exposition des arts déco qui a eu tant d'impact sur la couturière et l'a poussée à introduire dans la mode nombre de matériaux spécifiques du monde industriel moderne : plastique, latex, cellophane, crêpe de rayonne, tulle et tricots. »

À l'opposé une fois encore de la broderie fluide, légèrement grainée que privilégiait Vionnet, Schiaparelli accentue le relief, la tactilité de l'ornement ; les matériaux sont littéralement mis en relief : point de discrets vermicelles montés au Lunéville, mais des broderies « chardons » ou « hérissons », exécutées à la main suivant les techniques traditionnelles du « soulevé » ou du « bourré », celles dont on se servait pour les vêtements liturgiques ou militaires, sources d'inspiration de la couturière : des torsades d'or, de la laminette lisse, martelée ou gaufrée, exaltant la lumière, sertissant éclats de miroir et pierres semi-précieuses.

Du parfait accord entre la créatrice et le brodeur allait résulter, jusqu'à la déclaration de guerre, une succession de collections mémorables qui inscriront définitivement Schiaparelli dans l'histoire de la mode. Après le succès relatif des collections « Eskimo » d'octobre 1935 et « Parachute » de février 1936, la collection « Musique » donne le ton, un an plus tard : bijoux, ceintures et colliers en forme de tambours, mandolines et cornemuses sont assortis à de longues robes de crêpe de soie blanche rebrodées

page ci-contre   Schiaparelli, collection « païenne » 1938
page 78   Schiaparelli, 1939
page 82   Schiaparelli, cape Phœbus, 1938–1939
page 83   Schiaparelli, cape Phœbus dessinée par Christian Bérard dans *Vogue*, 1938

80

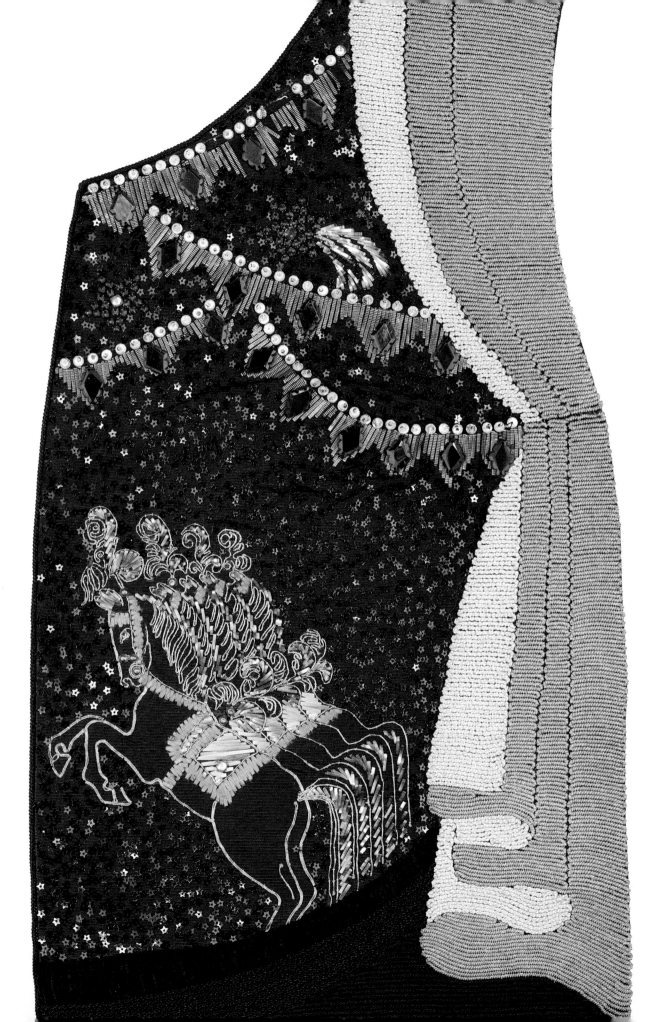

d'oiseaux chanteurs, de rubans et de semis de portées musicales. Elles précèdent les quatre collections de 1938 qui marquent, de l'avis unanime, le sommet de sa création, et de celle d'Albert Lesage.

La collection «Cirque», présentée en février, fut en elle-même un spectacle étonnant, au cours duquel équilibristes et acrobates se mêlèrent, avec toute la souplesse imaginable, au défilé gracieux des mannequins et dont Bérard laissera un superbe témoignage graphique dans *Vogue*. Rien d'étonnant à cela puisqu'il s'agissait d'un de ses propres sujets de prédilection, et il n'est pas interdit de penser qu'il prit une part active dans le choix et la mise en œuvre du motif par la couturière. Déclinant à sa manière un thème que Picasso avait remis en lumière dès le début du siècle, la collection proposait une éblouissante série de variations ou de détournements du vestiaire traditionnel des arts forains: chapeaux d'Auguste rose *shoking*, vestes à paillettes de Monsieur Loyal, hauts de forme d'écuyère et boléros de satin vif renforçaient de leur écho une profusion de broderies virtuoses sur le même registre: acrobates en vol, trapézistes, chevaux savants, carrousels d'éléphants, etc. Il n'était pas jusqu'aux boutons et bijoux (dessinés par Jean Schlumberger) qui ne prennent la forme de masques de clown, de sucres d'orge, de réglisses, de barbes à papa ou de chevaux parés. Schiaparelli «fixait» ainsi un thème qui restera une constante de son imaginaire, jusque dans l'illustration publicitaire de ses parfums qu'en donneront Bérard et surtout Vertès.

La collection «païenne», d'avril 1938, file pour sa part la métaphore végétale, pour laquelle Schiaparelli nourrissait une prédilection commune avec son amie, la poétesse Lise Deharme, et qui se déploie autour du thème d'une forêt mythique, peuplée d'elfes et de dieux antiques: «Des nymphes des bois portaient des vestes aux boutons en forme de hibou, de tête de cerf, de noisette, d'oiseau aux plumes étincelantes ou d'insecte. Des ceintures en feuillage encerclaient leur taille; des brindilles s'entrelaçaient sur leur poitrine comme de la broderie, s'enroulaient autour de leurs bras pour former des bracelets et se nichaient dans leurs cheveux, telles des barrettes, alors que des fougères ornaient leurs revers.» Pour donner relief et éclat aux arabesques de feuillage qui s'enroulent autour du corps et des fleurs brodées, Albert allia la laminette mate aux découpes de lamé et aux paillettes.

Faisant fonds, trois mois plus tard, de l'intérêt de Schiaparelli pour l'ésotérisme, les sciences occultes et l'astrologie, la collection «Astrologique» exploite cette fois-ci tous les aspects de la mythologie céleste et des puissances élémentaires ; la lune, le soleil, les étoiles et les planètes sont depuis toujours une source inépuisable de motifs ornementaux, mais ils offrent, dans cette collection, à la couturière et au brodeur l'occasion de créations devenues mythiques. En particulier celle d'un soleil de sequins rayonnant sur une cape de laine rose *shocking*, et d'une éclaboussure d'or sur un manteau de soie noire inspirée de l'attelage de la Fontaine de Neptune à Versailles.

Point d'orgue de cette succession de collections magistrales, et la dernière à thème, la «Commedia dell'arte» d'octobre 1938 prolonge à sa manière celle de février, en jouant à nouveau sur l'imaginaire du spectacle et de la représentation, cher à Schiaparelli. Elle lance ainsi sur la scène de la couture une troupe de Pierrots, d'Arlequins et Colombines, aux costumes losangés de feutre, de faille et de satin rebrodés, où se croisent l'influence de la musique baroque, de Tiepolo, de Picasso, de Bérard et de Severini qui en avait fait, depuis les années 1920, un motif obsessionnel. Tricornes de feutre, masques de gaze, clochettes tintinnabulant sur les accessoires complétaient une collection qui portait au plus haut point l'esprit de la mode de Schiaparelli : goût de la théâtralité, d'une légèreté ludique, du décalage et de l'ironie, de l'illusion et du trompe-l'œil (comme on le voit, parmi tant d'exemples, dans de fameuses broderies dessinées par Cocteau).

«Si vous observez les couturiers, résuma un demi-siècle plus tard François Lesage qui accompagna très jeune son père lors de ses visites à la couturière, vous verrez qu'ils reviennent aux mêmes motifs tous les 20 ou 25 ans. Schiaparelli ne l'a jamais fait. Pour elle, une bonne idée servait de tremplin à la suivante et elle ne se répétait jamais.» Encore fallait-il trouver à cette inépuisable fantaisie un juste interprète. Ce fut le cas d'Albert Lesage, comme le reconnut volontiers la couturière elle-même. «Si elle aimait quelque chose, poursuivait François, elle disait "Trrrrès bien" en roulant les r et ajoutait "Vous avez trrrès bien trrrravaillé".»

Millicent Rogers dans un ensemble Schiaparelli en velours noir.
Photographie de Horst P. Horst pour *Vogue*, 1938

L a relation entre Lesage et Schiaparelli devait se poursuivre, après la parenthèse des années de guerre, jusqu'à la fermeture de la maison en 1954. Elle ne retrouverait pourtant jamais pareille intensité, l'activité de mode de la couturière diminuant à mesure que s'affirmait le succès de ses parfums. Il reste que l'effet de cette collaboration fut sans doute plus décisif encore sur le trajet, et la situation, du brodeur que ne l'avait été le travail avec Vionnet. « Les livres de comptes qui indiquaient, résume Palmer White, un bénéfice de 800 000 francs en 1927 affichent, dix ans plus tard, la somme rondelette de 1 551 539 francs. » Et la réussite financière se double d'un autre atout, plus important encore, que l'on dirait aujourd'hui « d'image », Lesage gagnant en renommée grâce, en particulier, au succès des créations de Schiaparelli, et de la part évidente qu'y prenaient la broderie et l'ornement.

Porté par la dynamique de ce travail commun, par l'économie et l'*aura* internationales de la maison de couture, Albert songe à développer l'activité de l'atelier en renouant, en particulier, les liens avec les États-Unis qu'il avait quittés vingt ans plus tôt et qui constituaient un vaste marché en puissance. Réussissant une opération jusqu'alors totalement inédite dans le métier, il noue avec un brodeur new-yorkais (au nom pourtant bien français de Mr. Toussaint) un accord, analogue à ceux qui liaient certaines maisons de mode aux grands magasins américains ; il sera tenu de fournir régulièrement à son associé un ensemble saisonnier de collections adaptées au goût des clientes d'outre-Atlantique – transpositions dont il avait déjà quelque idée après son passage chez Marshall Field.

Le 28 août 1939, Albert Lesage prend place à bord du luxueux paquebot Normandie, lancé quelques années plus tôt, à destination de New York, pour y mettre au point les derniers détails d'une collaboration qui s'annonce fructueuse.

Le 1er septembre, trois jours seulement après le début de la traversée, Hitler envahit la Pologne. Le 3, la France et l'Angleterre déclarent la guerre à l'Allemagne. Albert n'arrive à New York que pour prendre acte de l'impossibilité de la collaboration annoncée face aux circonstances (et au décès inopiné de Mr. Toussaint). Abrégeant un séjour désormais sans objet, il parvient à retourner à Paris dans les derniers jours de septembre, voyageant cette fois-ci sur le tout nouveau Queen Elisabeth.

Marie-Louise, de son côté, s'est trouvée prise de court par la déclaration de guerre alors qu'elle séjourne au Mont-Dore, dans la résidence estivale où la famille se rend régulièrement, non seulement pour y passer de longues vacances, mais aussi parce que le climat de la région est bénéfique pour Jean-Louis, de santé toujours aussi précaire. Au retour d'Albert, la famille décide de rester à l'abri en province, tandis que ce dernier retournera seul à Paris pour tenter de gérer l'ingérable. On trouve un précepteur pour Jean-Louis, alors âgé de quinze ans et les jumeaux sont inscrits dans une école de la région.

Rue de la Grange-Batelière, Albert essaie de maintenir un minimum d'activité, aidé en cela par un monde de la mode déterminé à résister le plus longtemps possible aux circonstances. La Chambre syndicale de la Haute Couture, sous la direction de Lucien Lelong, annonce ainsi la présentation des collections d'été en février 1940; la presse et les acheteurs américains, bravant l'adversité, font le voyage en passant par Gênes avant de remonter vers Paris. Ils arrivent à temps pour assister aux défilés, sans se douter qu'ils ne verront les suivants que six ans plus tard. En juin, la France est envahie; les populations fuient vers le sud du pays. Albert n'a d'autre choix que de fermer l'atelier, de laisser Chaville aux mains de sa mère et de traverser à son tour la France en voiture en compagnie de son directeur des ventes, Christian Powel, et d'une première d'atelier prénommée Olga.

ci-dessus Schiaparelli, 1941
page 88 Schiaparelli, collection « Musique » 1937
page 92 Schiaparelli, 1938
page 93 Schiaparelli, 1937

Il restera neuf mois au Mont-Dore, qui échappe alors à l'emprise allemande. Incapable de rester inactif, il continue d'imaginer avec Marie-Louise projets et motifs dans l'espoir, vite déçu, d'un prochain retour à l'ordre. Aux troubles du temps, viennent s'ajouter les soucis familiaux : la pénurie de soins et de médicaments résultant de la situation contribue à dégrader l'état de santé de Jean-Louis ; il doit être placé en sanatorium à Crans-Montana, dans le Valais, tandis que ses grands-parents maternels, son frère et sa sœur s'installent à Thonon-les-Bains pour se rapprocher de lui. En mars 1941, n'y tenant plus, Albert décide de regagner Paris, accompagné de ses deux collaborateurs, et de rouvrir les ateliers. Il sollicite celles des maisons de couture qui, sous l'impulsion toujours de Lucien Lelong, essaient de poursuivre leurs activités : Schiaparelli bien sûr, Robert Piguet, Jacques Fath, qui vient de s'installer dans ses nouveaux salons, et Cristóbal Balenciaga, qui introduit précisément à ce moment, à l'instigation peut-être de Schiaparelli, la broderie et la passementerie dans ses modèles.

ci-dessus à gauche   Albert et François Lesage, 1942
ci-dessus à droite   Albert Lesage, avec ses enfants François et Christiane, 1941
page 94   Worth, 1948

Il ne suffit pourtant pas d'avoir des commandes, il faut pouvoir y répondre. Albert engage deux brodeuses, mais les effets des rationnements et de la pénurie de matériaux se font déjà sentir. Il peut, dans un premier temps, puiser dans le stock hérité de Michonet et dans ce qui lui reste de sa période faste. Il doit cependant vite faire avec les moyens du bord. « Il est difficile, écrit Palmer White, d'obtenir des bons pour les tissus. Il faut remplacer la soie par de la rayonne… quand on peut en trouver. Dénicher du fil devient une gageure. Albert, s'il veut être livré en fils d'or, doit glisser un louis au fournisseur. Les paillettes ? Il n'y faut point songer ! Les bœufs ont tout d'une denrée rare, comment donc fabriquer la gélatine nécessaire ? La mousseline, le taffetas, le satin et jusqu'à la rayonne se font rares ; on stocke le velours comme s'il se fût agi de lingots… Albert joue d'ingéniosité en adaptant à la broderie diverses substances naturelles : fibres animales et végétales, paille, raphia, lin. Il réalise même certaines pièces à partir du jute utilisé pour la confection des sacs de pommes de terre. Le fil à broder manque ? Albert recourt à la ficelle, voire à la corde… »

On a souvent dit que les Parisiennes firent de leur élégance, fût-elle d'expédients – socques de bois, semelles en pneus découpés, coutures de bas inexistants tracées au fard –, un signe d'affirmation, et de défiance face à l'occupant. La mode devient la force du faible : dans une broderie, rappelle White, exécutée par Lesage pour Schiaparelli en 1942, et représentant, en quelques traits d'or et de fuchsia, un fiacre sur un fond de soie aussi noire que l'était la nuit du couvre-feu, un couple qui s'embrasse semble affirmer avec insolence son indifférence face à l'oppression, et la liberté de son désir. Faisant de nécessité vertu, et composant avec la pénurie de produits chimiques, la mode n'a d'autre choix que de revenir à la non-couleur : aux perles de jais, aux arabesques et aux brandebourgs de passementeries en camaïeux de noir, dans des textiles souvent lourds et rêches (c'est le souvenir de cette mode contrainte et carénée que Dior voudra, de son propre aveu, exorciser avec sa collection légendaire de février 1947).

Dans son effort pour maintenir à flot l'atelier, qui lui sert aussi d'appartement et de bureau, Albert se contente d'aller, tous les quinze jours, à bicyclette à Chaville où se trouve toujours sa mère, et reste éloigné de sa famille pendant plus d'un an. Encore ne reverra-t-il Marie-Louise et les jumeaux que dans de funestes circonstances : Jean-Louis succombe à une méningite liée à la tuberculose en juin 1942. Albert parvient à traverser la zone libre pour rejoindre les siens. Il est cependant contraint de retourner rue de la Grange-Batelière au bout de quinze jours seulement. Il lui faudra cette fois attendre plus de deux ans, et la Libération, pour voir sa famille enfin réunie.

À Paris, la pression de l'occupant sur l'industrie de la mode s'accentue. Si la stratégie de Lelong, arguant de l'indissociabilité des métiers de la couture et de la capitale, parvient pendant les premières années de l'Occupation à éloigner la menace de démantèlement, la situation se tend au fur et à mesure de la progression des Alliés et de l'accroissement de la pénurie. L'oppression ne parvient cependant pas à réduire l'ingéniosité des créateurs et de leurs fournisseurs ; une certaine vie mondaine se maintient dans Paris, profitant aussi des revenus du marché noir et de l'impudeur des nouveaux riches qui tirent ressource de la détresse.

En janvier 1944 cependant, les Allemands ordonnent la fermeture de la maison Grès sous prétexte que les drapés emblématiques de la couturière ne respectent pas les limitations de métrages assignées (ils sanctionnent en fait l'irrévérence dont elle a fait preuve en plaçant au cœur de son défilé un passage provocateur de robes bleues, blanches et rouges) ; Balenciaga, surveillé de près depuis longtemps, subit le même sort ; et seules quelques maisons, plus souples avec l'occupant – Marcel Rochas, Maggy Rouff, Jacques Fath –, ne sont pas inquiétées. En mai 1944, la stratégie dilatoire de Lelong et de la Chambre de la Haute Couture a fait long feu : l'ensemble des maisons de mode parisiennes se voient intimer l'ordre de cesser toute activité sous huit semaines. C'est sans doute l'une des conséquences les moins connues et les plus décisives du 6 juin 1944 que d'avoir sauvé in extremis la haute couture française d'un diktat fatal.

L'euphorie de la Libération le cède vite aux difficultés de la situation. La pénurie persiste; on doit se contenter d'ersatz; la qualité des tissus reste médiocre; soies et fourrures sont inaccessibles; le métrage des tissus est toujours limité – d'où les réactions indignées qui accueilleront le dispendieux *New Look*, fixées pour toujours dans une célèbre photographie d'harengères déchirant avec rage la robe d'un mannequin lors d'une prise de vue. Il est d'autant plus essentiel, dans ces circonstances, de réaffirmer la tradition de l'élégance française, et le rôle central de Paris. Inaugurée en mars 1945 au Musée des Arts décoratifs, l'exposition du « Théâtre de la mode » est sans doute le signe le plus spectaculaire de cette volonté.

Reprenant l'usage des poupées de mode du XVIIIe siècle, qui permettaient de présenter en réduction les dernières créations parisiennes dans toutes les cours d'Europe, la Chambre syndicale de la Haute Couture demande à quarante couturiers, trente-six modistes et vingt coiffeurs de parer près de deux cents figurines au visage de plâtre et au corps en fil de fer de créations originales, qui représentent l'essence de la mode française. Mis en scène par Christian Bérard, dans des décors de Cocteau, Touchagues, Emilio Terry et d'autres, ce petit théâtre circulera pendant deux ans entre l'Europe et les États-Unis, mettant en lumière le savoir-faire et l'excellence des ateliers parisiens dans l'idée de reconquérir la clientèle étrangère et de la voir revenir dans la capitale. Quoique le nom de Lesage ne soit pas mentionné dans le catalogue de l'exposition, qui fait la part belle aux modistes, il n'est guère douteux que la maison soit discrètement présente sur certains modèles de ses commanditaires habituels – Lelong, Grès, Schiaparelli ou Balenciaga.

Albert Lesage, confronté à une crise aussi grave que celle qu'il avait traversée en 1931, cherche une nouvelle parade. Il la trouve, paradoxalement, dans le domaine où il avait échoué quinze ans plus tôt, celui des tissus. Il est vrai qu'il est aidé cette fois par l'un des plus prestigieux soyeux lyonnais, qui cherche ses entrées dans le monde de la haute couture. Président de la Chambre syndicale des tissus de Lyon, Jean Barrioz demande à Lesage de se faire son agent sur la scène parisienne, de présenter et promouvoir ses soieries auprès des couturiers dont il est familier, ce que ce dernier s'empresse d'accepter. Ajoutant à cette fonction celle de conseiller artistique et technique auprès de Barrioz, Albert, toujours en quête d'innovations, le pousse à s'intéresser aussi aux textiles artificiels obtenus à partir d'acétate de cellulose, fibre synthétique inventée dès 1865 mais dont certaines firmes – Rhodia en premier lieu – développent de nouveaux usages. (C'est en répondant de son côté à une autre campagne de promotion de l'acétate que Line Vautrin en tire le matériau qu'elle appelle Talosel, dont elle façonne ensuite bijoux, miroirs et objets aujourd'hui avidement recherchés.)

L'incursion d'Albert dans le textile lui permet à la fois de renforcer son offre et de pallier les baisses des commandes et la

page 100   Schiaparelli, 1952

pauvreté des matériaux disponibles dans la broderie. À l'indéfectible soutien de Schiaparelli, il peut aussi désormais ajouter les commandes d'un Balenciaga, dont la carrière prend alors véritablement son essor, et celles d'un nouveau venu, formé chez Molyneux et Lelong, qui ouvre, avec l'aide de sa mère, sa maison de couture en 1945 : Pierre Balmain. Architecte de formation, ce dernier propose une mode extrêmement structurée, régulièrement qualifiée de « sombre et sobre », qui ne dédaigne pas pour autant l'arabesque, le décor et l'ornement, en se fondant sur la grande tradition française.

Le coup d'éclat du 12 février 1947, et l'*aura* bien entretenue de Christian Dior, auront rétrospectivement contribué à rejeter dans l'ombre la réussite de Balmain, mais il connaît dès ses débuts un succès fulgurant qu'il saura prolonger jusque dans les années 1980 et qui l'amènera, en particulier, à habiller les plus grandes stars françaises et étrangères – de Danielle Darrieux, Brigitte Bardot et Michèle Morgan à Rita Hayworth, Sophia Loren ou Lana Turner. Il trouve immédiatement en Albert, puis en son héritier, une compréhension et une interprétation remarquables.

Il faudra attendre près de quarante ans pour que les noms de Dior et de Lesage, alors sous le magistère de François, se rapprochent. Car Christian Dior avait choisi de se tourner, en matière de broderie, vers l'un des anciens fournisseurs de Lelong : René Bégué, dit Rébé (1887-1987), qui restera jusqu'à la fermeture de sa maison, en 1966, le concurrent obstiné de Lesage et regrettera, sur le tard, « d'avoir cent ans et d'être passé à côté de ce qui aurait pu être une très belle amitié de métier ». S'il fallait opposer leurs deux approches, celle de Rébé s'appuie, résume Palmer White, « sur des techniques traditionnelles qui l'incitent à des effets de matières... Il joue de superpositions, d'associations (la laminette voisine avec le tube, le diamant, la cuvette) », ce qui donne souvent à sa broderie une densité, une texture, une opulence, dont Lesage fait un usage plus discret.

De leurs trois enfants, Marie-Louise et Albert voyaient en l'aîné celui qui était naturellement appelé à prendre la relève le moment venu. Esthète cultivé et raffiné, Jean-Louis ressemblait beaucoup à sa grand-mère, la comtesse Berthe, qui prit soin de lui tout au long de son adolescence, et particulièrement lors de son séjour en sanatorium. Sa disparition prématurée mit un terme à cette perspective. Par chance, ou nécessité, il se trouva que, des deux jumeaux, François ne dérogeait pas à l'esprit de famille et démontra très tôt un certain penchant pour le dessin, la couleur et l'aquarelle. Pudique, retenue dans l'expression de ses sentiments, Marie-Louise n'en était pas moins attentive, et soucieuse de la liberté de ses enfants; aussi choisit-elle de ne pas leur donner une éducation bourgeoise traditionnelle. Elle les inscrivit dans une école Montessori, dont la pédagogie favorise, comme l'on sait, l'appréhension sensorielle, progressive, ouverte du monde; et plutôt que des jeux et des jouets, elle leur offrait des livres d'art pour qu'ils se familiarisent avec une culture qui faisait, à ses yeux, le tissu même de la vie.

Rien d'aride, de contraint ni de poussiéreux dans tout cela: stricte et protectrice, selon son petit-fils Jean-François, Marie-

ci-dessus François Lesage, Los Angeles, 1948
page 104 Balmain, 1956–1957

Louise sait prendre le temps et s'adapter aux besoins et aux progrès des jumeaux. Qui plus est, les années passées – par la force des choses, et de la guerre – au Mont-Dore et à Thonon auront permis à Christiane et François de vivre en contact étroit avec la nature, de se familiariser avec ses cycles et ses formes – qui laisseront une empreinte profonde dans l'imaginaire du futur brodeur.

« Quand François a neuf ans, ajoute Palmer White, ses parents l'envoient prendre des leçons auprès d'un artiste de Versailles. À partir de reproductions d'œuvres de Léonard de Vinci ou de Michel-Ange, dessins ou sculptures, il apprend à travailler le plâtre, à en faire des moules. Le jeudi, il se rend en voiture à Paris avec son père qui le dépose rue Fontaine, chez sa grand-mère Adèle. Le déjeuner terminé, François redescend à pied jusqu'à la rue de la Grange-Batelière. Là, il va d'atelier en atelier saluer tout le monde, s'arrête pour observer les brodeuses au travail, puis étale ses affaires sur la première table disponible et se met à dessiner. »

François, comme le résume son fils, se retrouve ainsi dans le métier sans le savoir. Lorsqu'il n'est pas à Saint-Jean de Béthune – une école privée de Versailles qu'il a retrouvée à son retour à Paris en septembre 1945 (et qui sera aussi celle de Jean-François) –, il passe de plus en plus de temps dans l'atelier, qui a retrouvé son dynamisme et ne compte pas moins de vingt-cinq employées ; il dessine déjà des motifs de broderies, travaille à des échantillons, et prend l'habitude d'accompagner son père chez ses clients les plus importants – Schiaparelli bien sûr, et Balenciaga, mais aussi la « nouvelle vague » : Pierre Balmain, Jacques Fath, Jacques Heim ou Jacques Griffe. En 1946 – il a dix-sept ans –, ses parents lui font confiance au point de lui laisser la direction des équipes le temps d'un voyage dans le Sud. Et sa réussite au bac, en juin de la même année, n'est en fait que la dernière étape avant son entrée définitive dans la maison. Dès ce moment, et comme il ne cessera de le faire ensuite, il s'intéresse à tous les aspects de l'activité de l'atelier : non seulement aux dimensions esthétiques et créatives, mais aussi aux nécessités comptables (qu'il tiendra toujours à leur juste place), aux tractations avec les fournisseurs ou aux tournées avec les représentants des maisons de tissus.

Cette force nouvelle au sein d'une firme en pleine expansion dans un contexte encore marqué par la pénurie des années de guerre, il faut trouver à l'exploiter au mieux. Et quelle plus belle perspective, pour Albert, que celle d'une ouverture vers l'étranger, vers cet horizon américain qu'il avait laissé derrière lui vingt-cinq ans plus tôt ? Le sens esthétique semble infailliblement se doubler chez les Lesage, on le verra à une autre occasion, d'un certain penchant pour le nomadisme. Les coûts, sinon les risques d'une telle expédition n'étant pas négligeables à l'époque, François double sa mission de représentation et de recherche de partenaires nouveaux d'une autre, pour le compte d'un ami de la famille, Édouard Sirakian, de courtage en diamants.

Le 9 novembre 1946, il prend place à bord d'« un vieux charbonnier battant pavillon hondurien et manœuvré par un équipage grec ». La traversée sur le Myriam fut pour le moins houleuse : prévue sur neuf jours, elle en dura dix-sept : « à peine le navire avait-il pris la mer, poursuit le biographe, que la tempête se déchaina. La violence des éléments était telle que les passagers

ci-dessus   Marlene Dietrich sur le plateau de *La Scandaleuse de Berlin*, 1948
page 108   Balenciaga, 1957

durent s'attacher à leur couchette sans d'ailleurs pouvoir fermer l'œil de trois nuits! Le Myriam en arriva même à gîter de 37°. "Du pur boogie-woogie", écrira François à sa famille.» Détourné sur Baltimore à cause d'une grève, ultime épreuve après les aléas de la traversée, François Lesage gagne Philadelphie puis New York (et le quartier des diamantaires), avant de traverser d'Est en Ouest les États-Unis, de Cleveland à Chicago, puis de Saint Louis à Denver, en quête de contacts pour l'une ou l'autre de ses missions. Il se rend enfin de Salt Lake City à Los Angeles pour y retrouver la providentielle Simone Bouvet de Lozier, qui avait quitté New York pour la côte Ouest quelques années plus tôt.

Comme elle l'avait fait pour Albert, elle joue son rôle de marraine avec constance; elle introduit le jeune homme auprès de ses connaissances et amis à Los Angeles, ainsi que de nombre de figures de la communauté française de Hollywood, dont Charles Boyer est la figure de proue. Soucieux de parfaire sa connaissance d'une langue et d'une culture qu'il connaît mal, François s'installe, pour un moment pense-t-il, en colocation, suit des cours du soir à UCLA, s'inscrit en auditeur libre au Los Angeles City College ou assiste aux shows radiophoniques de NBC, le samedi soir pour se familiariser avec le langage parlé. Il n'en oublie pas pour autant sa double mission. Curieusement ses activités de courtier en pierres précieuses se révèlent plutôt infructueuses; les tractations menées au cours de ses diverses étapes ne donnent rien ou s'avèrent décevantes; c'est du côté de la broderie, en dépit des différences de goût qui séparent à ses yeux les deux cultures, que se dessinent d'intéressants débouchés.

Parmi les Français que Simone Bouvet de Lozier présente à François se trouve Jean-Louis Berthault, devenu, sous l'alibi de son seul prénom, l'un des créateurs les plus fameux de Hollywood. Ce couturier de la Columbia dont le titre de gloire était le long fourreau de soie noire de Rita Hayworth dans *Gilda* avait doublé ses activités professionnelles d'une entreprise personnelle: il habillait les stars les plus célèbres à titre privé (ce qui l'amènera à concevoir, entre autres, la fameuse robe couleur chair, constellée de paillettes, de Marylin Monroe en 1962). Rien de plus naturel dans ce contexte pour Jean-Louis que d'associer à ses créations les broderies d'un des plus célèbres ateliers parisiens. Aussi François fut-il chargé de faire venir tout un ensemble d'échantillons de la rue de la Grange-Batelière. Encouragé par ce premier succès, il entreprit de contacter les couturiers des autres studios – Adrian, Edith Head, Irene et Orry-Kelly –, figures eux aussi de la légende de Hollywood, qui l'accueillirent avec intérêt, et lui permirent incidemment de côtoyer certaines des plus grandes stars du moment, de Gene Tierney à Claudette Colbert, Olivia de Havilland et Lana Turner pour laquelle il dessina plusieurs costumes. «J'étais mignon, un peu zazou, je dessinais bien, je connaissais le métier, résume-t-il en 2009 pour *Le Monde*, j'ai habillé Lana Turner, Ava Gardner. Je savais exactement placer, là où il faut, la broderie sur Marlene Dietrich.»

Il semblait ainsi toucher au but de son voyage lorsqu'un obstacle imprévu surgit, sous la forme de droits de douane prohibitifs entre la France et les États-Unis, ce qui rendait la commercialisation des broderies parisiennes impossible. Une solution s'imposait: faire exécuter aux États-Unis les prototypes et modèles que lui enverrait Albert. Encore fallait-il trouver les équipes adéquates. Le hasard d'une rencontre – celle en l'occurrence d'une jeune brodeuse cubaine, Elsa Diaz, à la tête déjà d'un petit atelier – devait une nouvelle fois se révéler providentiel. Ils trouvèrent un terrain d'entente, puis un lieu où s'installer: une paradoxale maison en bois sur Sunset Boulevard, qu'ils décorèrent avec l'aide de la chambre de commerce française de Los Angeles. Travaillant à la fois pour le cinéma, les créateurs et une clientèle privée, l'atelier connut des débuts prometteurs: il ne fallut rapidement pas moins de dix brodeuses pour assurer le suivi des commandes. Avec en perspective le tournage annoncé par les studios de plusieurs épopées cinématographiques avec leurs lots de costumes, François considérait avec confiance l'avenir et le développement de l'atelier américain. Il envisageait même de prolonger son séjour pour faire face à la situation, lorsqu'une lettre de Paris vint tout remettre en cause.

L a lettre venait de son oncle, Louis Favot, et révélait à François l'état de santé inquiétant de son père, victime depuis quelques mois de graves troubles cardiaques, et à qui avait été imposé un repos absolu. Confiant la direction de la boutique de Sunset Boulevard à Elsa Diaz et Simone Bouvet de Lozier, François partit immédiatement pour New York, avant d'embarquer sur le premier bateau disponible, un navire de transport de troupes.

Il ne retrouva son oncle au Havre que fin juin et apprit qu'il arrivait quinze jours trop tard.

Marie-Louise reprit immédiatement la direction de la maison, et elle avait fort à faire : la disparition d'Albert ouvrait un vide dont les concurrents, Rébé le premier, ne manqueraient pas

d'essayer de profiter. Le succès de la collaboration dans le domaine du tissu avec les soyeux lyonnais avait eu pour conséquence un certain désinvestissement dans celui de la broderie; si quelques noms nouveaux – ceux de Jacques Heim, Jean Dessès ou Carven – étaient venus s'ajouter au registre des clients, d'autres, auxquels la maison avait été longtemps liée – Lelong, Piguet, Callot, Rochas – étaient partis. Marie-Louise pouvait compter sur la fidélité de Jacques Fath, Balmain et Balenciaga, mais aussi et surtout sur la détermination de François, héritier tout désigné. Il lui restait, malgré son expérience précoce, beaucoup à apprendre. Il n'était familier que de certains aspects du métier, n'avait qu'une vision partielle de la mise au point d'une broderie. Il n'avait jamais suivi l'élaboration d'un modèle dans sa totalité, de l'idée d'un motif à sa réalisation, des discussions avec les créateurs au placement final sur le vêtement.

S'il avait accompagné son père lors de ses visites auprès de certains couturiers, il ne connaissait pas véritablement le monde et les rituels de la mode auxquels l'avènement triomphal du *New Look* en 1947 avait donné un élan nouveau. La quinzaine d'années qui suivit la fin de la guerre fut marquée par une frénésie de fêtes et de bals, publics ou privés, improvisés ou somptueux où l'on rivalisait d'originalité et d'invention le temps d'une soirée, d'une mascarade ou d'une garden party. Il s'agissait à la fois d'un sursaut de soulagement, d'une célébration du retour à la vie après les horreurs de la guerre et des derniers feux d'une société mondaine dont les rites et les rythmes de vie remontaient au début du siècle et qui devait disparaître avec les années 1960.

Ce fut aussi, par la conjonction de talents remarquables, l'âge d'or de la haute couture parisienne. Schiaparelli, que François connaissait bien depuis ses visites avec Albert, persistait dans les fantaisies les plus extrêmes; elle eut une profonde influence sur le jeune brodeur et sur la vision de son métier – sur la nécessité d'expérimenter, de prendre des risques : grâce à elle, écrit Palmer White, «François eut l'idée de développer à son tour des thèmes pour ses propres collections de broderies. Grâce à elle encore, il se mit à employer des matériaux insolites, à rechercher des effets inattendus, amusants. Ainsi l'atelier Lesage mangea-t-il des

page 114   Balenciaga, 1956
page 116   Balenciaga, 1959
page 117   Grace Kelly en Balenciaga, photographiée avec le prince Rainier III, 1959

118

moules durant tout un hiver, car Elsa Schiaparelli voulait des broderies... coquilles incluses ». (L'histoire – celle de la mode en particulier – n'étant qu'un éternel recommencement, l'atelier subit à nouveau la même ordalie quelques décennies plus tard lorsque Christian Lacroix reprit, en hommage amusé, le procédé.)

François put aussi poursuivre et approfondir la relation avec l'autre client d'exception de la maison, Cristóbal Balenciaga, qui l'encouragea, à son tour, dans la voie de l'innovation : le noir des boléros et des vestes ajustées, aux connotations hispanisantes, trouvait un complément naturel dans celui des pampilles et des perles de jais contrastant avec le rouge sang d'un chemisier ou d'arabesques brodées. Avec Balenciaga, ajoute Palmer White, « François apprit à utiliser la dentelle de Chantilly, à l'appliquer sur satin, à faire des bordures baroques, à créer des éléments aux allures de cuir de Cordoue », matières et procédés qui trouveront un emploi nouveau, à plus de trente ans d'écart, dans sa collaboration avec Christian Lacroix. À côté des matériaux traditionnels, s'imposaient des créations récentes : dérivé de l'acétate de cellulose, que l'on a déjà évoqué à propos des tissus créés en collaboration avec Jean Barrioz, le rhodoïd se présente comme un film transparent, dur et brillant, que l'on peut teinter de diverses couleurs ; François eut l'idée de l'associer à de la chenille noire de façon à contraster les textures, relevant d'éclats cassants le pelucheux de cette dernière : « il en fit des cabochons, des triangles en relief, des pastilles enserrées dans un voile de cigaline, crépon de nylon chiffonné, qui donna à la broderie un aspect absolument neuf. »

L e héros du moment était cependant, bien évidemment, Christian Dior qui parvint, dans les dix ans que dura sa courte carrière, à prolonger le coup d'éclat du *New Look* par une succession de «lignes» au graphisme très marqué et une rare intuition commerciale (dans la création de parfums et d'accessoires par exemple). François parvint finalement à franchir la ligne de défense établie par Rébé autour du couturier en lui proposant des broderies moins opulentes, plus stylisées que celles auxquelles l'avait habitué son concurrent, en particulier pour les collections d'été aux matériaux plus souples et légers que ceux d'hiver. La relation que Lesage était parvenu à nouer avec la maison Dior fut cependant interrompue par la disparition brutale du couturier. Elle ne devait que mieux reprendre avec son successeur, Yves Saint Laurent.

« Comète dans le ciel de la mode », comme on le décrivit alors, Jacques Fath vit lui aussi sa carrière interrompue par une mort prématurée, des suites d'une leucémie, en 1954 ; l'éclat du succès de Dior a aussi rétrospectivement fait pâlir l'étoile de Fath, et obscurci l'importance de son rôle à l'époque. Moins formelle que celle de son aîné, sa mode se veut plus jeune et libre : elle trouve son emblème dans la féminité juvénile de Brigitte Bardot, qui porte plusieurs de ses modèles, et son incarnation dans la figure mutine de ses mannequins fétiches, Lucky ou Bettina. Aussi habile d'un point de vue commercial que Dior, avec lequel il entretenait une forme d'émulation, Fath se distinguait de celui-ci par la fluidité et l'ampleur de modèles qu'accentuait son habitude de draper les métrages de tissu à même le corps des mannequins.

Dans son désir de se présenter comme le couturier de la jeunesse et de la fraîcheur, il fila tout au long de sa carrière la métaphore des « jeunes filles en fleur », plaçant au cœur de sa création la thématique florale (il présenta en 1950 une collection « Lys » et donna à celle de 1953 des tonalités végétales). Comme il laissait toute latitude à François Lesage, ce dernier imagina pour lui aussi bien des brins de fougère en perles de verre teintées que des feuillages de crin brodés sur un fond de tulle. Il alla même, rapporte White, jusqu'à concevoir pour l'un des bals somptueux où Fath brillait avec sa femme Geneviève une robe éphémère : composée de brins d'asparagus, relevés d'éclats de strass entre deux épaisseurs de tulle, elle devait être vaporisée toutes les deux heures de façon à conserver sa fraîcheur au végétal.

Pierre Balmain, autre client du moment, partageait le même goût pour les motifs floraux, mais ils sont chez lui traversés de réminiscences historiques et renvoient – comme sa palette aux tonalités amorties de jaune paille et de vert sauge, de beige et de nacre, de vieux rose et d'argent – à la version stylisée qu'en donna le XVIIIe siècle. Le nom seul de ses modèles – « Versailles », ou « Zaïde » – suffit à le signifier. Formé chez Molyneux et Lelong, où il travailla avec Dior, Balmain échappera, lui, à la fatalité d'une disparition prématurée, restant à la tête de sa maison jusqu'à sa mort en 1982, ce qui en fit l'un des clients les plus fidèles de Lesage pendant près de quarante ans.

page 120   Création Lesage, automne-hiver 1958–1959
pages 122-123   Balmain, automne-hiver 1958–1959

Le nom de Balmain reste indéfectiblement associé à l'expression « Jolie Madame » dont il tira le nom d'un célèbre parfum, créé en 1949, mais aussi, dans la lancée, le thème de sa collection de 1952. Mêlant les réminiscences des caprices à la Pillement et des semis de fleurs ornant les gilets du xviiie siècle aux dentelles rebrodées, François fit de la robe phare de cette collection une éblouissante démonstration de virtuosité; chef-d'œuvre d'ingéniosité pourtant surpassé six ans plus tard par une autre robe emblématique, laconiquement dénommée « Paris », qui alliait les matériaux traditionnels, tels les rubans rococo, à d'autres totalement neufs, comme les paillettes de paille, les sequins martelés et les roses de soie aux couleurs fanées de la maison Judith Barbier.

À côté de son travail pour d'autres clients, célèbres à l'époque et que le temps a effacés, comme Jacques Griffe ou Jean Dessès – pour lequel François reprend la technique de l'ombré chère à Vionnet ou constelle une superbe robe à pétales de perles soufflées aux reflets irisés –, le jeune brodeur entame une collaboration avec un couturier de son âge, croisé quelques années plus tôt chez Schiaparelli dont il était l'un des collaborateurs, et qui ouvre sa propre maison en 1952 en la plaçant plutôt sous l'invocation de Balenciaga. François Lesage ne sait pas que le dialogue qu'il entame ainsi avec Hubert de Givenchy sera encore plus long que celui qui le liera à Pierre Balmain, et ne prendra fin qu'avec l'adieu du premier au monde de la couture, en 1995.

Balenciaga, Balmain et Givenchy restent les piliers de la maison Lesage dans la décennie suivant la mort de Dior – qui est aussi celle d'une redéfinition fondamentale du monde et des valeurs de la mode. La dynamique de la reconstruction, la progression des classes moyennes, l'urbanisation, la standardisation, les débuts de l'émancipation féminine, le changement des rythmes de vie conduisent, entre autres facteurs, à l'émergence et à l'affirmation d'un nouveau registre de création, plus accessible, moins formel que celui de la haute couture. C'est le grand moment de l'utopie futuriste, de la célébration du progrès et de l'innovation technologiques. Traduction de l'esprit du temps, la mode se veut dynamique, dégagée, épurée, adaptée à un corps libre et (fondamentalement) jeune.

Peu de place, supposera-t-on, pour les raffinements minutieux de la maison Lesage dans la mode monochrome d'un Courrèges, dans les jeux optiques d'un Cardin ou dans les cottes de maille d'un Paco Rabanne. Mais, le premier choc passé, les couturiers amis de Lesage savent adapter leur vision (Balenciaga ni Balmain n'ont jamais été, de toute façon, des adversaires de la litote et de l'épure); s'ils prennent à leur tour le biais de l'époque, ils n'en sacrifient pas pour autant leur goût des matières riches et précieuses, de ce supplément d'âme qui caractérise la haute couture.

La recherche constante de la nouveauté, pour ne pas dire de la modernité, qu'ont toujours cultivée, on l'a vu, les Lesage se traduit alors (comme quelques années plus tôt avec l'utilisation de l'acétate de cellulose) par l'introduction et l'expérimentation de matériaux nouveaux – ce que François développe à l'époque dans une rare pétition de principes : « L'art de la broderie traditionnelle, écrit-il, consiste à employer les mêmes techniques et les mêmes matériaux classiques, quel que soit le style du dessin. L'essence même de la broderie dans la haute couture est d'associer des techniques et des matériaux que nous n'avons pas coutume de voir réunis. C'est le secret de la création. On peut lancer de nouveaux textiles en tissant de la laine sur des métiers à soie ou de la soie sur des métiers à laine. La broderie se renouvelle avec l'introduction de toutes sortes d'éléments qui ne lui sont pas nécessairement destinés : plumes, fourrures, coquillages, cuirs, laines, cristaux de roche que nous pouvons tous intégrer aujourd'hui. Nos sequins, loin d'être placés un par un, peuvent être mis par paquets. Pour obtenir du relief, il suffit que la disposition des tubes suggère la profondeur... L'important, c'est de créer un effet neuf et toujours inattendu, de la réaliser à la perfection. À l'inverse de la machine, la main ignore les limites. »

Et Palmer White, qui a recueilli cette déclaration, d'en énumérer les résultats : ce sont des motifs de papier peint sur soie, des applications de mousseline sur toile d'organdi brodée au point de dentelle, des « sequins, strass et tubes sur du tulle ou du crêpe

page ci-contre   Balmain, 1955
page 126   Balenciaga, 1960

ci-dessus   Cristóbal Balenciaga, 1927
page 132   Balenciaga, 1967
page 133   Balenciaga, 1961

pour susciter opacité et transparence, motifs de rhodoïd découpés ou emboutis… effets de tissage obtenus grâce à l'association de fils de soie avec de la paille ou de la chenille de cellophane…». Jamais à court de ressource, François traite aussi «le thème des jardins vus à travers des stores vénitiens en recouvrant un ensemble fleuri de baguettes de rhodoïd. Il joue de cabochons disposés sur des fonds de mosaïques multicolores, de galons de cellophane tressés, incorpore à ses broderies des plumes enserrées dans un tulle protecteur… Il obtient de nouveaux effets en créant des fonds rythmés de paillettes, de petites fleurs, de feuilles de trèfle, d'étoiles, de rectangles et de plumes de plastique, de cabochons et de tartans écossais». Ce ne sont là que les premiers effets de cette capacité jubilatoire à innover qui sera définitivement associée au nom de François Lesage, digne héritier de la tradition familiale, et qui fera son succès.

L'ouverture, ces années-là, de sa propre maison par Yves Saint Laurent après son passage chez Dior marque aussi un tournant, et coïncide avec l'avènement de nouveaux créateurs dans la haute couture, plus ou moins proches en âge de Lesage, dont ils resteront tout au long de leur carrière les partenaires privilégiés: Emmanuel Ungaro et Jean-Louis Scherrer, dans leurs maisons respectives, Marc Bohan chez Dior, Michel Goma chez Patou ou Jules-François Crahay chez Lanvin. Sur les lignes simplifiées du moment (entre «mini» et «maxi»), usant de motifs volontiers géométriques ou abstraits, ils persistent à s'inscrire dans une vision du métier dont Balenciaga sera parmi les premiers à juger, en fermant sa maison en 1968, qu'elle ne correspond plus à l'esprit du temps. Yves Saint Laurent la soutiendra avec splendeur pendant plus de trente ans, avant d'en arriver à la même conclusion, Mais il aura entre-temps été l'un des principaux acteurs d'une redéfinition de la mode, et de l'apparition d'un nouveau registre de création.

S'il est évident qu'Yves Saint Laurent aura considéré jusqu'à la fin de sa carrière la haute couture comme son véritable moyen d'expression, on ne saurait oublier que la création de la ligne Rive Gauche en 1966 en fit aussi l'un des protagonistes essentiels de l'avènement du prêt-à-porter – qui devait fournir quelques décennies plus tard, on y reviendra, un terrain d'expérimentation inépuisable à François Lesage. À ses débuts, la collaboration entre le brodeur et le couturier, dont sortiront de véritables chefs-d'œuvre, se situe cependant dans le droit fil de la tradition de la couture parisienne : lorsqu'Yves Saint Laurent se tourne vers Lesage, c'est d'abord vers celui qui fut l'interlocuteur de Vionnet et de Schiaparelli, figures de sa mémoire et de sa vision de la mode. Les dizaines de lèvres de strass constellant un manteau du soir la collection printemps-été 1971 offrent comme un premier hommage à la créatrice de la place Vendôme, hommage qui se prolonge de loin en loin dans les collections du couturier : par exemple dans les variations en 1979-1980 sur les motifs de la *commedia dell'arte* réinventés par Cocteau et Picasso, dans le col brodé de strass et de lames d'or d'une veste de satin de l'hiver 1980-1981 ou dans le soleil de broderies rayonnantes sur lequel se détachent deux oiseaux de la collection « Braque » en 1988.

Dans les années 1970, l'une des premières réussites de la collaboration entre Lesage et Yves Saint Laurent consiste en une série de longs cardigans brodés de motifs aux multiples variations (« imitations de pulls irlandais, pieds de poule en trompe-l'œil, imitation lézard, écaille, croco, écorces d'arbres et bien d'autres »). Défiant la résistance des matériaux pour répondre aux exigences des créateurs (Yves Saint Laurent, mais aussi Marc Bohan chez Dior), François travaille aussi bien des matières rigides, comme le cuir, que réputées impossibles à cause de leur fluidité élastique, comme le jersey (on doit le renforcer d'une doublure que l'on élimine, une fois la broderie achevée).

Ces exploits ne sont pourtant que le prélude à une succession de défilés Yves Saint Laurent devenus légendaires dans l'histoire de la mode, et pour lesquels Lesage fit preuve d'une virtuosité stupéfiante. Collection « russe » de 1976, puis « chinoise » l'année suivante, collection « Diaghilev et Picasso » de 1979 – que suivront celles dédiées à Apollinaire et Cocteau, à Matisse, Léger ou Braque (pour laquelle la réalisation de plastrons en forme d'aile d'oiseau exigea des trésors d'inventivité). Succession qui culmine dans l'« hommage aux artistes » de 1988 dont les chefs-d'œuvre restent évidemment les vestes entièrement brodées sur le motif des iris et des tournesols de Van Gogh : exigeant plus de six cents heures de travail, elles furent réputées les plus chères du monde. Mais Yves Saint Laurent pouvait aussi bien s'amuser à semer des citations en lettres de suède noir relevées de strass sur le satin rose *shocking*

page ci-contre   Cape Yves Saint Laurent, collection « Braque », haute couture printemps-été 1988. Photographiée lors du défilé rétrospectif Yves Saint Laurent, janvier 2002

136   *page 134*   Yves Saint Laurent, Hommage à ma Maison, haute couture printemps-été 1990

d'une veste du soir, ou faire resplendir « les yeux d'Elsa » en lames de strass et d'or rehaussées de jais sur un fond de velours bleu Nattier.

Au début des années 1980, en conséquence de ce regain d'activité, l'atelier s'est considérablement développé : il comprend un chef dessinateur, cinq dessinatrices, deux modélistes, une assistante, une chef de fabrication, des échantillonneuses et les brodeuses ; fidèle à l'esprit qui restera le sien, François considère ses collaborateurs comme une seconde famille, qui n'est pas sans prendre parfois le pas sur la première : « au moment des collections, dit-il à *L'Officiel de la Mode*, nous couchons ici. Des lits de camp sont prévus. Le soir, je fais moi-même la cuisine. Le dimanche à midi, nous sommes quarante à déjeuner. » Cette forme de vie en phalanstère (que pratiquera plus tard Azzedine Alaïa dans son atelier de la rue de Moussy) se justifie aussi par la fréquente nécessité de répondre aux demandes toujours urgentes, et toujours tardives, des créateurs (travers qui reste aujourd'hui encore l'apanage des maisons de mode pour lesquelles nul travail ne semble valide s'il n'est fait dans l'urgence). Il en résulte une équation vertigineuse qui rassemble en une seule donnée contradictoire les délais impossibles, les quarante heures nécessaires à la mise au point du moindre échantillon (de vingt-cinq sur vingt-cinq centimètres) et la nécessité de trouver une idée qui satisfasse le désir du couturier. « Une feuille qui tombe, une couleur d'automne peuvent être le point de départ d'une idée, explique alors François, j'ai trouvé le thème de la dernière collection à trois heures du matin en feuilletant un journal : tout est parti d'un camélia. La collection était née. » Alliance de hasard heureux et de discipline acharnée qui définira le travail de l'atelier, de saison en saison. Les années suivantes verront encore s'emballer cette mécanique de précision.

Rien qui ne soit plus fait pour attiser l'imagination et la créativité de François que cette exaltation de l'ornement, que cette infinie liberté de l'imagination, que ce jeu sur les apparences. François Lesage partage avec Yves Saint Laurent le goût du trompe-l'œil et des coqs à l'âne visuels, goût qu'il développera plus tard lorsqu'il lancera une ligne d'accessoires : plastrons en

page ci-contre   Yves Saint Laurent, 1983
page 138   Katoucha Niane porte un modèle de la collection « Braque »
d'Yves Saint Laurent, haute couture printemps-été 1988. Photographie prise
lors du défilé rétrospectif Yves Saint Laurent, janvier 2002.
page 139   Yves Saint Laurent, collection « Aria », haute couture printemps-été 1988

141

faux-relief sur des robes du soir, faux-plis – au sens propre – sur des jupes, pseudo-ceintures de cordes brodées... « À ces trouvailles, poursuit Palmer White, il ajoute de nouvelles techniques en appliquant un à un des motifs prédécoupés qu'il fixe sur le tissu grâce à de nouveaux films thermofusibles. Ce procédé va lui permettre des miracles jusqu'alors impossibles avec la gutta-percha, substance gommo-résineuse qui colle trop vite et laisse des traces. Au cours des années suivantes, François perfectionne cette méthode et peut ainsi apposer sur ces créations des films thermoplastiques ayant l'aspect des feuilles d'or que le doreur des Invalides appliquait, du temps d'Albert Lesage, sur les robes d'Elsa Schiaparelli. »

François ne réserve cependant pas ses tours de force à Yves Saint Laurent; pour la collection indienne présentée par Jean-Louis Scherrer pour l'été 1981, il rivalise en virtuosité avec les brodeurs de Madras dont son fils utilisera ensuite le savoir-faire : il adapte les motifs traditionnels du cachemire avec des fils d'or et des appliques de lamé sur un fond rebrodé de paillettes vert sauge; en hommage à Fortuny, il propose à Givenchy et Balmain une interprétation des motifs caractéristiques du couturier vénitien, en utilisant des films thermofusibles qui lui permettent d'appliquer des aplats d'or sur de la mousseline de soie, de la panne et des velours froissés, matériaux de prédilection de Fortuny. Pour Hanae Mori enfin, avec laquelle il commence à collaborer trois ans après l'ouverture de sa maison de couture, en 1980, il imagine aussi bien des nuées de papillons diaphanes, emblèmes de la créatrice, qu'un semis de cristaux de neige en strass et fils d'argent sur un boléro de satin bleu nuit, ou une longue veste entièrement brodée de feuillages en camaïeux de paillettes mauves et bleues sur fond noir.

Autant que par le *power suit*, par une nouvelle définition de la féminité, par la silhouette carénée et les fortunes récentes, les années 1980 sont marquées par l'émergence de la « mode de la mode », l'affirmation du prêt-à-porter, qui se développe internationalement, et par le surgissement de nouveaux créateurs dont l'individualité devient immédiatement image de marque. L'une des conséquences obliques, et imprévues, de cette transformation pour la maison Lesage sera une troisième aventure américaine, totalement couronnée de succès cette fois. Dans leur contraste même avec leurs confrères européens (leur mode est considérée, depuis Claire McCardell et d'autres, plus simple, fonctionnelle, mieux adaptée au goût d'une large clientèle que celle de Paris), les créateurs new-yorkais avaient acquis une importance nouvelle, en particulier depuis un défilé historique, réunissant à Versailles, en 1973, certains grands noms de la couture des deux continents, dans l'idée d'affirmer une communauté de statut.

On n'associe pas spontanément la définition que l'on pourrait qualifier de pragmatique de la mode américaine au culte débridé de l'ornement et des broderies étincelantes. Au début de l'été 1982 pourtant, Calvin Klein, qui tenait pour ainsi dire le haut de l'image des créateurs d'outre-Atlantique, saisit le prétexte des présentations des défilés parisiens pour franchir le seuil de la Grange-Batelière. Devant le savant désordre de l'atelier, les tiroirs débordant de perles, de tubes, de broderies, d'échantillons, le couturier réagit, pour reprendre l'expression de François Lesage, comme « un enfant dans une pâtisserie ». « Conquis, poursuit Palmer White, il en commanda des dizaines et des dizaines pour la collection qu'il devait présenter à la fin du mois d'octobre, soit trois mois plus tard. La maison Lesage travailla jour et nuit tandis que l'assistant de Calvin Klein sautait tous les trois jours dans un Concorde pour emporter les modèles terminés. » Le succès amenant le succès, et face à l'accueil que reçut la collection, François se décida, quoiqu' « un peu intimidé » selon son biographe, à présenter ses modèles – comme il l'avait fait, cette fois-là sans complexe, à Los Angeles quarante-six ans plus tôt – à l'aristocratie de la couture new-yorkaise : Bill Blass, Geoffrey Beene ou Oscar de la Renta, qu'il devait retrouver plus tard à la tête de Pierre Balmain, auxquels allaient s'ajouter Carolina Herrera, Mary McFadden et Carolyne Roehm. Une nouvelle nuée de fidèles venait ainsi s'ajouter à sa clientèle.

La couture parisienne n'était pas en reste, et ce moment est en particulier pour Lesage celui d'une rencontre capitale avec l'un des acteurs les plus en vue du monde de la mode dont le transfert et le changement de statut défraient alors la chronique. On verra les conséquences imprévues, et radicales, qu'elles devaient avoir sur le destin de la maison. Dans la haute couture, et surtout le prêt-à-porter, l'atmosphère est alors à l'émulation et aux défis décomplexés ; les créateurs semblent vouloir rivaliser en inventivité et – de Klimt à Kandinsky, des ailes d'insectes aux motifs tribaux ou à une plage jonchée de débris (réalisée pour

page ci-contre Détail d'une veste créée par Karl Lagerfeld pour Simone Veil
à l'occasion de sa réception à l'Académie française, 2010
page 146 École Lesage, 1996

148

Thierry Mugler) – François se voit donner, comme, de son côté, le parurier Robert Goossens, les sources d'inspiration les plus hétéroclites et les plus baroques. «Un jour, rapporte *Le Monde*, Yves Saint Laurent l'appelle : "venez voir !" Il accourt. Saint Laurent lui montre le reflet du lustre en cristal et du ciel de Paris dans les miroirs de Lalanne, et lui dit : "je voudrais ça." M. Lesage revient avec trois versions, les lumières du matin, du midi et du soir. Saint Laurent s'exclame : "C'est merveilleux ! On va toutes les faire !" À raison de trois cent cinquante heures de broderie pour chaque pièce... »

Ces année-là ne sont pas ennemies de l'excès (on se contentera d'évoquer les onze mille heures de travail et le million de dollars requis pour l'ornementation de la cape, de la robe et de la traîne de l'épouse d'un potentat africain qui se voulut empereur en 1977). Elles sont surtout celles d'un bouleversement dans la haute couture – dont le chiffre d'affaires, rappelle Palmer White, augmente de vingt-cinq pour cent entre 1980 et 1981 – et du surgissement, dans un fracas de formes et de couleurs, de Christian Lacroix. L'entente entre le jeune créateur et François fut immédiate, au point que le premier reconnut le second comme son parrain de mode.

Rien ne pouvait mieux satisfaire au goût du « risqué » (comme disent en français les Anglo-Saxons) dont a toujours fait preuve Lesage que les effets de collage et la liberté de mélanges chers à Lacroix. Ce fut, dans la collection Patou de l'été 1985, une chemise, mi-texane mi-camarguaise, d'organza jaune d'or, rebrodée de sequins, sur laquelle se détachaient des cœurs de jais et de fragments de miroir ; des découpes, l'année suivante, de cuir repoussé, doré ou couleur bronze, aux motifs animaliers ou floraux, dont François proposa toute une gamme et que le couturier compliqua de motifs de bois pétrifié ; un bustier de velours noir aux larges spirales d'or mat, inspiré des dessins de Bakst, qu'accompagnait à l'été 1986 une robe feu, peinte à la main, parcourue de grandes volutes noires... L'ouverture de sa propre maison par Christian Lacroix le 26 juillet 1987 devait sceller, plus qu'une collaboration, une amitié qui ne s'interromprait qu'avec la disparition de François vingt-cinq ans plus tard.

Cause ou effet, la vision jubilatoire que portait Lacroix s'imposa à un moment où le prêt-à-porter, qui ne cessait de gagner en importance (financière et médiatique) et dont le chiffre d'affaires atteignait en 1982 le milliard de francs, semblait prendre des allures de haute couture. S'ouvrit alors une période d'une dizaine d'années où tout sembla possible : affirmant leur désir d'opulence, les créateurs commencèrent à intégrer dans leur prêt-à-porter des broderies que l'usage et leur coût réservaient jusqu'alors à la haute couture – ce qui eut pour effet immédiat de stimuler l'activité de l'atelier, et d'en accroître le nombre d'employées. Afin d'équilibrer les moments d'intense production, précédant les collections, et les temps intermédiaires, où il fallait désormais faire travailler une centaine de brodeuses, François décida d'ajouter un nouveau registre à ses activités – et incidemment un autre terrain d'expérimentation – en créant une ligne d'accessoires et de bijoux brodés qui seraient vendus dans une boutique écrin, place Vendôme (coïncidence remarquable : cette boutique avait auparavant été celle de Schiaparelli).

Il s'adjoignit pour cela, en 1985, les services d'un jeune styliste, Gérard Trémolet, qui avait commencé sa carrière, à vingt ans, chez Jean-Louis Scherrer, avant de rentrer dans une maison d'accessoires dont il dirigeait l'ensemble de la production, de la conception à la mise en place commerciale, ce qui était évidemment un atout majeur pour Lesage. Pour François, c'était aussi une façon de renouer avec un épisode ancien de l'histoire de la maison : les bijoux et objets brodés qu'Albert avait exécutés pour Schiaparelli dans les années 1930. Lesage put ainsi proposer en nom propre des manchettes et bracelets, colliers et boucles d'oreilles, sacs, étoles, châles, ceintures et sautoirs, souvent en trompe-l'œil, dans les matériaux les plus divers : cristaux et paillettes aussi bien que tessères d'un stock ancien de mosaïques, ou perles de jais et pierres du Rhin du XIXᵉ siècle.

Insensiblement, François Lesage s'était imposé comme un créateur à part entière, l'interlocuteur, une fois encore, plutôt que le fournisseur des grands couturiers. Cette décennie est pour lui celle d'une reconnaissance, sinon d'une consécration. Il reçoit le Grand prix des Métiers d'art, ainsi que la médaille de la ville de Paris en 1984, puis le grand prix de la Création de la ville cinq ans plus tard. Rare distinction, la maison est admise en 1990 au sein du Comité Colbert, qui rassemble, illustre et défend les plus grandes signatures du luxe français. Une première exposition consacrée à l'histoire de Lesage est organisée au Fashion Institute of Technology de New York en 1987, et précède d'un an une autre rétrospective au Musée Galliera, reprise ensuite à Tokyo et Los Angeles.

page ci-contre   Fei Fei Sun porte un modèle Chanel, haute couture printemps-été 1984.
Photographie de Steven Meisel pour le numéro de mai 2015 du *Vogue* américain
page 154   Chanel, 1983

Mettant à profit cette période de vaches grasses, par essence précaire, François investit dans le futur : il recherche et accumule tout ce qu'il peut trouver de matériaux rares ou délaissés, provenant des stocks de maisons fermées ou en voie de l'être avant leur dispersion (dont soixante tonnes de perles et de paillettes anciennes) ; il classe tant bien que mal les cinquante mille échantillons des archives, dont ceux de Michonet, entassés rue de la Grange-Batelière ; il rachète Hamelin, firme de broderie pour ameublement, dont le siège se trouvait rue du Mail, et qui jouera un rôle imprévu dans le développement futur de la maison. Dans le respect et l'admiration qu'il porte à toutes les formes de talents, il partage aussi l'aventure d'un jeune couturier danois dont le hasard avait fait son voisin d'immeuble : fort de ce soutien, Lars Hillingso (1938-2005), qui créera ensuite plusieurs tenues pour Margrethe de Danemark et sa mère Ingrid de Suède, connaîtra pendant une dizaine d'années le succès avec sa marque « Lars, Paris » que François soutiendra avec une rare libéralité, et dont il exécutera régulièrement les broderies des robes de soirée.

Enfin, s'inquiétant de l'avenir d'un artisanat dont la seule force tient à l'excellence et au renouvellement de ses « petites mains », François décide en 1992 d'adjoindre aux ateliers une école destinée à perpétuer le savoir-faire unique de brodeuses dont certaines (surnommées « les anciennes ») étaient nées au tout début du XXᵉ siècle – école qui fait désormais partie intégrante de l'entreprise Lesage, connaît un succès international et forme aussi bien des passionnées de broderie que de futurs talents de la mode.

Généreux de nature, et plus cigale que fourmi, François ne vit cependant pas arriver le temps des vaches maigres, pas plus qu'il ne pouvait imaginer l'ampleur de la crise dont l'économie serait l'objet à la fin des années 1980. Les effets cumulés du second choc pétrolier, de la récession, de la chute de l'emploi industriel, de l'effondrement de la bourse – en même temps que de fortunes hâtivement constituées – se traduisirent par la disparition soudaine d'une clientèle, en particulier moyen-orientale, qui avait jusque-là dépensé sans compter. À cela, s'ajouta – intuition une fois encore ou symptôme – une redéfinition totale du champ de la mode, avec l'arrivée des créateurs japonais, la vague de la déconstruction, l'esthétique minimaliste, la contestation grunge : peu de place dans ces visions ascétiques, sinon aucune, pour le plaisir de l'accessoire, la sensualité de l'ornement, l'accent vif et enlevé d'une broderie. Il fallut fermer la boutique de la place Vendôme.

François mettait en regard la crise de 92 avec celle de 29 : si la seconde semblait, du point de vue général, plus radicale que la première, elle était tout aussi extrême en ce qui concernait Lesage : de même qu'Albert dans les années 1930, François était confronté à un abrupt revers de situation. En dépit de la relation quasi paternelle qui le liait à sa « famille » de brodeuses, il dut se résoudre à licencier quelques-unes de ses « filles », sans espoir de reprise étant donné la concurrence nouvelle d'ateliers beaucoup moins chers dans une économie de la mode qui ne connaissait plus désormais de frontières. Il alla même jusqu'à puiser largement dans sa fortune personnelle pour maintenir l'atelier à flots.

Tandis que s'amorçait le mouvement de concentration et de polarisation autour de quelques groupes de luxe qui n'a cessé de s'affirmer depuis, la figure du « styliste », interprète de tendances, supposé capter ou traduire l'instant (et faire fonds des nécessités du marketing), s'imposait aux dépens de celle du couturier, dont la vision du présent s'inscrit dans un imaginaire propre, variant au cours du temps. Le retrait d'Yves Saint Laurent en 2002, celui, aussi injuste et regrettable que prématuré, sept ans plus tard, de Christian Lacroix, le « filleul » de François, sont les deux signes les plus éclatants de cette transformation. L'avenir des maisons résolument indépendantes, comme l'avait toujours été Lesage, tributaires en outre d'une définition de la couture devenue pro-blématique, semblait au moins incertain. Le mal appelant le remède, il fallut toute l'intelligence, et l'intérêt bien compris, d'une des maisons phares de l'industrie de la mode, Chanel, pour aider François, telle une *Dea ex machina*, à sortir de l'impasse ; qu'elle se soit elle aussi définie comme une entreprise de famille, discrète dans sa visibilité même, ne peut relever du simple hasard.

ci-dessus   Inès de La Fressange porte un modèle Chanel, haute couture automne-hiver 1983–1984
double page suivante   Chanel, haute couture automne-hiver 2016–2017

Une autre perspective oblique, lumineuse, familiale et imprévue, allait pourtant s'ouvrir dans ces années troublées de l'histoire de Lesage.

François avait eu trois enfants – Martine, Jean-Louis et Marion – de son premier mariage avec Colette Oudenot, ancienne styliste chez Jacques Griffe, et un quatrième, une dizaine d'années plus tard, de sa seconde épouse, Gisela Grube von Klewitz, créatrice de masques pour l'opéra. Né le 28 décembre 1965 – le même jour, à quelques décennies d'écart, que sa grand-mère maternelle qui appartenait à l'aristocratie berlinoise et dont il aimait la distinction discrète –, Jean-François démontra très tôt une sensibilité esthé-tique dont avaient fait preuve avant lui son père, son grand-père, et

ci-dessus   Jean-François Lesage, Pondichéry, 2009
page 164   Atelier Vastrakala, Chennai, Inde

jusqu'à son arrière-grand-père, Gustave, qui avait été responsable d'édition chez Hachette, où il s'occupait en particulier des techniques de gravure et d'illustration.

François, de son côté, n'était pas Albert : prématurément séparé de son père par les circonstances que l'on a vues, élevé par ses grands-parents, il avait une conception rien moins que fusionnelle de la famille. Les enfants devaient à ses yeux rester libres, comme lui-même l'avait été, de trouver et suivre leur propre voie. Quoique profondément aimant, et tendre, il n'était pas très présent, absorbé comme il l'était par son travail, et son autre famille symbolique, plurielle, de l'atelier. Plus ou autant qu'un père, il était pour Jean-François un modèle, un guide, un parrain, un ami, une présence bienveillante.

Passionné d'histoire dès l'enfance, ce dernier aimait à se perdre dans les lectures de récits et de biographies, et il nourrissait un penchant particulier pour le décor et les cadres de vie des siècles passés, qu'il s'amusait parfois à reconstituer en bricolant du polystyrène. Ayant passé son enfance dans la maison familiale à Chaville, il fit ensuite ses études – sans grand enthousiasme, à vrai dire – à Saint-Jean de Béthune, où François l'avait précédé. Échappant à la fatalité qui avait malgré tout poussé ce dernier à prendre la suite de son père, il passa un bac littéraire, puis poursuivit des études de droit et d'histoire de l'art à l'École du Louvre pour devenir commissaire-priseur, faisant ainsi son métier de la passion qui l'avait amené à fréquenter la salle des ventes de Versailles, et les antiquaires dans la foulée, dès l'âge de seize ans.

Un voyage en Inde dont la culture l'avait toujours fasciné, et qu'il avait visitée pour la première fois quand il avait dix-neuf ans, allait totalement changer la donne, et modifier le cours de sa vie. Il évoque même un moment clef – illumination ou scène primitive – lorsqu'un soir de black-out à Bénarès, il fut saisi par le spectacle de la seule tache de lumière qui se détachait sur cet océan d'obscurité : s'y découpait la silhouette d'un brodeur au travail dans la solitude de son atelier, tout à sa tâche, comme indifférent à la réalité qui l'entourait. « Ma rencontre, confie-t-il à un journaliste, avec des brodeurs indiens à Bénarès au début des années 90 a réveillé en moi le virus familial, tout en annihilant l'envie d'une autre destinée. »

Il découvre au cours d'un deuxième voyage, à Madras cette fois, la tradition immémoriale des villages de brodeurs dans la région. Liant son goût du décor, sa passion indienne et l'activité emblématique de la famille, il imagine de créer un studio utilisant le savoir-faire des brodeurs indiens pour exécuter certaines des commandes de Hamelin. Quoi de plus naturel en effet, pour un passionné d'histoire des formes et des objets, que ce retour au commerce de la broderie entre les comptoirs de l'Inde et la France, tel qu'on le pratiqua à la fin du XVIII siècle et, par-delà, dès les premiers temps d'une technique mythiquement venue de Perse ?

C'est ainsi qu'en 1993, franchissant un pas supplémentaire, il crée avec son ami Patrick Savouret et deux partenaires indiens, Malavika Shivakumar et Sandeep Rao, une association qui reflète la nature mixte de l'entreprise, la société Vastrakala («l'art du tissu» en sanskrit); il s'y donne pour but de rassembler, et de faire travailler dans les meilleures conditions possibles, les brodeurs jusqu'alors dispersés dans différents villages de la province du Tamil Nadu (État dont Madras, devenue Chennaï, est la capitale). Fournissant Paris en broderies dont le coût est sans comparaison avec celui des ateliers de la capitale, il assure à ses brodeurs un revenu et un cadre de vie incomparables en Inde, faisant preuve d'un souci éthique qui ne l'a jamais quitté. «Je ne travaille pas, explique-t-il en 2010, avec l'idée en tête que la broderie est française ou indienne, parce qu'elle est perse. Mais je marie les spécificités françaises et indiennes pour donner à notre broderie une plus-value inégalable. La France est un creuset d'expérimentation, alors que l'Inde est fidèle au maintien et à l'équilibre de sa tradition. C'est pour cela qu'il faut imaginer un partage des forces et des faiblesses.»

Munis de leurs aiguilles et de leurs crochets, suivant les procédures millénaires du métier (dessin, piqure des contours du motif, transfert et ponçage), brodant entre deux et cinq centimètres carrés par heure, adoptant suivant l'occasion les techniques universelles du point lancé et du point velours, du point riche et du point d'ombre, les artisans de Madras réalisent d'incroyables tours de force, ne serait-ce que par l'ampleur des surfaces auxquelles ils sont le plus souvent confrontés.

double page précédente   Chambre de Jeanne Lanvin créée en 1925, désormais au
Musée des Arts décoratifs, Paris. La broderie, créée en collaboration avec F.-J. Graf,
est une reproduction à l'identique de l'originale.

Sous l'impulsion de Jean-François, et grâce aux liens qu'il avait noués dans ses activités antérieures, ils ne tardent pas à travailler pour les décorateurs les plus en vue du moment : Alberto Pinto, Jacques Garcia, François-Josef Graf, Juan-Pablo Molyneux, Jacques Grange, Roberto Peregalli, Jean-Louis Deniot, Peter Marino et bien d'autres. Mais les milliers d'heures de travail des brodeurs ne sont pas réservées qu'à une clientèle privée et fortunée ; c'est autant la réussite de prestigieuses commandes publiques qui assure la renommée et le succès de l'entreprise. Si le premier exploit de la maison est la réplique à l'identique du décor de l'Opéra Garnier de Monte-Carlo (« nous avons refait le bandeau du rideau de scène, les lambrequins de la loge princière et des loges latérales d'après une photo ancienne dans un délai de six semaines »), c'est sans doute la restauration de la chambre de Jeanne Lanvin au Musée des Arts décoratifs – dont les murs, les rideaux, radiateurs et bouchons de radiateur sont entièrement brodés – qui en est la manifestation la plus visible. Mais il ne s'agit là que de repères dans la voie toujours ouverte des défis qui se présentent chaque jour et comprennent des travaux aussi divers que la restauration de la chambre du roi et du lit à baldaquin de Madame Fouquet à Vaux-le-Vicomte, la salle à manger d'état du vice-roi à Delhi ou le mobilier, les tapisseries et tentures d'un salon du château de Moritzburg près de Dresde.

Plutôt sceptique au départ, et gardant son quant à soi (aller s'installer en Inde lui paraissait « inimaginable »), François ne tarda pas à reconnaître le bien-fondé de l'entreprise, allant jusqu'à rendre visite à son fils plusieurs fois à Madras. Cette ramification imprévue de l'histoire de Lesage se dessinait au moment où les ateliers de Paris recommençaient à travailler pour une couture dynamisée par l'arrivée au sein des grandes maisons françaises de créateurs étrangers – John Galliano, Marc Jacobs, Alexander McQueen, pour ne citer qu'eux –, mais ce regain d'activité ne suffisait pas à lever toutes les hypothèques sur le devenir de l'entreprise et la sauvegarde du savoir-faire unique que l'on y cultivait.

Si l'on peut mettre au passif de la nouvelle définition de la mode focalisée et mondialisée qui émergea pendant les dernières années du XXᵉ siècle une certaine prédominance du marketing et du retour sur investissement, il faut saluer, à l'inverse, l'intelligence qu'eurent certains acteurs de se dégager de cette emprise immédiate, en misant sur le long terme. Tributaire du tour de main unique de ses artisans et paruriers, Chanel en particulier prit très vite conscience de la situation incertaine dans laquelle se trouvaient certains d'entre eux qui risquaient de bientôt disparaître faute de successeurs.

Le rachat en 1985 du parurier Desrues, à l'initiative de Françoise Montenay qui dirigeait alors Chanel, fut le point de départ d'une succession d'autres, la maison de la rue Cambon se donnant pour mission de sauvegarder des savoir-faire essentiels, au service des plus grands noms de la mode. Le passage d'un siècle à l'autre vit donc la création d'une filiale, significativement nommée

Paraffection, destinée à acquérir et soutenir plusieurs maisons d'art qui la fournissaient depuis parfois l'époque de Mademoiselle Chanel. À Desrues, vinrent progressivement s'ajouter le plumassier Lemarié, le bottier Massaro, le chapelier Michel, l'orfèvre Goossens – pour ne citer que ces quelques noms – au sein d'une structure qui compte à présent, sous la direction du successeur de Françoise Montenay, Bruno Pavlovsky, président des activités mode de Chanel, plus d'une trentaine de maisons et manufactures, et qui semble toujours ouverte à de nouvelles possibilités d'acquisition.

Nul ne semblait plus justifié que Lesage à faire partie de cet ensemble, la raison la plus visible en étant la collaboration et l'estime réciproque qui le lièrent à Karl Lagerfeld dès l'entrée de ce dernier chez Chanel. Figure centrale de l'essor du prêt-à-porter dans les années 1970, le couturier avait créé la sensation en entrant, en 1983, dans une maison qui faisait alors figure de belle endormie, et qu'il se proposait de réveiller avec le sens et le savoir de la mode qui le caractérisaient. Fidèle à son goût des jeux d'esprit et des clins d'œil, Lagerfeld se lança alors dans le travail d'interprétation de l'univers de Chanel. Initiant une collaboration dont ni l'un ni l'autre ne pouvaient alors prévoir les conséquences, il se tourna vers Lesage pour les collections de haute couture, lui donnant comme première source d'inspiration les fameux paravents de Coromandel dont Chanel s'était entourée sa vie durant. « En 1983, avec Karl, résuma Lesage pour *Le Monde*, ça a démarré tout seul : allez voir les Coromandel, m'avait-il dit, et c'était parti. »

Ce n'était là, en fait, que le point de départ d'une série de variations sur le motif dont les plus mémorables furent sans doute celles de trois manteaux brodés de la collection haute couture automne-hiver 1996 qui n'exigèrent chacun pas moins de huit cents heures de travail. C'était aussi le premier d'innombrables tours de force et de démonstrations virtuoses (restée dans les mémoires, une robe brodée de fils d'or, inspirée d'un objet d'art hindou de la haute couture printemps-été 1996, nécessita près de mille deux cents heures de travail).

Jouant de façon ludique et décalée avec les thèmes exemplaires de la créatrice de la rue Cambon – le camélia, les perles, le matelassé, les chaînes, les bijoux fantaisie, et même le tweed –,

page ci-contre   Shalom Harlow dans une robe créée par Karl Lagerfeld pour la collection Chanel haute couture printemps-été 1996. Photographie d'Irving Penn pour le numéro du *Vogue* américain d'avril 1996.

174   *page 172*   Chanel, haute couture automne-hiver 1983–1984

Lagerfeld proposa à Lesage de les traiter, au fil des collections, dans les matériaux les plus inattendus – béton, plastique, bois, raphia, métal –, autant de suggestions qui ne pouvaient qu'en appeler au goût du risque et au désir d'innovation du brodeur.

Une somptueuse robe brille, dès la première collection haute couture de l'été 1983, des feux de bijoux baroques brodés en trompe-l'œil, parures illusoires qui trouveront une nouvelle interprétation, à plus de trente ans d'écart, dans les collections de l'hiver 2016. Le losange matelassé et la chaînette d'or du sac Chanel font à leur tour l'objet d'une transposition malicieuse sur un tailleur rebrodé de paillettes noires et gansé d'une chaîne en trompe-l'œil de l'automne-hiver 1986. Motif qui revient quatre ans plus tard, sur un mode plus précieux, entièrement brodé de perles, avant de donner lieu sur un tailleur de la collection automne-hiver 2015 à un étonnant effet 3D, qui vaudra à cette création les honneurs du Metropolitan Museum de New York.

Constituée d'une véritable cage de camélias ajourés en tulle brodé, une robe du soir de 1997 offre l'exposition la plus spectaculaire d'un thème insistant d'un bout à l'autre de la collaboration entre Lesage et Lagerfeld, sous les formes les plus diverses et dans un graphisme parfois très stylisé, brodé de perles, de paillettes ou de chaînes. La référence récurrente à Chanel – qui inspire aussi bien les motifs de mosaïques de la collection «Paris-Byzance» de 2010 que ceux, étoilés, de la collection «Paris-Dallas» de 2013 – ne constitue pas pour autant la source unique à laquelle puise, au cours des années, l'imaginaire de Lagerfeld, et François Lesage se verra aussi bien proposer des interprétations de Kandinsky (en 1986 puis 1998), Malevitch (en 2002) ou Popova (en 2008) que de ce XVIIIe siècle qui représente aux yeux du couturier l'une de ses sources d'inspiration privilégiées: de la blancheur mate des biscuits de Sèvres (haute couture printemps-été 1985) aux tonalités d'un Watteau ou d'une boîte de nacre précieuse. Entrée chez Chanel en 1987, Virginie Viard, qui prendra la direction artistique des collections mode en 2019, fera ses premiers pas au studio de création de la maison en charge de ces broderies pour les collections de haute couture, créant un lien étroit avec le couturier et François Lesage.

L'offre faite à François, en 2002, de faire entrer sa maison dans Paraffection était à la fois comme la conséquence logique de cette longue collaboration et la réponse toute trouvée au souci du brodeur de sauvegarder l'entreprise, d'assurer le futur de sa « famille », le développement de l'école et de toutes les formes de transmission d'un savoir pour lesquelles il avait lutté depuis tant d'années. C'était certes aussi ne plus être *totalement* maître chez soi, perdre un peu de la souveraineté dont il avait toujours été si jaloux, mais le sacrifice était léger, car Chanel avait l'intelligence supplémentaire de laisser toute liberté de création aux maisons et à ceux qui leur avaient donné leur identité, après leur entrée dans Paraffection. La complicité de François avec Karl Lagerfeld s'en trouvait renforcée, sans que cela signifie pour autant une collaboration exclusive avec la rue Cambon : le projet même de sa nouvelle filiale était d'assurer la subsistance, à tous les sens du mot, des maisons choisies, c'est-à-dire *aussi* de leur permettre de continuer leur collaboration avec leurs clients réguliers et de répondre aux demandes nouvelles qui se présenteraient.

La dernière décennie de la vie de François Lesage fut ainsi délivrée du souci de la survivance, et des contraintes de la gestion ordinaire, ce qui lui permettait de se consacrer à sa passion d'inventer : à la fois pour des clients familiers, tels Valentino, John Galliano (chez Dior) ou Marc Jacobs (chez Vuitton), mais aussi pour des créateurs alors au début de leur trajet, comme Alexandre Vauthier, Jason Wu ou L'Wren Scott.

Sa disparition, le 1er décembre 2011, ne lui permit pas de voir la traduction littérale, et admirable, de ce dialogue entre l'ancien et le nouveau – entre deux moments aussi de l'histoire de Lesage – avec la collection de dix-huit modèles qu'imagina, en juillet 2013, Christian Lacroix pour Schiaparelli : occasion symbolique pour les ateliers de boucler la boucle, de donner corps au dialogue entre deux univers exubérants, consonnants, et de se surpasser dans l'exécution d'une soutache de jais sur un boléro rouge sang, ou dans la sublimation d'une écrevisse décorative à la carapace et aux antennes constellées de perles.

L'intégration dans un grand groupe, la volonté de développer et de promouvoir la marque, les demandes et la prospection de nouveaux clients, tout cela n'était évidemment pas sans conséquences. Peu après le rachat de Lesage par Chanel, il devint évident que les locaux de la Grange-Batelière étaient désormais trop exigus, et malcommodes, pour répondre aux exigences de la situation. Dans un souci compréhensible d'économie, aux multiples sens du terme, la maison de la rue Cambon décida de regrouper la plupart des métiers d'art que comprenait Paraffection dans un lieu unique, spacieux et fonctionnel.

Les ateliers et les archives Lesage partirent ainsi rejoindre ceux de Lemarié, Massaro, Maison Michel ou Goossens dans un ancien site industriel de plusieurs milliers de mètres carrés sur les bords du canal de l'Ourcq, à Pantin – quartier alors au début d'une transformation qui en a fait depuis un pôle important de la création de mode. Cette décision n'impliquait pas de renoncer aux cinq étages de la rue de la Grange-Batelière, partie intégrante de l'identité de Lesage. On se proposa d'y développer l'école, qui faisait face à des candidatures de plus en plus nombreuses, avant

d'accueillir un peu plus tard les bureaux parisiens de l'entreprise de Jean-François, elle aussi rentrée désormais dans le cercle des métiers d'art sous le nom de « Lesage intérieurs ».

Ce que l'on perdait en poésie, on le gagnait en capacité et en efficacité. Quatre-vingt tonnes de fournitures et plus de soixante-quinze mille échantillons de broderies firent ainsi en 2012 le voyage des petits appartements, bourgeois et contournés, du IXᵉ arrondissement aux espaces lumineux et fonctionnels, fussent-ils légèrement aseptisés, de la banlieue nord.

Entrée trente ans plus tôt, sur les conseils d'une amie, chez Lesage qu'elle n'avait pas quitté depuis, Murielle Lemoine, rapidement devenue responsable des achats, avant de s'occuper des relations avec le prêt-à-porter aux côtés de François, fut le témoin d'une transformation dont ce dernier ne vit que l'amorce : la crise du début des années 1990 liée à la première guerre du Golfe s'était traduite par un bouleversement total du champ, et de la définition même, de la mode, entraînant une réduction drastique du nombre des clientes de la haute couture et la progression exponentielle d'un prêt-à-porter qui changeait à son tour de nature, se rapprochant toujours plus de la sophistication de la couture. C'était la conclusion à proprement parler renversante du processus entamé dans les années 1970. Tel l'effet du battement d'aile d'un papillon, le déménagement à Pantin n'était au fond qu'un lointain effet de cette mutation, comme l'était la disparition de nombre d'ateliers et de fournisseurs (en ce qui concerne la seule activité de Lesage, ils passèrent en une trentaine d'années de près de cinq cents à un peu plus d'une centaine).

Une autre parade imaginée par François face à cette situation et à la restriction des travaux de broderies pour la haute couture avait été de se tourner, comme Albert avant lui, vers l'industrie textile pour y développer de nouvelles activités. « Je vais croiser des fils », décréta-t-il, répondant d'abord de manière plutôt empirique au désir de Karl Lagerfeld de « réinventer » le matériau emblématique de Chanel, à savoir le tweed. Les premiers essais, tissés par un atelier auquel il s'était adressé, évoquaient plus la serpillière qu'autre chose, ce dont ce tweed aventureux garda ironiquement l'appellation. Il fut ensuite confié à une spécialiste

page ci-contre   Chanel, haute couture printemps-été 2016
page 182   Chanel, prêt-à-porter printemps-été 2017
pages 184–185   Gigi Hadid avec Karl Lagerfeld pendant les essayages
de la collection Chanel haute couture printemps-été 2016

187

ci-dessus   Hubert Barrère, 2018
page 188   Vittoria Ceretti porte le modèle en tweed Diane,
Chanel collection croisière 2017–2018
page 189   Chanel, collection croisière « Versailles » 2012–2013
page 190   Chanel, prêt-à-porter printemps-été 2013
page 191   Chanel, prêt-à-porter printemps-été 2014

de ce genre de tissage, Maria Messner, dont l'entreprise, située dans le sud-ouest de la France, se donnait comme principe «de tisser l'impossible». Créée en 1996, sa société ACT 3 (pour «Association Création Tissage») avait aussi beaucoup travaillé avec Christian Lacroix et, comme l'indiquait sa devise, ne reculait devant aucun défi. Couleurs, textures, matériaux, rien qui n'échappe à la recherche de l'innovation et au désir d'imprévu. De la volonté initiale de Lagerfeld d'échapper à l'usage et à l'image classique du tweed, en la défaisant littéralement, sortit ce «tweed serpillière» déconstruit, effiloché, intégrant les matériaux les plus disparates et les plus inattendus au gré des collections (jusqu'à inclure des fermetures éclair ou des fils de nylon).

De ces multiples expériences allait surgir un champ de création inédit pour Lesage. La recherche sur le tweed permit d'ouvrir de multiples horizons, jusqu'à justifier la création d'un secteur dédié dans l'activité des ateliers. Suivant la politique habituelle de la maison, et des Métiers d'art en général, aux deux créatrices amenées à se consacrer exclusivement aux travaux pour Chanel, s'ajouta une équipe répondant aux besoins des autres créateurs et aux commandes ponctuelles.

Autre acteur de la réinvention de Lesage, Hubert Barrère avait croisé à de multiples reprises le chemin de François Lesage. Appartenant à la race des rêveurs, le jeune Hubert avait passé son enfance à lire et à dessiner, fasciné par l'univers de la mode et ne s'imaginant pas d'autre destin. Il lui fallut pourtant mettre ses rêves de côté pour mener de patientes études de notariat et satisfaire ainsi aux injonctions familiales. Mais rien ne saurait submerger une passion profonde. Laissant ses études en plan au grand dam de ses parents, il choisit de s'inscrire à l'École de la Chambre Syndicale de la Couture Parisienne pour y suivre une formation de styliste modéliste. La vie d'expédients et de petits boulots que supposait un tel choix n'était rien face au bonheur de suivre enfin sa vraie voie, celle qui allait l'amener à rencontrer François Lesage.

Son passage chez divers brodeurs concurrents directs de la Grange-Batelière n'avait en rien obéré la relation entre les deux hommes, qui se voyaient régulièrement pour déjeuner et discuter. L'admiration pour François Lesage et sa maison, le souci

ci-dessus   Dalila Betka et Véronique Barbier dans l'atelier Lesage de Pantin, 2018
page 194   Chanel, haute couture automne-hiver 2013–2014
page 195   Chanel, haute couture automne-hiver 2013–2014
page 196   Chanel, haute couture automne-hiver 2015–2016
page 197   Ondria Hardin porte un modèle Chanel, haute couture automne-hiver 2015–2016

ci-dessus Margot Perotin (à gauche) et Caroline Maréchal (à droite) dans l'atelier Lesage de Pantin, 2018
page 200 Chanel, défilé Métiers d'art « Paris–New York » 2018–2019
page 201 Chanel, haute couture automne-hiver 2013–2014
pages 202–203 Chanel, haute couture automne-hiver 2013–2014
page 204 Dior, haute couture automne-hiver 2017–2018
page 205 Valentino, haute couture printemps-été 2014

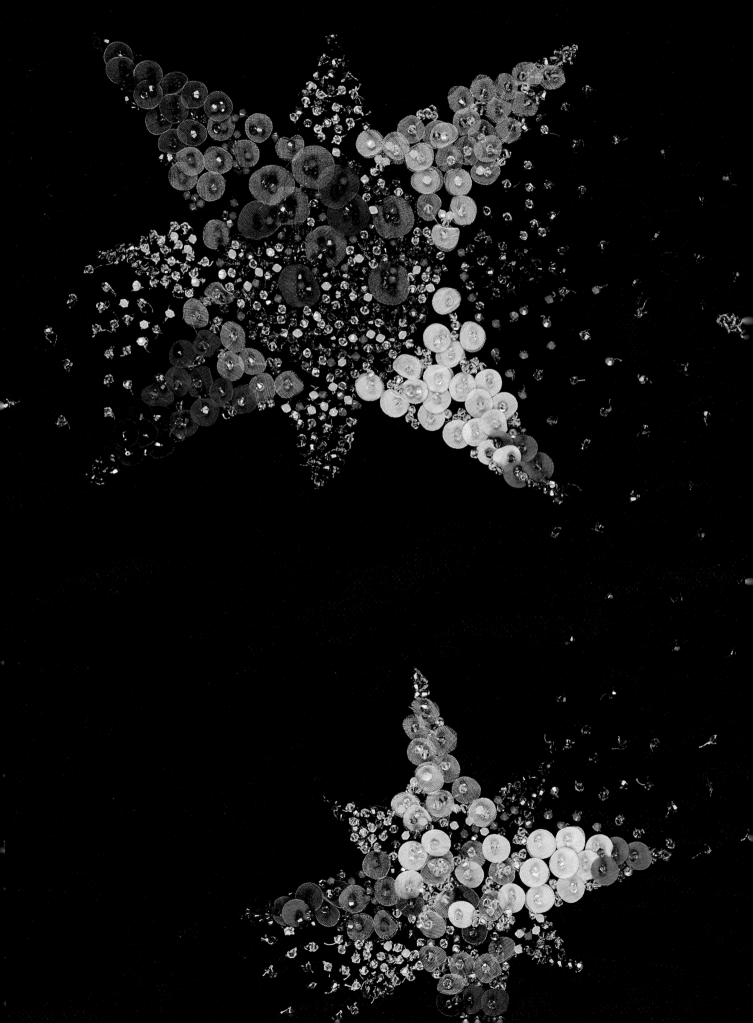

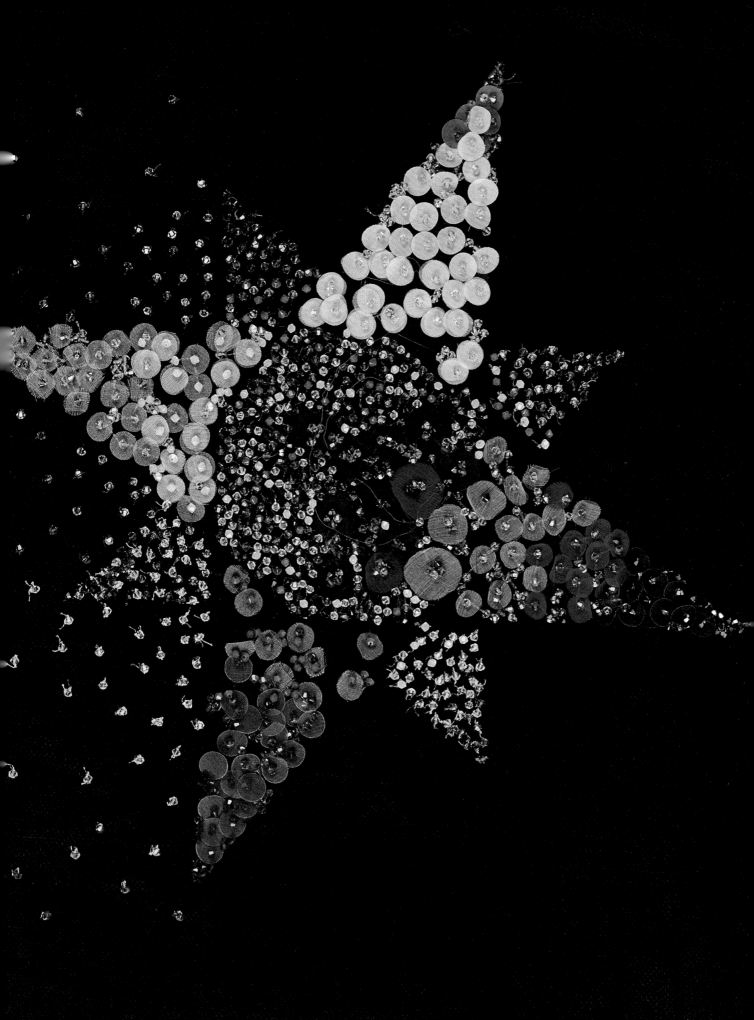

de sauvegarder son héritage, la collaboration nouée dès 1997 avec Karl Lagerfeld et Virginie Viard (alors directrice du studio), la connaissance des broderies historiques des créations de Chanel, amenèrent Hubert Barrère à accepter la proposition de Paraffection et à se voir confier, chez Lesage, la direction artistique de la maison, et plus particulièrement les relations avec la maison de la rue Cambon dont les huit collections annuelles n'exigent chacune pas moins de cinquante à cent échantillons.

Initiés au début des années 2000, les défilés destinés à mettre en lumière le travail des Métiers d'art, présentés chaque année dans une ville différente, demandent un effort particulier de virtuosité et d'invention, car il ne s'agit pas seulement d'une démonstration de savoir-faire, mais aussi de broder les accessoires – sacs, gants et chaussures – conçus en résonance avec les robes, tailleurs et manteaux dans les matériaux, encore une fois, les moins prévisibles.

La volonté de respecter tradition et savoir-faire sans pour autant s'en tenir à une formule figée, le souci d'innovation qui constitue depuis Albert et François un leitmotiv de l'histoire de Lesage, et l'irruption aujourd'hui des nouvelles technologies, comme le laser ou la 3D, semblent repousser de fois en fois les limites du possible. Le même souci de l'avenir se traduit par la perspective d'un second déplacement géographique des ateliers, et leur installation, en 2020, dans une «maison de mode», Porte d'Aubervilliers, dont Chanel a confié la conception à l'architecte Rudy Ricciotti, et qui assurera la possibilité de nouveaux développements à la créativité des artisans brodeurs et des maisons des Métiers d'art.

Comme dans tant d'autres domaines où les capacités humaines semblent désormais débordées par l'avancée technologique, chacun des acteurs de l'histoire présente de Lesage sait bien pourtant que la véritable raison d'être – et le futur – de la maison ne tient qu'à ces quelques gestes que décrivait déjà, à la fin du xviiie siècle, Charles-Germain de Saint-Aubin et à l'intelligence de cette main invisible qui, après avoir piqué la feuille de papier, transféré le dessin en une fine pluie de craie et bien fixé son tissu, commence, avec l'aiguille et le crochet, son lent, très lent travail de patience.

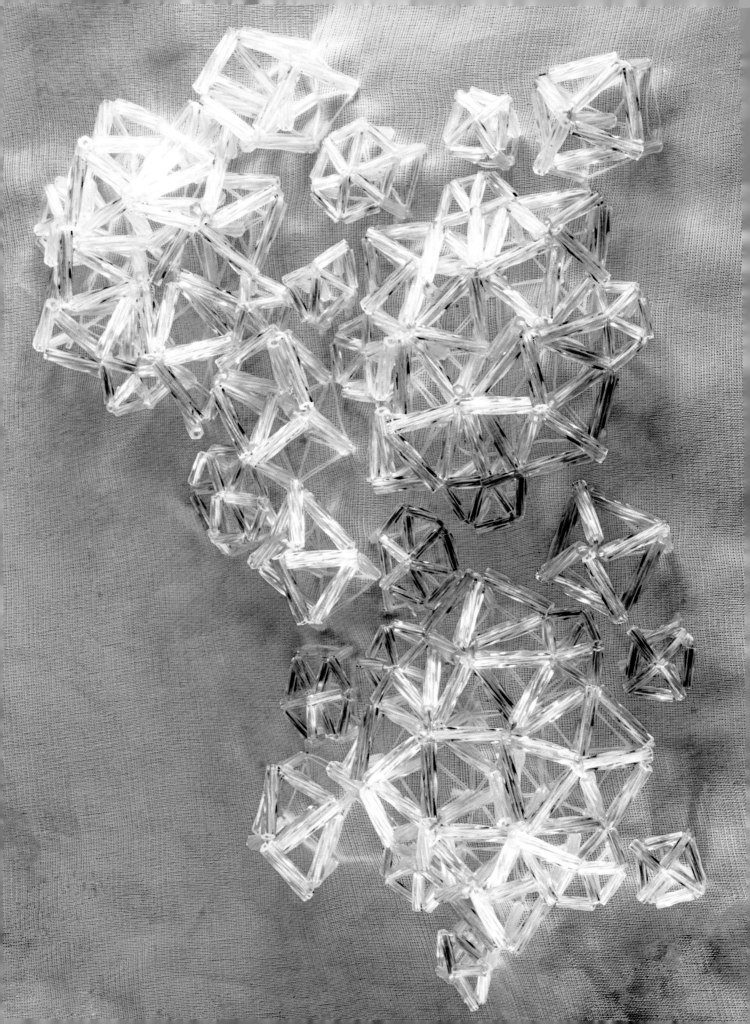

ci-dessus   François Lesage au 13 rue de la Grange-Batelière, Paris, 2001

NOTES

Si Lesage a été l'objet d'innombrables articles depuis sa création, il n'existe qu'un véritable livre sur la maison – celui de Palmer White, *Haute Couture Embroidery: The Art of Lesage* (Simon & Schuster, New York, 1994), traduit en français la même année sous le titre *Lesage, Maître-Brodeur de la Haute Couture*, aux Éditions du Chêne, Paris.

Visiblement écrit sur les conseils et sous le regard vigilent de François Lesage, ce livre reste la source essentielle à laquelle puiser pour tout ce qui concerne l'histoire de la maison jusqu'à la fin des années 1980 ; et le présent ouvrage ne saurait minimiser sa dette à son égard.

p. 11 « tout se briserait sans eux », célèbre citation de Madame Necker

p. 15 « tout l'élan que donne un régime monarchique... », H. Baudrillart, *Histoire du luxe privé et public*, Paris, 1881, IV, p. 583

p. 19 « à développer ni l'épargne chez les pauvres, ni la vertu chez les riches... », *ibid.*, p. 655

p. 19 « la broderie connut un tel essor que plus de quarante ateliers », Palmer White, *Lesage, Maître-Brodeur de la Haute Couture*, Éditions du Chêne, Paris, 1994, p. 25

p. 26 « Il était temps, lui sembla-t-il, de s'en aller chercher le bonheur, la vie – ailleurs. », *ibid.*, p. 33

p. 37 « l'aînée des trois sœurs, une perfectionniste », *ibid.*, p. 47

p. 39 « jamais par une fermeture à glissière, le vêtement tombe en plis harmonieux. », *ibid.*, p. 48

p. 51 « de dessiner sur coton l'emplacement destiné à la broderie. », *ibid.*, p. 37

p. 57 « va jusqu'à utiliser une table de logarithmes pour calculer les proportions », *ibid.*, p. 48

p. 62 « Albert craint de plus en plus que ce chiffre ne passe à neuf. », *ibid.*, p. 58

p. 69 Selon sa biographe, Meryle Secrest, *Elsa Schiaparelli: A Biography*, Fig Tree, Londres, 2014

p. 69 « le gouffre entre les styles décontracté et habillé », *ibid.*, p. 77

p. 69 « un triomphe en terme de mélange des couleurs », *ibid.*, p. 78

p. 80 « latex, cellophane, crêpe de rayonne, tulle et tricots », White, *op. cit.*, p. 62

p. 85 « de l'avis unanime, le sommet de sa création, et de celle d'Albert Lesage », Palmer White, *Elsa Schiaparelli: Empress of Paris Fashion*, Aurum, Londres, 1986, pp. 164–170

p. 85 « alors que des fougères ornaient leurs revers. », *ibid.*, p. 170

p. 86 « et elle ne se répétait jamais », entretien avec François Lesage dans *L'Express*, 8 juin 1984, cité in Secrest, *op. cit.*, p. 198

p. 89 « la somme rondelette de 1 551 539 francs », *Lesage, Maître-Brodeur, op. cit.*, p. 66

p. 97 « Albert recourt à la ficelle, voire à la corde », *ibid.*, p. 74

p. 103 « ce qui aurait pu être une très belle amitié de métier », *La Dépêche*, 11 avril 2009

p. 107 « étale ses affaires sur la première table disponible et se met à dessiner », White, *Lesage, Maître-Brodeur, op. cit.*, p. 83

p. 111 « écrira François à sa famille », *ibid.*, p. 86

p. 112 « pour laquelle il dessina plusieurs costumes », *L'Officiel de la Mode*, nº 680, 1982, pp. 282-283

p. 112 « placer, là où il faut, la broderie sur Marlene Dietrich. », « François Lesage, artificier de la haute couture », *M le Mag (Le Monde)*, 27 janvier 2009

p. 118 « à rechercher des effets inattendus, amusants », White, *Lesage, Maitre-Brodeur, op. cit.*, p. 100

p. 119 « à créer des éléments aux allures de cuir de Cordoue », *ibid.*, p. 102

p. 119 « nylon chiffonné, qui donna à la broderie un aspect absolument neuf », *ibid.*, p. 102

p 124 « vaporisée toutes les deux heures de façon à conserver sa fraîcheur au végétal », *ibid.*, p. 99

p. 128 « À l'inverse de la machine, la main ignore les limites », *ibid.*, p. 108

p. 131 « l'association de fils de soie avec de la paille ou de la chenille de cellophane... », *ibid.*, p. 109

p. 131 « plumes de plastique, de cabochons et de tartans écossais », *ibid.*, p. 110

p. 136 « écaille, croco, écorces d'arbres et bien d'autres », *ibid.*, p. 118

p. 141 « en lames de strass et d'or rehaussées de jais », *ibid.*, p. 124

p. 141 « La collection était née », *L'Officiel de la Mode*, , art. cit.

p. 148 « pour emporter les modèles terminés » : White, *Lesage, Maitre-Brodeur, op. cit.*, pp. 32-33

p. 151 « À raison de trois cent cinquante heures de broderie pour chaque pièce... », *M le Mag (Le Monde)*, art. cit.

p. 159 « dont ceux de Michonet, entassés rue de la Grange-Batelière », Veronica Horwell, « François Lesage », *The Guardian*, 5 décembre 2011

p. 167 « tout en annihilant l'envie d'une autre destinée », Olivier Michel, « La broderie française renaît à Madras », *Le Figaro Magazine*, 2 janvier 2010

p. 170 « imaginer un partage des forces et des faiblesses. », *ibid.*

p. 171 « une photo ancienne dans un délai de six semaines », *ibid.*

CRÉDITS PHOTOGRAPHIQUES

p. 140   Jean Marie del Moral
p. 143   Courtesy archives Lesage et Chanel, Paris
pp. 144–146 Jean Marie del Moral
p. 149   Courtesy archives Lesage et Chanel, Paris
pp. 150,
152–153   Jean Marie del Moral
p. 154   © Olivier Saillant
p. 157   © Steven Meisel/Art + Commerce
p. 158   © Olivier Saillant
p. 161   Dick Ballarian. Courtesy archives Lesage
             et Chanel, Paris
pp. 162–166 Courtesy archives Lesage et Chanel, Paris
p. 168   Musée des Arts décoratifs, Paris. © MAD,
             Paris/Tholance
p. 169   Musée des Arts décoratifs, Paris. © MAD,
             Paris/Philippe Chancel
p. 172   Courtesy archives Lesage et Chanel, Paris
p. 175   Irving Penn, *Vogue* © Condé Nast
p. 176   Musée des Arts décoratifs, Paris/Jean
             Tholance/akg-images
p. 179   Cathleen Naundorf, 15.11.2016.
             Photostudio, Paris

p. 180   Cathleen Naundorf, 07.04.2016.
             Photostudio, Paris
p. 181   Cathleen Naundorf, 07.04.2016.
             Photostudio, Paris
p. 182   Jean Marie del Moral
pp. 184–185 Benoît Peverelli. Courtesy archives Lesage
             et Chanel, Paris
pp. 186–191 Courtesy archives Lesage et Chanel, Paris
p. 192   Jean Philippe Raibaud
p. 194   Courtesy archives Lesage et Chanel, Paris
p. 195   firstVIEW.com
pp. 196–203 Courtesy archives Lesage et Chanel, Paris
p. 204   Victor Virgile/Gamma-Rapho
             via Getty Images
p. 205   Pascal Le Segretain/Getty Images
pp. 206–209 Courtesy archives Lesage et Chanel, Paris
p. 210   Jean Marie del Moral
pp. 211–223 Courtesy archives Lesage et Chanel, Paris

REMERCIEMENTS

L'auteur et l'éditeur tiennent à remercier, pour l'aide et la confiance qu'elles leur ont accordées durant l'élaboration du présent ouvrage, les personnes suivantes :

Chez Lesage   Jean-François Lesage, Caroline Le Borgne, Hubert Barrère, Murielle Lemoine

Chez Chanel   Marie-Louise de Clermont-Tonnerre, Laurence Delamare, Cécile Goddet-Dirles, Nathalie Vibert, Fanny de Kervenoael, Agnès Brisson-Personnaz

INDEX

220

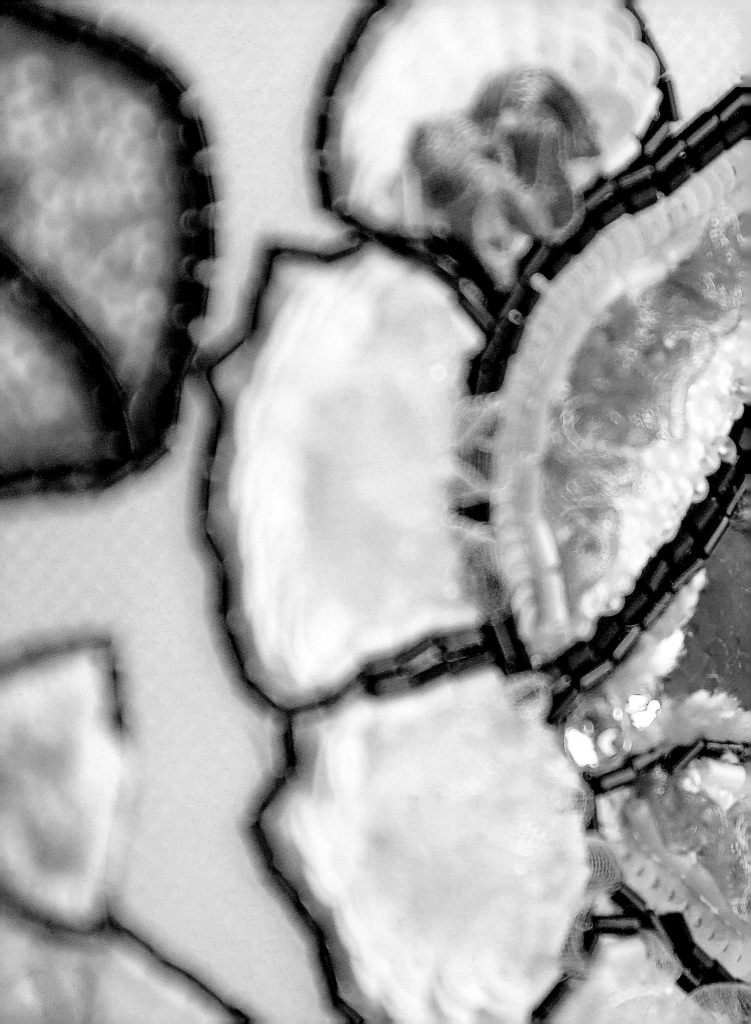

En couverture Chanel, haute couture automne-hiver 1983 © Olivier Saillant
p. 2 Chanel, haute couture printemps-été 2017
pp. 4–5 Atelier Lesage, Pantin
pp. 6–7 François Lesage dans l'ancien atelier du 13 rue de la Grange-Batelière, Paris
pp. 222–223 Pièce d'étude de l'école de broderie d'Art Lesage

L'édition originale de cet ouvrage a paru sous le titre *Maison Lesage
Haute Couture Embroidery* chez Thames & Hudson Ltd, Londres

Lesage Brodeur © 2020 Thames & Hudson Ltd, Londres
Texte © 2020 Patrick Mauriès
Photographies © 2020 (voir crédits photographiques page 217)

Maquette intérieure et typographie par Studio Mathias Clottu
Lettrines créées par Adrien Vasquez
Relecture par Anne Levine

Cet ouvrage a été reproduit et achevé d'imprimer en septembre 2019
par l'imprimerie Artron pour Thames & Hudson.

Dépôt légal : 1er trimestre 2020
ISBN 978-0-500-02249-8
Imprimé en Chine

ACID RAIN

A review of the phenomenon in the EEC and Europe

A report prepared for the
Commission of the European Communities,
Directorate-General for Environment,
Consumer Protection and Nuclear Safety

by
ENVIRONMENTAL RESOURCES LIMITED

Graham & Trotman
for the Commission of the European Communities

Published in 1983 by
Graham & Trotman Limited
Sterling House, 66 Wilton Road
London SW1V 1DE, United Kingdom

for the Commission of the European Communities,
Directorate-General Information Market and Innovation

EUR. 8684
© ECSC, EEC, EAEC, Brussels and Luxembourg, 1983
ISBN 0 86010 501 6

Printed and bound in Great Britain by
Biddles Ltd, Guildford and King's Lynn

CONTENTS

CONTENTS (continued)

CONTENTS (continued)

page no.

SUMMARY

The report examines the extent of environmental damage in the Community and in certain other European countries that may be attributable to acid pollutant emissions within Member States. The study assesses the evidence for possible causal effects and considers the physical, chemical and biological processes which have been suggested as damage mechanisms.

Concern in Europe has grown in the past few years as a result of observed damage to forests found principally in central and southern Germany, and also because of the loss of fish populations in the lakes of parts of south west Norway and Sweden. More recently, a few lakes, rivers and streams in Scotland, England and Wales, with geological and upper river catchments similar in character to those areas of Scandinavia referred to, have also reported absence or death of fish. Acid precipitation is considered a possible contributory cause. Loss of needles from pine trees has also been found in other areas of the Community. Less well appreciated is the existence of damage to building materials, caused by short range acid pollutant effects and the possibility under certain conditions that yields of some crops and vegetables are affected by the dry deposition of acid pollutants and their derivative products.

Historically most attention has focused on SO_2, and its oxidised 'wet' form, sulphuric acid. Overall emissions of SO_2 in the Community have declined in the last ten years and this trend may well continue. Without further abatement measures, this decline is not likely to be more than 15% by 2000. Recent investigations in Europe and work in the USA suggest that NO_x emissions, which arise from both stationary and vehicle fossil fuel combustion and which are on a rising trend, may also contribute significantly to plant and tree damage. In particular ozone, of which NO_x is a chemical precursor, can, at certain concentrations under summer climate conditions, cause damage or yield effects to some trees and plants, possibly in conjunction with SO_2 and NO_x.

However, it has not been unequivocably established that these environmental impacts are caused by acid pollutant emissions, nor is the relative importance of other factors properly identified. Also considerable further investigations are required to understand the mechanisms involved. Nevertheless circumstantial evidence would suggest that acid emissions and their subsequent chemical transformation and precipitation are at least a partial contributory cause to these observed effects and may be giving rise to as yet unidentified impacts, some of which could be irreversible.

The costs of SO_2 and NO_x emissions control are considerable. They also increase on an upward rising curve in relation to the amount of SO_2 and NO_x removed. The benefits of control measures are currently impossible to assess with accuracy, and in any case some effects cannot be readily evaluated in economic terms. In considering any future control strategies, it should be recognised that the relative costs and benefits certainly vary from one Member State to another, and that, for some countries, transboundary effects are probably also a significant factor.

1.   INTRODUCTION

1.1   Aim of the Report

The aim of this study is to report on and evaluate:

-        the extent of environmental damage claimed to arise from precipitation of acid pollutants;

-        the physical, chemical and biochemical mechanisms by which acid pollutant emissions can cause environmental change;

-        the trends in emissions and deposition of acid pollutants and their derivatives.

ERL has also been asked to consider the costs and possible benefits of alternative emission control options with the aim of limiting any effect, and to suggest areas where further research work is needed.

1.2   Definition and Scope of the Phenonmenon

1.2.1   Long range vis-à-vis local effects

Emissions of air pollutants can give rise to local, regional and international impact depending on the particular circumstances. We have interpreted our brief to be concerned principally with long-range rather than local effects, in other words impacts which result in many cases after pollutants have been mixed in the turbulent 'mixing layer' of the atmosphere and which therefore cannot be attributed to any particular local source. In these situations the pollutants are generally (but not always) more dispersed and of lower concentrations than would be the case with ground level concentrations (emissions) resulting from local source(s).

Nevertheless Section 9 of the report does examine the impact on buildings of acid pollutants, since in many urban environments this damage can be quite widespread. Also the report does consider the importance of distance from sources as a factor in influencing the likely type of pollutant which may cause damage, its deposition level and resultant impact. On the other hand respiratory health effects caused by high urban SO_2 with particulate concentrations was considered not to be part of the 'acid rain' phenomenon.

1.2.2   Geographical scope

The focus of this study has inevitably been on the acid rain phenomenon in the context of Europe, but it is not limited to the European Community since emissions arising from within the Member States have an effect beyond it, and vice versa. However, the occurrence of acid rain in North America means that many of the cause and effect relationships observed there are of relevance to further understanding of the phenomenon in Europe. North American experience will therefore be referred to at appropriate points during the course of the report.

1.3   **Acknowledgements**

During the course of its investigations ERL has received an enormous amount of assistance in the way of information, advice and comment from a large number of experts in government and industrial organisations, and academic research workers in several EEC Member States, and in North America. We would like to record our sincere thanks for this generous assistance.

FINDINGS AND CONCLUSIONS

1.   **WHAT IS ACID RAIN?**

In a strict definition, acid rain refers to the wet precipitation of pollutants SO_2/SO_3 and NO_2/HNO_3, which have dissolved in cloud and rain droplets to form sulphuric and nitric acids. However, the term has come to be more generally applied to include dry precipitation of the gaseous pollutants and their gaseous and particulate derivatives.

This study also includes an examination of the role and possible ecological effects of ozone, a so called photo-oxidant (not acidic), of which the gaseous pollutant NO_x is an important precursor. Thus effects covered under the heading of acid precipitation include those possibly caused by ozone.

2.   **WHAT IS THE EXTENT OF ENVIRONMENTAL DAMAGE CAUSED BY ACID PRECIPITATION?**

In Table 1 below, we summarise the effects believed to be caused by acid precipitation and where they have been observed, indicating the certainty with which such effects have been established - see also Section 2.

Table 1

SUMMARY OF EFFECTS REPORTED TO BE CAUSED BY ACID PRECIPITATION

	ESTABLISHED	PROBABLE	POSSIBLE
FORESTS			
- acute visible damage	Pine/spruce California/ Virginia USA, Canada, GDR and Czechoslovakia	Pine/spruce FR Germany and Poland	
- growth(1)/ chronic effects			Certain pine and spruce species in areas of FR Germany, Netherlands, France, E coast USA and Canada
CROPS/VEGETABLES			
- acute damage		Tobacco southern USA.	
- growth effect(2) chronic damage		Principally winter wheat, soya, maize, peanut, radish and grapes, throughout parts of USA	Certain crops root vegetables/ grass species and grapes in certain areas of continental Europe and UK

continued/...

Table 1 continued			
SUMMARY OF EFFECTS REPORTED TO BE CAUSED BY ACID PRECIPITATION			
	ESTABLISHED	PROBABLE	POSSIBLE
OTHER TERRESTRIAL FLORA/FAUNA	Damage to or disappearance of lichen, canthar-ella, certain fungi. Reduction in diversity of flora in certain areas close to urban communities		
FISH POPULATION LOSS		Lakes, rivers in: southern Norway; south/central Sweden; Canada; Adirondacks, USA	Certain lochs in SW Scotland. Certain streams and rivers of Scotland, NW England & Wales
OTHER ORGANIC FLORA/FAUNA	Change and/or loss in phyto- and zoo-plankton, benthic (bottom sediment living) communities, cycling of nutrients, organic matter decomposi-tion, diversity and type of flora - parts of Canada, USA, Scandinavia, Scotland and Eastern Europe		
BUILDINGS	Materials including sandstone, limestone, stained glass and most metals		
HEALTH THREAT			Sweden - danger of heavy metal uptake in drinking water from copper/lead piping. USA - bio-accumulation of mercury/cadmium

Notes:
(1)   Some offsetting positive growth effects in some nitrogen deficient forest areas.
(2)   Some offsetting positive growth effects in some sulphur-deficient agricultural areas.

In addition to what might be considered apparent effects, acid precipitation contributes to 'unseen' acidification of soil. In certain areas where the natural buffering capacity is low - see 8 below, soil acidification leads to loss of certain tree and other plant nutrients and change in soil chemistry. In the long term (more than 50 years), this process could produce other apparent environmental change, and might be irreversible.

3.   **WHAT HAPPENS TO ACID POLLUTANTS AFTER THEY ARE EMITTED?**

Acid pollutants go through one of three stage routes before interacting with the environment:

Route 1	Route 2	Route 3
Emission	Emission	Emission
Dispersion	Chemical transform-	Chemical transforma-
Dry deposition	ation/dispersion	tion/dispersion
	Dry deposition	Wet deposition

This process and the principal chemical substances involved are illustrated in Figure 1 overleaf - see Sections 4.3-4.5.

4.   **WHICH OF THE EMITTED ACID POLLUTANTS, THEIR SUBSEQUENT DERIVATIVES AND THEIR DEPOSITION PROCESSES ARE THE MOST IMPORTANT IN CAUSING ENVIRONMENTAL DAMAGE?**

It depends upon what is being acted upon, the climate (therefore the time of year) and/or upon how far the receptor is from the source of emissions.

Dry deposition, Routes 1 and 2, involving gaseous pollutants and their derivatives, are more important close to the source (up to 300 kilometres)(Section 4.4.5). Wet deposition in the form of acid rain becomes increasingly important at longer distances. In southern Norway, parts of western Sweden and NW Scotland, areas of high rainfall and no large local sources of pollutant, wet deposition accounts for 65-80% of acid precipitation. In most areas of Germany, Netherlands, eastern France, the UK, Belgium and Denmark, wet and dry deposition are of roughly equal importance, with dry deposition predominating in summertime. In central Germany and the Black Forest area, acid mists may be of particular significance.

In dry deposition, SO_2 increasingly predominates over NO_2 as the major dry acid pollutant away from the source, although ozone may be a potentially critical pollutant at long distances from the sources. In areas where acid rain is dominant, sulphuric and nitric acids contribute in about a 70/30 ratio to overall acidity of rain (Section 4.4.6). It is probable that there is not a linear relationship between SO_2 emissions and SO_4^{2-} deposition as the supply of oxidants/catalysts may be a limiting factor. Opinions differ on the degree of this effect for wet deposition (acid rain)(Section 4.3.2(iii)).

FIGURE 1: PROCESSES AND CHEMICAL COMPOUNDS IN POLLUTANT EMISSIONS AND ACID PRECIPITATION

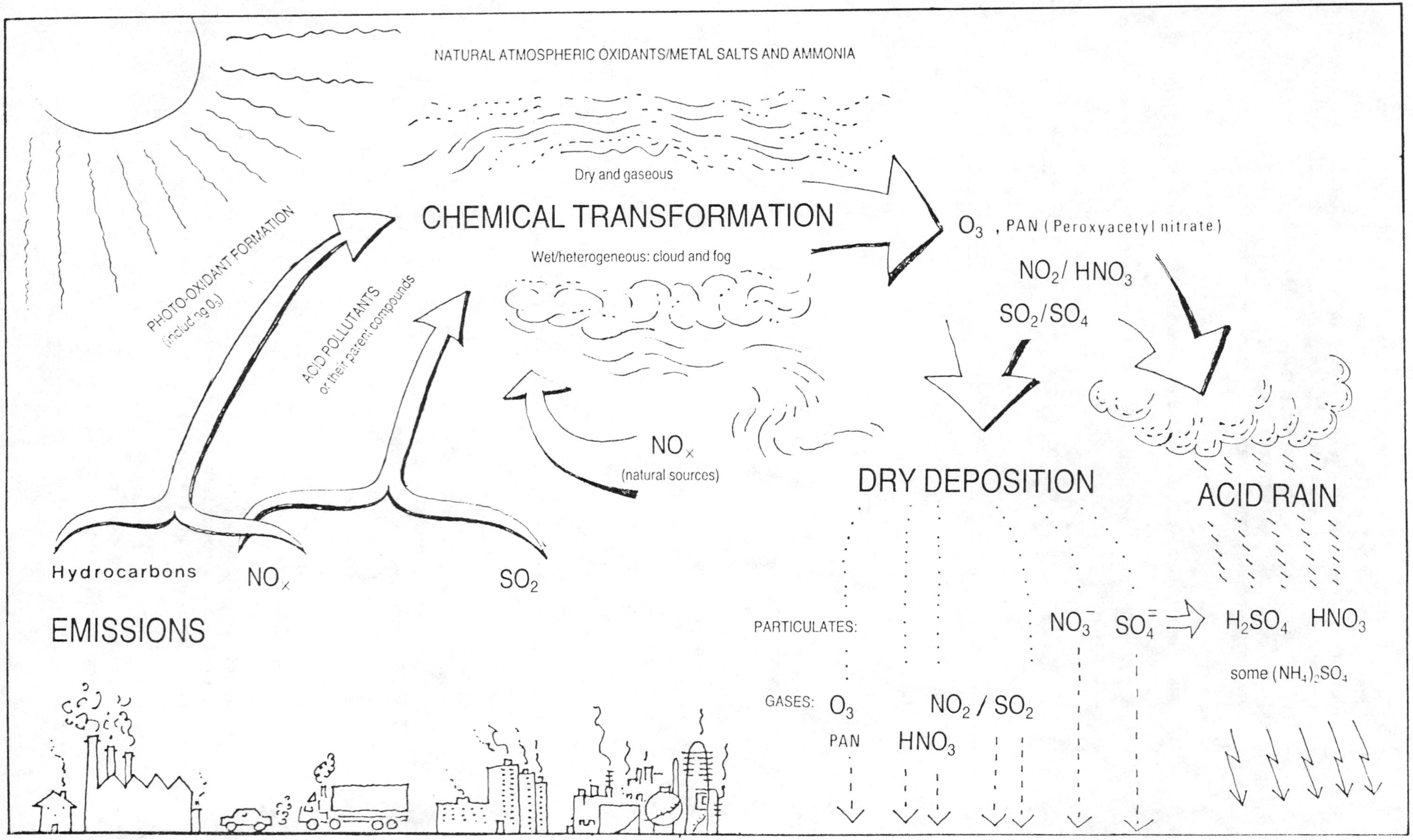

5. **ARE EEC ACID POLLUTANT SO_2 AND NO_x EMISSIONS INCREASING?**

Sulphur dioxide emissions are estimated to have fallen about 15%
since 1973. Previous to that they had been increasing since the
1940's. Under current energy and emissions abatement policies
(not taking account of new proposed German Government action),
SO_2 emissions in the EEC are unlikely to increase much in the
1980-2000 period, and could well fall (by about 15%). On the
other hand, without further controls, NO_x emissions are likely to
go on increasing, 5-20% by 2000.

6. **WHAT ARE THE PRINCIPAL SOURCES OF EMISSIONS?**

Over 90% of SO_2 emissions in Europe are from man-made sources.
By 2000 approximately 40-55% of these emissions are, on current
abatement policies, expected to come from coal and lignite fired
power stations. These sources contribute a somewhat higher share
to SO_2 transported over long distances than low level emitters.
In some Member States, most notably France, this share is
considerably less.

About half of NO_x present in the atmosphere and at ground level
in rural areas, is emitted from man-made sources, of which
vehicles and stationary emitters contribute about 50% each.
Close to urban areas this anthropogenic share is significantly
higher. By 2000, it is estimated that on current abatement
policies, vehicles will contribute 50-60% of NO_x emissions in the
Community, and coal fired power stations about 25-30%.

7. **HOW DO ACID POLLUTANTS CAUSE IMPACTS UPON THE ENVIRONMENT?**

Some damage is caused by direct mechanisms, that is the emitted
pollutant(s), or chemical derivative(s), interact(s) bio-
chemically with building material or the plant leaf/stomata
itself (themselves) - Section 2. However, the pollutants and
their derivatives can also have effects via indirect mechanisms
on flora and fauna by causing change in soil or aquatic
ecosystems (Sections 5.3 and 5.4). The situation with respect to
different observed effects is shown in Figure 2 overleaf.

In the case of forest damage, it is possible that both direct and
indirect mechanisms are involved.

8. **WHAT IS THE SIGNIFICANCE OF DIRECT OR INDIRECT MECHANISMS IN
    POSSIBLE ACID PRECIPITATION EFFECTS?**

Because effects on fish and aquatic species, and possibly on
trees, depend upon changes in the soil and aquatic ecology
(Figure 3 overleaf), which in turn is subject to many other
chemical and biological influences:

8.

FIGURE 2:   ACID POLLUTANT IMPACTS - DIRECT OR INDIRECT PROCESS?

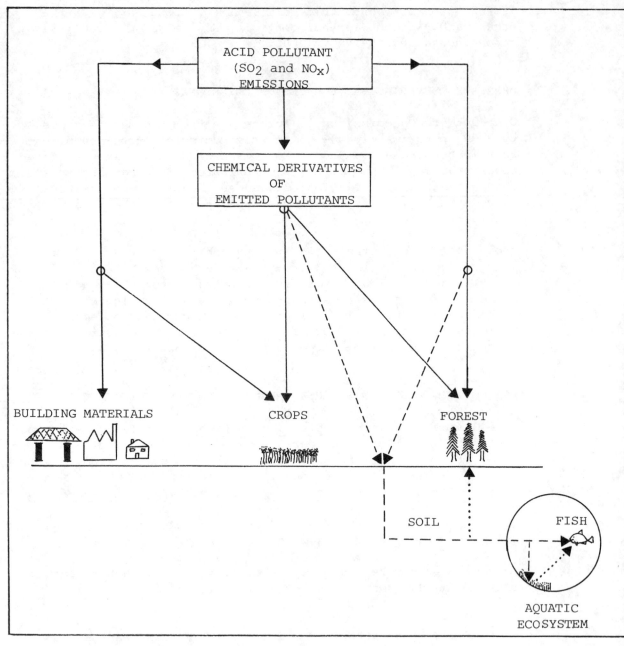

KEY: ——▶ Direct Process

– – ▶ Indirect Process

······▶ Possible Indirect Process

FIGURE 3: ECOLOGICAL PATHWAYS FOR AIR POLLUTANTS

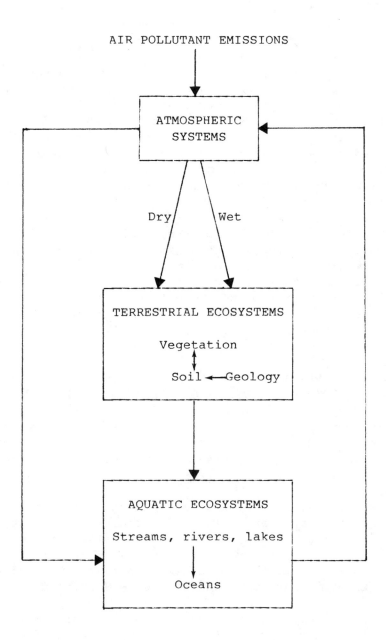

o   It is harder to identify the extent to which environ-
         mental damage/change is caused by acid precipitation in
         relation to other possible factors.

o   Observable effects can take longer to become apparent.

o   The resultant change in the ecosystem, if caused by acid
         precipitation, may or may not be reversible through a
         reduction in pollutant emissions.

It would however be wrong to conclude that direct effects caused
by acid precipitation or associated photo-oxidants can be easily
detected. Where damage to plants/trees is chronic or causes
growth effects, these changes are often masked by changes in
other factors, most notably climate, so that possible effects
caused by gaseous pollutants can only be established by appropriate field experiments and tests. Soil chemistry may also have
an important influence on the extent of direct gaseous pollutant
effects (Section 5.5).

Also, the influence of other natural and possibly anthropogenic
factors, e.g. supply of oxidants, and sunlight are important in
determining the degree of atmospheric conversion of pollutant
emissions to their damaging derivatives. In other words,
sulphate deposition and ozone formation may not be linearly
related to the amounts of SO_2 and NO_x respectively which are
emitted (Sections 4.3.2, iii and 4.5).

9.   **HOW WIDESPREAD IN EEC MEMBER STATES IS SOIL ACIDIFICATION AND
      LOSS OF NUTRIENTS RESULTING FROM ACID PRECIPITATION?**

In calcareous soils, which constitute a majority of soils to be
found in EEC Member States, the availability of neutralising base
metal cations is sufficient to prevent significant
acidification.

Nevertheless, in many neutral and acid soil areas, often used for
agriculture and particularly for coniferous forestry, acid
precipitation is not naturally neutralised in the soil. However,
it may be seen from Figure 4 overleaf that acidification from
acid precipitation is often small compared to acidification from
other natural and man-made sources - Section 5.4.

In intensively cultivated areas, soil acidification from the
nitrification process, following application of nitrogen
fertilisers, far outweighs any effect from acid precipitation -
Section 5.4.3. The potential loss of nutrients caused by this
process are made up by application of the other fertilisers
(Section 5.5). Only in the poor soils of pine and spruce forests
is the acidification caused by acid precipitation substantial in
relation to other sources. It may also be seen that forestry
practices themselves can be a significant cause of soil acidification - Section 5.4.4. However, an important distinction
should be made between organic acids formed from natural acidification processes, which are 'weak acids', and acidification

FIGURE 4: SOURCE OF ACID INPUTS TO SOIL

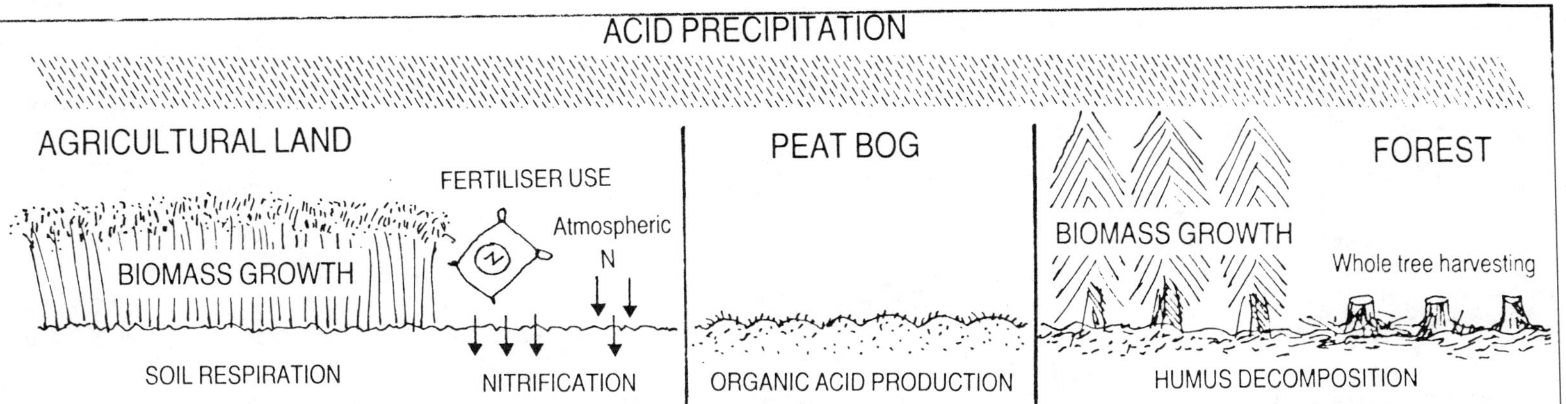

SOURCE:	AGRICULTURAL LAND	PEAT BOG	FOREST: SPRUCE/MED. SOIL	FOREST: PINE/POOR SOIL
FERTILISER/NITRIFICATION	65-80% (1)			
BIOMASS GROWTH			20-40% (2)	5-10%
TREE HARVESTING			10-15% (3)	0-10% (3)
HUMUS DECOMPOSITION/ ORGANIC ACID PRODUCTION		70-90%	20-40% (2)	10-15%
SOIL RESPIRATION	10-20%			0-5%
ACID PRECIPITATION	5-20%	10-30%	25-50%	60-80%

Notes:
(1) Nitrifications in soils where artificial fertilisation has taken place supplies the large majority of H^+ input to soils. No fertilisation of forest soils assumed.
(2) Young trees (10-25 years) contribute three times as much H^+ as old trees (40 years) through cation exchange.
(3) Whole tree felling produces twice H^+ input to soil than thinning/trunk harvesting practices.

from anthropogenic causes, including acid precipitation, which are 'strong acids' - sulphuric and nitric acids. Although 'weak acids' can cause quite high levels of acidity, their impact upon soil and water chemistry, especialy in relation to mobilisation of toxic aluminium ions and leaching of other base and heavy metals, is less than that of 'strong acids' (Sections 5.4.4 and 5.5.5).

10. **WHICH SOILS AND WATER CATCHMENTS ARE MOST SUSCEPTIBLE TO ACID PRECIPITATION, AND WHAT ARE THE EFFECTS?**

Many acid soils are adequately buffered against further 'unnatural' acidification by sufficient supply of base cations (calcium and magnesium) from natural weathering of bedrock. However, on siliceous soils overlying hard granite bedrock, the upper horizon particularly can gradually lose its base cation neutralising capability under the influence of acid rain (Section 5.5.6). Such areas are to be found in parts of Scotland, southern Norway and western Sweden. Some loss of nutrients may have occurred from certain poor mountainous forested soils of central and southern Germany. The exact route taken by water run-off through soils can be critical in determining the degree of cation exchange.

A consequence of this process is a gradual acidifying of the soil solution, water run-off and of the downstream rivers and lakes. As well as lowering of pH (in some cases down to 4.0), acidification mobilises aluminium in soluble form into the rivers and lakes (Section 5.5.3). The strength of acidity in affected surface waters can be particularly marked during the first snow melt and in run-off from storms after a dry period. This is because an accumulation of strong acid cations (H^+) and/or anions has occurred in the catchment area. In dry periods sulphur accumulates in dry deposited form which is then oxidised and dissolved by the wet precipitation.

11. **WHAT IS THE EXTENT OF FOREST DAMAGE IN WESTERN EUROPE CAUSE BY AIR POLLUTION?**

Acid precipitation, or ozone as a direct derivative of NO_x emissions, has been cited as a major cause of acute damage and death to fir and spruce trees found in parts of Bavaria, the Black Forest and Solling over the last five years. Chronic damage (loss of needles) has also been found quite widely and also necrosis of beach trees. More recently, damage attributed to acid precipitation is believed to have occurred in North Rhine Westphalia (Section 6.2).

Outside the FR of Germany, widespread chronic damage to pine trees may have occurred as a result of air pollution impacts in the eastern area of the Netherlands. Change in the forest litter ecology has also been observed. Previous claims of loss of growth to Scandinavian coniferous forests as a result of acid rain have not been substantiated. Damage to forests in East Germany and Czechoslovakia, as a result of exposure to high SO_2

concentrations and acid rain is known to be quite widespread. In the USA some acute/chronic tree damage or death induced by ozone has been found in California and Virginia, and downstream from high SO_2 emission sources in Canada and Finland (Section 6.1.2).

12.   **WHAT IS THE CAUSE OF TREE DAMAGE IN GERMAN FORESTS?**

The first point to be made is that many research workers in this field, including those strongly supporting the view that gaseous pollutants are the main cause of forest damage, consider that other factors besides acid rain have contributed to the damage (Section 6.2). The principal 'natural' factors cited are fragile soils at elevated (>500 metre) heights, age of the trees, the drought of 1976 and inappropriate forestry management. Pathogens could also be a contributory cause, their effects partly induced by climatic conditions.

Nevertheless, the scale of the damage and the spatial and temporal manner of its occurrence strongly suggest that acid precipitation and/or ozone are likely be the principal causes. The precise mechanism of damage is not yet established. At least two, not necessarily mutually exclusive, causes have been hypothesised (Section 6.3).

The first publicised hypothesis by Ulrich is that tree damage is caused by soil acidification which induces aluminium attack on the roots of trees followed by pathogens (Section 6.3.1). Others have argued that the spatial occurrence of observed tree damage and evidence of soil chemistry do not support this hypothesis.

There is a growing view that damage is directly caused by ozone attack on the needles, probably in synergistic conjunction with sulphur dioxide and possibly NO_x (Section 6.3.2). Certainly high episodic concentrations of ozone (Section 4.5.3) have been found in summertime in affected areas; also SO_2 concentrations can reach relatively high annual average (20-50 $\mu g/m^3$) and episodic levels for rural areas as a result of stable air systems and unfavourable air streams from polluted industrial areas in FR Germany, and also in the German DR and Czechoslovakia. Acidic mists can also be persistent in wintertime in some forest areas. Ozone attack could increase the susceptibility of trees to leaf/needle injury caused directly by acid mists.

Many take the view that more than one of the mechanisms could be contributory to the cause, although direct damage mechanism theories now have more widespread support.

13.   **IS TREE DAMAGE LIKELY TO OCCUR IN OTHER EEC MEMBER STATES?**

IUFRO (International Union of Forestry Research Organisations) has set a guideline of ambient annual average maximum SO_2 concentrations of 25 $\mu g/m^3$ as an upper threshold for protecting spruce and fir forests in susceptible situations. Such

concentrations are found (see Figure 4.4(a) Section 4.4.2) in
other forested areas of Europe and more widespread acid
precipitation induced damage is certainly possible, and indeed
concern is growing in eastern Netherlands over the condition of
pine trees. However, the relatively high SO_2 and ozone
concentrations that can occur in central and southern Germany
together with the high altitudes of many of the damaged forest
areas, the relatively poor soils for such forestry in some parts
and the climate, contribute to a susceptibility to acid
pollutant/ozone damage not matched in most other forest areas of
Western Europe (Section 6.4).

14. **WHAT POLLUTION DAMAGE OR YIELD LOSS OF CROPS HAS BEEN FOUND IN
EEC MEMBER STATES?**

No significant visible damage attributed to direct SO_2/NO_x or
ozone attacks has been observed. Nor has any firm evidence for
loss of yield in susceptible crops been produced. However, until
very recently, nor has any such loss been looked for in a systematic way using properly controlled field (as opposed to
laboratory) experiments. But in the last five years peak/hourly
summer ozone concentrations have been found in many rural areas
of the EEC Member States - UK, Netherlands, Germany and Belgium -
(Section 4.5.3) at levels which are known from American
experience to be toxic to certain plants and crops, and cause
loss of yield (5-40%). Preliminary evidence from $SO_2/NO_x/F^-$
filtered ambient air/open top chamber experiments in the UK and
in the Netherlands would also suggest high ambient SO_2 (most
likely episodic peaks at critical times in the growing season),
probably in conjunction with NO_x and ozone, can also cause loss
of crop yields (10-25%). Particularly susceptible species are
known to be winter wheat, soyabean, clover, grapes, radish,
lettuce and potatoes, and possibly barley. High ozone
concentrations have been observed up to 200 kilometres from major
urban conglomerations - in Germany at even greater distances. On
the other hand, the higher episodic SO_2 concentrations are mostly
found close to urban/industrial sources.

It should be emphasised that the size of loss will be highly
dependent upon the climate and possibly upon soil factors. The
variations in the former, together with pest/fungal attack, etc.,
are likely to mask air pollutant effects. Nevertheless it is
apparent that crop damage potential from acid pollutant/ozone may
well be significant in almost all EEC Member States.

15. **WHAT IS THE EXTENT OF ACID PRECIPITATION DAMAGE AND OF ACIDIFIED
AQUATIC ECOSYSTEMS IN WESTERN EUROPE?**

Within the EEC Member States, loss of fisheries as a result of
acidified surface waters is confined principally to some 20 lakes
of the Galloway area of SW Scotland, and disappearance of fish
from other streams in Scotland, and also from certain streams and
rivers in the Lake District of England and possibly in West
Wales. Fish kills have been reported on release of trout from

hatcheries, particularly young fish, and acid precipitation may have been the main contributory cause to the disappearance of fish in certain rivers and streams of Scotland and NW England where the presence of pine and spruce forests was also shown to be a factor.

The most affected area of Western Europe covers southern Norway and parts of south and central Sweden where acid rain has probably been a major factor causing disappearance of fish. In the four southernmost counties of Norway, more than half the fish stocks have been lost during the 1940-80 period in an area covering 20,000 km^2 (Section 8.5.2); in Sweden loss of fish has occurred in some 3,000-4,000 lakes (Section 8.5.1). Most affected are trout and salmon species, but also perch, char and pike. Fish kills have been reported in a number of rivers of the region, as well as in Scotland and NW England.

Acidification, the process of which may be considered as taking place in three separate buffering stages (Section 8.4), has resulted in the reduction in the pH range of lakes in these most affected areas from 5.0-6.5 down to 4.5. Elsewhere acidification not necessarily with any marked pH change has occurred in several lakes of Scotland and some in Germany, Belgium, Netherlands and Denmark (Section 8.2.1). The most reliable evidence for acidification is provided by the evidence of diatoms in layers of bottom sediments in lakes. These support the view that a fairly rapid increase in acidification of waters has taken place since the 1940's, and in some instances, from earlier in the century. Considerable changes in aquatic biology take place as pH is lowered below 5.0. In SW Sweden, pH values of 4-5 have been recorded in some groundwater, making it unfit for human consumption and leading to concern in rural areas over leaching of copper from copper piping systems.

16.   **WHAT IS THE MECHANISM OF FISH DEATHS CAUSED BY ACIDIFIED WATERS?**

A lowering of pH is believed to damage the sodium balance of the gill membranes of fish, although fish can adapt to a certain amount of gradual pH reduction. If the change is sharp, damage is much more severe and episodic pulses of low pH water at snow melt may be a major factor in disappearance of fish. Most evidence now supports the view that dissolved aluminium ion, toxic to fish at low concentrations in pH ranges around 5.0, is the principal damaging agent. As acidification increases, aluminium ion concentration increases in relation to dissolved calcium ion, which, up to certain aluminium concentrations in its toxic form, would offset the damaging properties of Al^{3+}.

Critical to the vulnerability of lakes to acidification are the characteristics of the associated catchments. In the Sorlandet lakes of southernmost Norway, generally good correlation has been found between fish status and pH (or dissolved excess sulphate ion), if lakes are grouped according to their buffering capacity or catchment characteristics (Section 8.8.1). It is a matter of some doubt as to whether reducing the acidity (raising pH) of

rain in this area would always result in sufficient permanent
recovery of base cation concentrations in the catchment and lakes
so as to lead to increased fish populations (Section 8.8.2).
Liming of catchments may assist this process but there are
practical and possibly ecological difficulties. On the other
hand, it is likely that further loss of fisheries could take
place if the acidity of rain is not reduced.

17. **DAMAGE TO BUILDINGS**

Sulphur dioxide attacks certain building materials, principally
carbon, steel, zinc, and limestone, marble and sandstone where
calcium carbonate is used as a binder (Section 9.1). Humidity is
an important factor in determining the susceptibility of these
materials to acid attacks by SO_2 (Section 9.3). Additional
damage costs to buildings, over and above the replacement cost of
materials, arises when historic buildings are attacked.

Damage to buildings arises only from relatively high concentrations of SO_2 close to urban and industrial emission sources.
Nevertheless, according to the findings of recent studies, the
total cost of building material damage in the Community as a
result of sulphur dioxide attack could be of the order of $0.5-
2.7 billion/year (Section 11.2.5).

18. **WHAT WOULD BE THE BENEFITS OF EMISSIONS CONTROL?**

In most attempts at cost/benefit analysis of environmental
control strategies, it is much easier to identify emission
control costs than to assess the benefits that would be derived
from such controls. A detailed cost/benefit analysis of control
strategy options for limiting the environmental effects of acid
pollutant emissions, and their derivatives, was outside the scope
of the study. In any case, absence of data would render the
exercise in some areas of damage fairly meaningless.

Because of the relatively recent awareness of the possible
environmental effects caused by acid precipitation, and in view
of the considerable difficulties of either assessing the dose/
response relationships of low or epidsodic concentrations of
these pollutants on vegetation or evaluating over time the
indirect effects caused in soil and aquatic ecosystems, the
problems are compounded (Section 11.1).

Once sufficient further experimental work has been undertaken in
key areas, it should be possible to assess direct or economic
costs associated with possible damage caused by acid precipitation and associated pollutants. In Section 11.2, some very broad
orders of magnitude of damage costs have been made based on
current knowledge. These should not be considered as adequate
assessments of economic damage costs (in the case of crop damage
they relate to 1982 EEC crop output value, and are based on ERL's
own assumptions from very sparse data), but they do give orders
of the upper magnitude of possible direct economic damage costs
attributable to acid pollutant emissions.

   i. Forest damage (loss of output) in
      FR Germany (Section 11.2.2)   = 0.2×10^9/year

  ii. 10% loss in yield of susceptible
      crops applied to 40% of growing
      area for these crops   = 1.0×10^9/year

 iii. Loss of fisheries value in affected
      (Section 11.2.3) Scandinavian,
      Scottish lakes and rivers
      (Section 11.2.4)   = 0.03×10^9/year

  iv. Damage (materials replacement cost)
      to buildings (Section 11.2.5)   = $0.5-2.7 \times 10^9$/year

Apart from the uncertainty in assessing these costs, in the case
of fisheries loss the damage costs shown are not the benefit
value that would be derived from reducing emissions by the amount
necessary to prevent further damage (Section 11.2.4). In other
words it is probable that some catchment/lake acidification
effects are irreversible, so that net fisheries output benefit
from a reduction in rain acidity sufficient to prevent further
acidification might be only some 25-50% of this estimated
economic damage cost.

However, society does not perceive possible environmental damage
from acid rain only in terms of that which is economically
measurable. Other impacts, which some would argue are of at
least equal importance, include adverse change in the ecology of
areas, e.g. loss and diversity of species, the deterioration of
forests, visible air pollution, damage to historic buildings. In
theory, assessments of the value society places on these can be
made (Section 11.1.2); in practice such evaluations are
notoriously difficult and the appropriate political response to
wide concern is probably a better way for society to deal with
such questions.

19.   **WHAT ARE THE COSTS OF EMISSION CONTROL STRATEGIES?**

1.   Sulphur dioxide

Estimates of sulphur emission control options, and the resultant
reduction in emissions by 2000 are discussed in Section 11.3 and
summarised in Table 2 overleaf.

Table 2		
ANNUALISED FOR ADDITIONAL (1) SULPHUR REMOVAL COSTS FOR TOTAL EEC SO_2 EMISSION IN 2000		
	$ x 10^9/year	Reduction on Total 2000 EEC Emissions
Gas Oil: 0.4-0.3% S.wt	0.7-1.0	2%
Fuel Oil: 2.5-1.75% S.wt	0.4-0.6	6%
Flue gas desulphurisation in large (>25 MW) coal/lignite boilers		
- new >25 MW plants only(1)	0.2-0.7	6-20%
- new + 70% existing plant	2.9-4.3	45-53%
Fluidised lime bed boilers		
- in new industrial coal boilers <25 MW	0.03-0.1	4- 7%
- in 50% of existing + new	0.6-0.7	7-10%

(1) Does not include cost of FGD in new coal power stations in Germany and Holand, which is assumed to be part of existing policy - see page 135.

It may be seen that the most cost-effective option, introduction of FGD in new coal fired power stations, would reduce Community sulphur emissions by 2000 by a relatively small amount, 6-20%, (the high end of the range relating to a high economic growth case). This strategy would probably not reduce ground level concentrations by the same percentage amount in areas where the cost of damage may be highest, i.e. urban buildings and agriculture/horticulture crop yields. Control of sulphur levels by use of fluidised bed systems in new coal fired boilers with lime beds would also appear relatively cost-effective, but as a control policy might have the effect of driving industrial consumers ordering new boiler plant away from coal to oil. The cost of introducing fluidised (lime) bed boilers as a means of limiting SO_2 emissions from industrial coal combustion in new boilers is the estimated additional cost of FBC over conventional stoker boilers.

Desulphurisation of oil fuels has been limited to what is seen to be cost-effective. Higher levels of sulphur removal from fuel oil would require very expensive residual desulphurisation or FGD on low load factor power plants. Such measures would only reduce total EEC emissions by a further 13-16%.

It may be seen, therefore, that to achieve more than a 18-35% (degree of sulphur removal shown for oil fuels and new coal fired plant) reduction overall in SO_2 emissions by 2000 would be very

costly. However, change in fuel consumption pattern in certain
critical areas including use of low sulphur imported coals might
achieve a somewhat higher reduction in a more cost-effective
manner over time.

2. NO_x

Anthropogenic NO_x emissions contribute roughly half of total
atmospheric concentrations of NO_x. In urban areas and close to
large emitters, the proportion is very much higher. While NO_x is
itself a potentially damaging acid pollutant, being largely
converted in wet and dry deposition to HNO_3 (nitric acid),
perhaps the greatest significance of emitted NO_x is as a
precursor of ozone, known to be the most phytotoxic of all
gaseous pollutants in terms of direct effect on plants, and
possibly one of the principal causes of any tree and crop damage
and growth effects.

Stationary emissions of NO_x are believed to contribute about half
of man-made emissions, the main contributors being high temperature fossil furnaces and boilers, of which coal combustion in
power stations contributes on a per tonne of fuel burnt about
twice that of fuel oil burnt in power station boilers - a major
reason for the expected increase in NO_x emissions (Table 11.3(e),
Section 11.3.2). By a number of measures concerned with
adjusting furnace combustion conditions, it is believed that NO_x
emissions could be reduced in new boilers by 40-70%. There is
less scope for introducing such measures in existing boilers,
perhaps 25-40% overall, and the unit capital costs of achieving
such reductions would be higher than with new boilers. The cost
of introducing such controls on new and on 70% of existing
boilers and other high NO_x emitters (certain chemical plants) is
estimated to carry an annualised capital and operating cost by
2000 of $0.1-0.4 \times 10^9$/year. Some of this reduction in emissions
would in any case be achieved if flue gas desulphurisation were
fitted for purposes of controlling SO_2. Fluidised bed coal
boilers also emit less NO_x than stoker-type boilers.

Vehicles contribute the other 50% of man-made NO_x emissions.
Under the current EEC/UMECE regulations, vehicle manufacturers
have agreed to adapt combustion conditions in the engine in order
to achieve a 15-30% reduction in NO_x emissions from new cars by
1985. Given the expected increase in car population, admittedly
offset by greater fuel efficiency, this improvement in emissions
is unlikely to mean very large overall reduction in vehicle NO_x
emissions by 2000. Further reductions in vehicle NO_x emissions
would have to be achieved by catalytic exhaust control systems.

Overall it can be seen that a quite large and far reaching
programme would be needed to realise a reduction in NO_x emissions
from stationary and vehicle emitters in order to produce a
significant reduction in ambient NO_x and ozone concentrations.
It would need to embrace oil as well as coal consumers. However,
its cost would be considerably less than introduction of SO_2
controls. However, NO_x emission controls could have the adverse
side effect of decreasing efficiency of fuel combustion if very
ambitious NO_x emission controls were introduced quickly.

20. **WHAT ACTION IS JUSTIFIED IN THE LIGHT OF CONTROL STRATEGY COSTS AND THEIR POSSIBLE BENEFITS?**

It is clearly not possible to make an overall judgement on this matter given the unknowns and uncertainties in the degree of possible damage being caused by acid pollutant emissions. However, some uncertainty will always exist and should not be an excuse for postponement of any action. Probabilistic methods for dealing with uncertainty in cost/benefit analysis in this area have been developed by a UNECE expert group.

In Section 11.5, certain observations are made on the costs of control in relation to possible benefits and, in the light of this, Section 11.6 suggests possible future priorities on control action and research activities. Some of the more important points which emerge are:

o   In total, the orders of magnitude of direct damage costs are similar to the costs of control which would realise a 25-50% reduction in SO_2 and NO_x emissions. However, this is not a helpful comparison as it ignores where possible damage is arising in relation to the principal emissions likely to be causing that damage.

o   While coal fired power stations and large high stack industrial emitters contribute a substantial proportion of total SO_2 and NO_x emitted, if action were only directed to these sources it would not address a considerable proportion of urban damage to buildings, and the possible loss of yield to horticultural crops close to urban areas.

o   Other than damage being caused to aquatic ecosystems in Scandinavia, for which only two Member States contribute significantly to acid precipitation there, most environmental damage from acid pollutant emissions probably arises from emissions within each of the Member States. Netherlands, and possibly eastern France, Belgium and Luxembourg may be suffering some environmental damage from imported pollutants. FR Germany almost certainly is experiencing some tree damage as a result of East European SO_2/NO_x emissions. The extent of damage among Member States varies very considerably, as does the pattern of fossil fuel combustion. As a result the net benefit of emissions control will vary considerably among Member States.

o   It is probable that if and where loss of crop yield and forest damage is occurring, control of NO_x emissions will require at least as much attention as SO_2 emissions.

o   Building damage tends to be relegated to a lower priority than damage to the natural environment. It is probable that SO_2-caused building damage represents the highest direct environmental damage cost from acid pollutants. Control costs for this damage are also likely to be high. Better understanding is needed of the costs of control and the costs of building damage.

o   There is an urgent need for more field experimentation work to assess the degree and location of possible damage and/or yield loss to susceptible crops. Better understanding is needed of the principal pollutant damage mechanisms for spruce and fir trees, and the responses of different catchment areas to changes in acidity of precipitation and to liming.

o   From the analysis of emission trends and their sources, in relation to possible effects, it follows that, if a substantial reduction in SO_2 and NO_x emissions should be considered necessary within a 10-15 year time period, control action would need to:

    i. be directed at most major categories of fossil fuel consumers;

    ii. include existing as well as new consumers.

2.   APPARENT EFFECTS

2.1   Scope

This section describes the effects and extent of damage that have been claimed as being the possible direct or indirect results of acid precipitation. It is not intended that this section should consider the validity of these claims but simply identify the range of possible effects.

These effects fall into the following categories:

o   damage to **trees, flora** and **crops** by direct deposition on leaves and stems and indirectly by affecting the root environment, i.e. the soil;

o   damage to **fish** populations and to other **aquatic flora** and **fauna** due to acidification of lakes and rivers;

o   damage to **buildings**;

o   **health and human effects** as a result of changes in water quality.

2.2   Trees

The possible affects that may be caused to trees range from death, visible damage and reduced growth to stimulation of forest productivity.

Three areas in particular have been highlighted as suffering from such damage:

o   **Central Europe,** southern and central FR Germany particularly, but also recently Westphalia, German DR and Czechoslovakia, where reduced tree growth and the progressive dying of trees over 1 million hectares of land is reported.

Infrared photography can assess the extent of the deaths, and there are claims that in the worst areas of the Bayerische Wald in Bavaria about 30-40% of firs on south-facing, semi-arid slopes are dying at present.

Deciduous trees are less affected. The majority of trees affected are spruce and fir, although Ulrich includes evidence of damage to beech and some other deciduous types.

Some claim a change in tree species assemblage or diversity is occurring.

o   **Southern Scandinavia.** Despite lower total deposition
        levels than southern Germany and markedly less dry
        deposition of SO_2 and NO_x, it was believed in the early
        1970's that acid precipitation had affected forest
        growth in the 1950-65 period. However, the view is now
        that no clear evidence exists for either increased or
        reduced tree growth in southern Norway or Sweden as a
        result of acid precipitation.

o   **North America.** Reduced growth of red spruce and white
        pine since the middle 1950's has been recorded in New
        York, and of pitch, shortleaf and loblolly pine in New
        Jersey. Death and acute ozone damage to pine has been
        reported in the San Bernadino Mountains in California,
        and on a lesser scale to certain tree species in the
        Blue Ridge Mountains of Virginia.

Literature covering other European countries in general has not
claimed evidence of damage due to acid pollutant emissions.

The possibility of stimulating tree growth derives from the
provision of soluble nitrates in forest ecosystems deficient in
nitrogen.

2.3   Crops

Claims regarding effects on crops have been deduced from United
States experience or from laboratory or controlled atmosphere
experiments. The following possible effects have been suggested:

o   reduced yields of crops such as winter and spring wheat,
        barley, potatoes, beet, radish, lucerne, clover,
        soyabeans and certain grass species;

o   increases in yields of certain crops in sulphur
        deficient soils.

2.4   Other Terrestrial Flora and Fauna

Damage claimed to terrestrial flora and fauna has largely focused
on species rather than countries:

o   The disappearance of or damage to lichens, and
        Cantharella (e.g. from low calcium soils in the
        Netherlands).

o   A reduction in the species richness of flora per unit
        area.

o   Visible leaf damage i.e. necrosis and chlorosis.

2.5   Fish and Other Aquatic Flora and Fauna

The following effects in aquatic ecosystems have been claimed:

o   the reduction and loss of fish populations, particularly salmon and trout;

o   the reduction and/or loss of amphibian populations;

o   changes in phyto- and zoo-plankton and benthic communities;

o   increased growth of sphagnum, a weed prevalent in small lakes;

o   changes in the cycling of algal nutrients in lakes;

o   consistent differences in flora and fauna in lakes with different levels of acidity but with comparable ionic and nutrient compositions, e.g. reduced species richness per unit area and changed special assemblage;

o   the replacement of bacteria by fungi as the main decomposing agent.

Changed fish populations include:

o   In southern **Norway,** an area of 28,000 km^2 has been examined. 1,750 out of 5,000 lakes there are thought to have lost fish populations; 900 others are seriously affected. If the present loss rate continues, 80% of brown trout populations will be lost in this region by 1990.

o   In southern and central **Sweden,** fisheries damage is observed in 2,500 lakes; on the basis of lake chemistry, it is estimated that a total of 18,000 lakes with pH <5.5 are also experiencing fisheries damage. Fish damaged include roach, salmon, trout, perch, minnow, char, grayling and pike.

o   In parts of **Scotland,** fish have disappeared from certain lochs; in **Scotland, England and Wales,** certain upper catchment streams have little or no fish population, which is surprising on the evidence of the catchments, and fish kills have been recorded in certain rivers.

o   In northern **USA** in the Adirondack Mountains, the fish populations in at least 180 lakes (representing 2.5% of the surface water of lakes and ponds) have been lost since the 1930's.

o   In the La Cloche Mountain area of **southern Ontario, Canada** 24% of lakes surveyed had no fish at all. 56% of these fishless lakes are known to have suffered a reduction in fish species composition. Smallmouth bass, walleye, white suckers, northern pike, lake trout, lake herring, perch and rock bass have been affected.

o   In **Nova Scotia,** records of angling catches dating back to 1900 show a severe decrease in salmon runs in 7-9 rivers. Populations in 8-13 additional rivers have declined significantly.

In all cases, the majority of fish affected are salmonid.

2.6   Buildings

The major effect of acid pollutant emissions on buildings is claimed to be the increased deterioration of building materials.

It is generally acknowledged that most of this damage occurs in the area of the pollutant source and is therefore a **local** rather than a regional effect.

The following materials show evidence of this damage:

o   sandstone, containing calcium carbonate as a binder

o   limestone and marble

o   stained glass

o   most metals.

Such damage has been widely catalogued in relation to historic buildings in most European countries. Examples include:

o   the Parthenon in Athens,

o   historic buildings in Venice and London,

o   monuments, libraries and archives in the Netherlands,

o   churches and historic buildings in West Germany,

o   building facades in the Bordeaux area of France.

Many economic assessments of the cost of material damage from air pollution have been carried out.

2.7   Health

Potential threats to humans may occur as a result of:

o   exposure to a higher heavy metal intake from drinking water provided in lead or copper plumbing. In Sweden it has been claimed that a high copper intake has caused diarrhoea in infants;

o   exposure to a higher heavy metal intake, particularly
    mercury and cadmium from the bioaccumulation process in
    aquatic food chains.

3. EMISSIONS AND PHYSICAL TRANSPORT

3.1 Introduction

In this section we consider the future probable trends in SO_2 and NO_x emissions from within the European Community which give rise to acid precipitation (in dry and wet form), and to other pollutants of possible concern, principally ozone.

This is followed by a brief description of the physical transport of pollutants, and the resulting sulphur budgets of European countries as calculated by the UNECE EMEP Programme [1].

Two sets of emission forecasts are produced, based on assumptions of high and low economic growth in the Community. The higher forecasts adopt the projections of the DG XVII paper [2] giving projections of fossil fuel use in coal-using sectors of the Community based on 2.5% per annum economic growth 1980-2000, to which consistent forecasts of other fossil fuel use in the Member States have been added. Although a more recent Commission forecast [3] giving lower energy use projections has been developed, the forecast only extended as far as 1990. It was therefore felt that the earlier forecast provided a useful upper limit to emissions. The low forecast adopted was developed by ERL in its recent study on Coal and the Environment (see Sections 2.1-2.4) [4] and assumes a low economic growth forecast of 1.0% p.a.

3.2 Forecast of Sulphurous Fuels Emissions

3.2.1 Total emissions

In the northern hemisphere anthropogenic sources of sulphur are believed to account for around 90% of sulphur in the atmosphere. In coastal areas this percentage is rather lower as the sea is a significant source of sulphate. Globally, natural sources, principally volcanoes and to a much lesser extent marsh gases account for 50% of sulphur in the atmosphere.

Based on the economic growth forecasts discussed above, forecast sulphurous fuel consumption in the EEC is shown in Table 3.2(a).

---

[1] The Cooperative Programme for Monitoring and Evaluation of Long Range Transmission of Air Pollutants in Europe. UNECE.

[2] The Outlook for Coal Production and Use in the Community. COM(80)117.

[3] Review of Member States' Energy Policy Programmes and Progress Towards 1990 Objectives. COM(82)326 final.

[4] Environmental Impact of Future Coal Production and Use in the EEC. Environmental Resources Limited. Graham and Trotman for the Commission of the European Communities, 1983.

Table 3.2(a)			
FORECAST SULPHUROUS FUEL CONSUMPTION IN THE EEC (MILLION TONNE)			
	1980	1990	2000

Case I

	1980	1990	2000
Distillates(1)	176	180	190
Fuel Oil:			
- industry	69	60	45
- power plants	60	50	30
Hard Coal	316	385	475
Lignite	145	155	160

Case II

	1980	1990	2000
Distillates(1)	176	180	180
Fuel Oil:			
- industry	69	55	45
- power plants	61	40	25
Hard Coal	316	320	350
Lignite	145	155	160

(1)   Jet and burning kerosene account for only 17 million tonnes.

Sources: Case 1 High Economic Growth (1980-2000 GDP 2.5% per annum); COM(80)117.
Case 2 Low Economic Growth (1980-2000 GDP 1% pa); Environmental Impact of Future Coal production and Use in the EEC. Graham & Trotman for the CEC, 1983.

In 1980, average sulphur levels of these fuels were estimated to be:

	% S.wt.
Distillates	0.4
Fuel oil	2.5
Coal	1.5
Lignite	0.35

It is not considered that there is sufficient firm evidence concerning change in the mix of crude oils and coals consumed in the EEC to alter these average levels over the 1980-2000 period. However, in projecting future emissions (see Table 3.2(b) overleaf), account is taken of sulphur control policies existing at the end of 1982. The new policies in the Netherlands and Germany assume that all new coal and lignite fired power stations will have to install Flue Gas Desulphurisation. As a result, SO_2 emissions are some 1.1 and 0.2 million tonnes less than they otherwise would be in the High and Low Cases respectively. The figures do not take account of the latest Federal German Government proposals to reduce sulphur emissions 30% by 1993.

Table 3.2(b)				
FORECAST SO$_2$ EMISSIONS IN THE EEC (MILLION TONNES)				
	1980	1990	2000	1980/2000 Increase
Case I				
Distillates	1.4	1.4	1.5	
Fuel Oil	6.5	5.8	3.8	
Coal	8.5	10.3	11.8	
Lignite	1.0	0.9	0.9	
Other Sources[1]	1.3	1.1	1.0	
Total	18.6	19.5	19.0	+2%
Case II				
Distillates	1.4	1.4	1.4	
Fuel Oil	6.5	4.8	3.5	
Coal	8.5	8.6	9.3	
Lignite	1.0	0.9	0.9	
Other Sources[1]	1.3	1.0	0.8	
Total	18.6	16.7	15.9	-15%

(1)   Other industrial sources include steel plants, sulphuric acid manufacture and smelters.

From Table 3.2(b), it may be seen that on current abatement policies, sulphur emissions are not expected to rise significantly, taking the Community as a whole, and could well fall. Of particular note in this respect is the fall in sulphur emissions from fuel oil combustion relative to those of coal.

There is not expected to be a great variation from this overall trend within individual Member States, although some countries, such as the Netherlands, will have to introduce stricter abatement policies, not reflected here, to prevent increased emissions. The position in the Netherlands comes about because of the relative fall in natural gas consumption relative to coal, and to some extent fuel oil. A fall in French SO$_2$ emissions is likely, principally as a result of their strong nuclear programme, and possibly also in the UK as fuel oil consumption falls in relation to natural gas consumption.

3.2.2   Contribution to emissions and long range transport

From the disaggregated analysis of the forecasts above, it is estimated that coal and lignite fired power stations will contribute overall approximately 45-55% of total emissions by the year 2000.

Section 3.6 discusses the importance of emission height to long range transport of air pollutants. It is generally believed that high stack emissions contribute about 15% more to long range transport than low level emissions. Broadly, coal and lignite fired power stations in the Community would be expected to contribute about 45-60% to long range transport of sulphur emissions.

3.3 NOx Emissions

3.3.1 Sources of NO_x

Natural sources of NO_x, principally chemical and bacterial denitrification in soil, account for very approximately 50% of NO_x in the atmosphere. One should also add that ammonia sources (principally fertilisers) also make some contribution to total NO_x.

3.3.2 Based on emission factors which have been adopted in OECD/LR TAP [1] and the Warren Spring Report [2] studies and the forecasts of fossil fuel use (including gasoline consumption not shown in Table 3.2(a) above), total anthropogenic sources of NO_x emissions in the EEC are estimated as follows:

Table 3.3(a)			
FORECAST NOx EMISSIONS FROM FOSSIL FUEL COMBUSTION (MILLION TONNES)			
	1980	2000	1980/2000 Increase
Case I	9.2	11.1	21%
Case II	9.2	9.7	5%
Source: ERL estimates: See Environmental Impact of Future Coal Production and Use in EEC. Graham & Trotman for the CEC, 1983.			

These forecasts assume NO_x emission controls on vehicles in conformity with the latest adopted modifications to the EEC Directive 70/220 implementing the Geneva UNECE regulation No 15/04.

[1] Measurements and Findings of the OECD Programme on Long Range Transport of Air Pollutants; OECD Paris 1979.

[2] Air Pollution from Oxides of Nitrogen, Carbon and Hydrocarbons. A.P. Apling, Warren Spring Report, WSP LR 306.

It may be seen that unlike SO_2, NO_x emissions are still on a rising trend and believed to have increased 40-50% over the last 10-15 years. Aircraft air-sampling over the North Sea has often found unexpectedly large concentrations of NO_x, which are difficult to account for by emissions from known sources.

Of the total emissions, vehicles are expected to contribute approximately 50-60% by 2000 and coal fired power stations 25-30%. The contribution from coal increases somewhat over the period.

Sources of NO_x, other than fossil fuel combustions, account for a substantial proportion of average ground level concentrations and acid precipitation. It is believed that the contribution in rural areas from such sources is at least half. Close to urban areas the contribution from man-made sources, principally vehicles, is very much higher.

3.3.3   Within the last five years evidence has been accumulating to show that **ozone**, a photo-oxidant pollutant for which NO_2 is the most important precursor, occurs in concentrations that are signifi-cant in rural areas of Europe up to 100-150 km from large urban areas (in Germany over longer distances). It may be assumed that these concentrations have increased, in view of NO_x emissions increases - see Section 4.5.

3.4   **Implications for any Future Control Policy**

From the analysis of expected future levels of SO_2 and NO_x emissions, it may be seen that if in the future any substantial reduction in emissions should be considered necessary within a 10-15 year time period in order to limit possible effects of acid precipitation or ozone, control action would need to:

   i.   be directed at most major categories of fossil fuel consumers;

   ii.   include existing as well as new consumers.

3.5   **Physical Transport**

3.5.1   Once a pollutant has been emitted into the atmosphere its behaviour is governed by the physical and chemical nature of the environment in which it finds itself.

The series of processes which it undergoes - transport and dispersion, chemical transformation and deposition etc. - define its pathway through the atmosphere. For sulphur, this pathway averages between one and five days, i.e. between a few hundred and more than a thousand kilometres.

The following sections deal with the transport and diffusion processes of pollutants. Chemical transformation and deposition processes are discussed in Chapter 4.

3.5.2 Characteristics of the mixing layer

The flow field in the mixing layer (or planetary boundary layer) of the atmosphere is responsible for pollutant transport between a source and the receptor sites.

This field is almost always in a state of change and is characterised by a spectrum of atmospheric motions ranging from micro-scale eddies, through meso-scale to synoptic-scale circulations. The elements of the field critical to pollutant transport are wind speed and wind direction.

Wind speed increases with height as the effect of surface roughness is diminished. Thus the higher a pollutant's effective injection height (stack height plus plume rise) the greater the transport wind speed it experiences.

3.5.3 Variations in the mixing layer

The mixing layer experiences diurnal and seasonal variations which affect pollutant transport and diffusion.

Diurnal variations in the mixing layer may be associated with inversions. These may form at night time when surface long-wave radiation cools the near surface air and causes the formation of a ground-based stable layer or inversion. Pollutants emitted into this layer undergo little mixing or dilution, while those emitted above it may be slowly mixed through a large depth of the atmosphere above the ground-based inversion without reaching the surface. In the morning, as solar radiation heats the surface and causes convective mixing, the stable layer is eroded from below and pollutants mix through progressively greater depths of the atmosphere, frequently up to one or two kilometres, depending on the time of year and the meteorological conditions.

Seasonal variations in the mixing layer affect the frequency of different air masses and hence of different pollutant concentrations a receptor site experiences. Figure 3.5(a) shows the frequency of different air masses experienced in January, at Kew in the UK. Polar maritime air (mP) is less pollutant-loaded than continental polar (cP) air, is unstable and has a frequency of 30% or more in all months, except March. True continental polar air only affects the British Isles between December-February, and is basically very stable. Similar air mass frequencies would be experienced in north west Europe. In Germany, the incidence of air mass movements from the south is very low.

Several authors have attempted to catalogue circulation patterns over the twelve month cycle. Lamb's results for Britain are shown in Figure 3.5(b). Anticyclonic conditions in the UK are most likely to occur in late May, early June and in September.

FIGURE 3.5(a): **AVERAGE AIR MASS FREQUENCIES FOR KEW IN JANUARY**

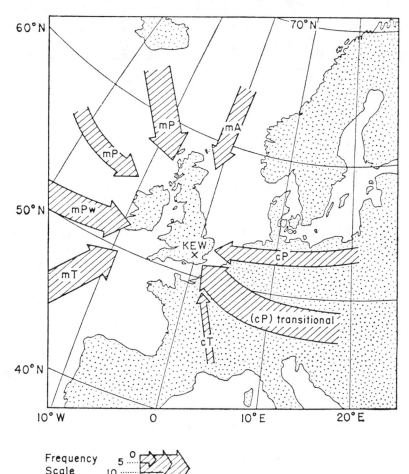

Source: Belasco, *Weather,* **3, 1948.**

FIGURE 3.5(b): **PERCENTAGE FREQUENCIES OF DIFFERENT AIR MASSES FOR BRITAIN, 1898–1947**

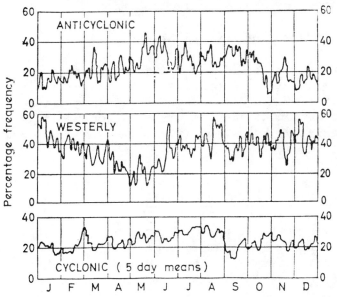

Source: H.H. Lamb, *Quart.Jour.Roy.Met.Soc.* 76, 1950.

Anticyclonic conditions persist for longer in the continental land mass. These conditions in emission areas often lead to marked pollutant deposition:

o   when emissions from diverse sources over a broad area accumulate in stagnating air associated with anticyclonic conditions. The pollutants become well mixed by day-time convection, and are slowly transported in the southerly flows to the west of the high pressure centres, to affect areas several hundreds of kilometres across for a couple of days at a time;

o   a related transport situation is responsible for many of the episodes of excessive sulphate and hydrogen ion deposition in Scandinavia. The air in stagnant anticyclonic conditions over Europe becomes heavily polluted and is then drawn into a frontal area of a depression running along the northern edge of the anticyclone. Only modest rainfall at the front is needed to produce relatively large depositions.

3.5.4   Variations in mixing layer height

Mixing height is an important parameter as it governs not only vertical dilution of the pollutant but also horizontal dilution by wind shear effects. Unstable air masses normally have a deeper and more active mixing layer than stable air masses. Thus plumes emitted into a stable atmosphere undergo little vertical or horizontal diffusion and can travel intact for several hundred kilometres before being dispersed or incorporated into cloud. Figure 3.5(c) shows such a narrow, coherent plume observed by satellite over Ontario, Canada.

Mixing height varies seasonally and diurnally. It peaks in the afternoon and seasonally in summer, and over Europe may range from a few tens of metres in stable conditions to about 2000 metres in very unstable conditions.

3.5.5   The process of precipitation

Pollutants are also dispersed (and removed from the atmosphere) by precipitation processes which are highly effective scavengers of SO_2 in the air. Thus a polluting air mass may lose a proportion of its pollutant en route, if it experiences precipitation. Deposition of SO_2 and NO_x are discussed in Section 4.4.

3.6   The Effect of Emission Height

It is generally acknowledged that emission height makes a relatively small difference to long range pollutant transport under Western European conditions averaged over the year. In summertime (when emissions are lower), the efect of stack height is more pronounced. Stack height influences arise either from the fact that low level emissions deposit a slightly larger percentage of their pollutant locally before entering the mixing layer than high level emissions; or from occasions when there **are** inversion conditions, and low level emissions are trapped beneath the inversion and do not enter the mixing layer to undergo transport.

FIGURE 3.5(c): PLUME OUTLINE, SUDBURY ONTARIO

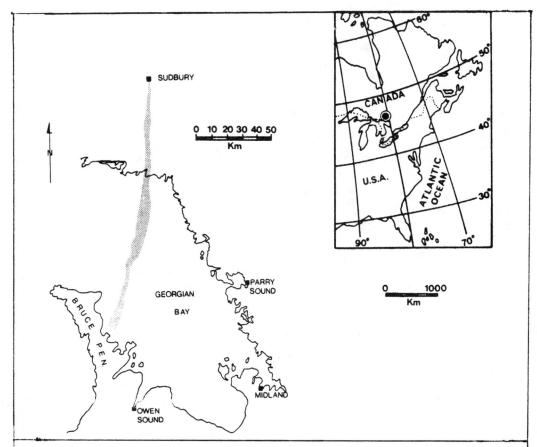

Tracing from ERTS photograph, showing the outline of a plume from the 381 m nickel smelter stack at Sudbury, Ontario, crossing Georgian Bay, 1040 EST, September 1972 (Munn 1976). The inset shows the map location in central Ontario, Canada.

In long-range pollutant transport models, account of the former is taken by adding a 15% surcharge to high level emitters.

The inversion effect is difficult to assess accurately as the frequency and height of inversions varies over Europe. As a result relatively few people have attempted to quantify the effect of inversions. One French paper concluded that on account of the frequency of inversions and of stable and unstable conditions, emission height was important 50% of the time in summer and 80% of the time in winter.

3.7   National Sulphur Budgets

3.7.1   Under the OECD LRTP Programme, a Lagrangian air pollution
dispersion model was developed to calculate the sulphur budgets,
that is the sources and receipts of total deposition of sulphur
for European countries. The model simulates the movement and
deposition of sulphur emissions according to:

o   total sulphur emissions in each country;

o   the prevailing wind direction, air movement in relation
         to the earth's rotation, rainfall and other climatic
         factors affecting the transport of SO_2 pollutants in the
         mixing layer;

o   the scavenging of SO_2 and SO_4 and their rate of
         deposition in wet and dry forms.

This work was updated by the Norwegian Meteorological Institute
as part of the First Phase of the ECE Cooperative Programme for
Monitoring and Evaluation of Long Range Transmission of Air
Pollutants which was published in 1980. [1]

3.7.2   The results, giving the calculated total amounts of sulphur
emitted and received by each European country for the winter half
year 1978/79, are presented in Figure 3.7(a) and Table 3.7(a)
overleaf. Subsequent monitoring and measurement in certain
countries has verified the accuracy of the predicted results up
to $\pm$ 50%.

The following points are of note:

o   overall the EEC exports 25-60% of its sulphur emissions;

o   the principal net importers of deposited sulphur in the
         EEC are Netherlands (77% of total deposits are imports),
         and Belgium (58%), $\pm$ 50% in each case;

o   in southern Norway, some 40-75% of sulphur deposition is
         emitted in EEC countries, the principal contributors
         being the UK and to a lesser extent FR Germany.
         However, some 25-50% of their deposition is unaccounted
         for and a further 10% (approximately) derives from other
         countries. This large uncertainty factor arises from
         the heavy rainfall of the area which deposits droplets
         that have picked up low concentrations of SO_2 from a
         very widely distributed area of the northern hemisphere.

The very approximate nature of these sulphur budgets is clear
from the discussion of the results of the EMEP Programme.

---

[1] Summary Report of the Western Meteorological Synthesising
Centre for the First Phase of the ECE Cooperative EMEP Programme
- ECE, Geneva, 1980.

FIGURE 3.7(a):   SOURCE OF 1980 DEPOSITION OF SULPHUR IN EUROPE

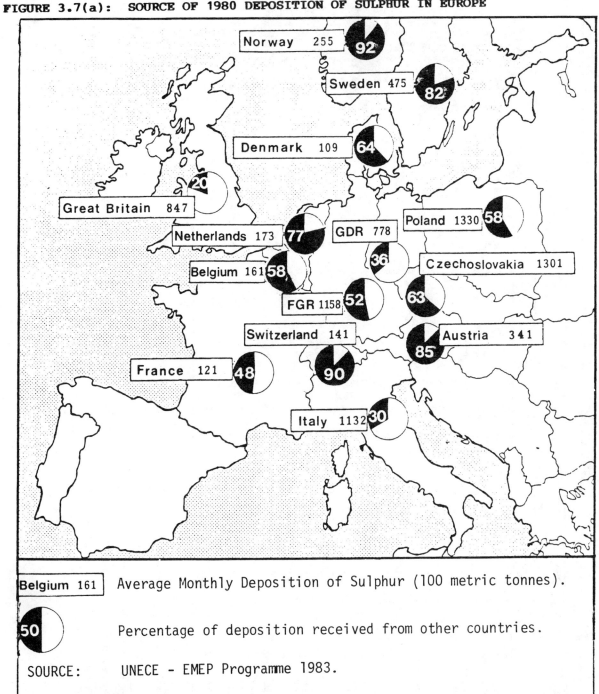

| Belgium 161 | Average Monthly Deposition of Sulphur (100 metric tonnes). |

Percentage of deposition received from other countries.

SOURCE: UNECE - EMEP Programme 1983.

The large variation possible from year to year, and from season
to season, is principally a function of climatic change.
However, they do establish broad patterns of exports and imports
of sulphur in Europe, although in sensitive areas such as
southern Norway, the source of a large proportion of the sulphur
precipitation cannot be accounted for.

Table 3.7(a)

CALCULATED 1980 SULPHUR BUDGETS FOR TOTAL DRY AND WET DEPOSITION (AVERAGE MONTHLY) FOR EUROPEAN COUNTRIES

− 100 metric tonnes of sulphur

R/E	AL	A	B	BG	CS	DK	SF	F	DDR	D	GR	H	IS	IRL	I	L	NL	N	PL	P	R	E	S	CH	TR	SU	UK	YU	RE	UND	SUM	Q1	Q2
AL	10	0	0	0	0	0	0	0	0	0	2	2	0	0	8	0	0	0	0	0	2	0	0	0	0	0	0	13	0	12	67	42	
A	0	52	3	0	35	0	0	20	24	32	0	14	0	0	56	0	2	0	13	0	0	2	0	3	0	0	8	35	0	30	341	179	
B	0	0	67	0	0	0	0	28	2	24	0	0	0	0	0	0	4	0	0	0	0	0	0	0	0	0	18	0	0	9	161	317	337
BG	0	0	0	153	8	0	0	2	6	2	7	12	0	0	8	0	0	0	7	0	34	0	0	0	3	12	2	45	0	29	346	417	
CS	0	22	10	2	483	2	0	45	195	108	0	68	0	0	39	0	7	0	95	0	14	4	0	2	0	14	32	53	0	91	1301	1250	
DK	0	0	0	0	3	39	0	3	12	11	0	0	0	0	0	0	0	0	4	0	0	0	0	0	0	0	11	0	0	11	109	190	
SF	0	0	2	0	8	3	77	5	19	15	0	3	0	2	2	0	2	2	15	0	2	0	14	0	0	43	14	3	0	55	293	225	
F	0	0	33	0	0	0	0	629	20	98	0	0	0	0	41	4	12	0	0	0	0	66	0	7	0	3	99	6	0	166	1212	1500	
DDR	0	0	8	0	56	3	0	20	497	85	0	4	0	0	3	0	6	0	23	0	0	0	0	0	0	3	22	6	0	26	778	1667	
D	0	8	37	0	48	4	0	108	118	561	0	6	0	0	24	5	23	0	18	0	8	6	0	6	0	3	72	15	0	80	1158	1513	
GR	3	0	0	34	4	0	0	3	3	3	93	5	0	0	14	0	0	0	2	0	0	0	0	0	4	4	0	27	0	31	253	293	
H	0	9	0	0	46	0	0	7	18	13	0	194	0	0	27	0	0	0	21	0	16	0	0	0	0	4	3	75	0	20	467	625	
IS	0	0	0	0	0	0	0	0	0	0	0	0	0	18	0	0	0	0	0	0	0	0	0	0	0	0	0	0	0	18	24	5	
IRL	0	0	0	0	0	0	0	0	0	0	0	0	0	18	0	3	0	0	0	0	3	0	0	0	0	0	27	0	0	26	65	73	
I	0	0	2	0	12	0	0	53	11	22	0	11	0	18	793	3	0	0	6	0	3	17	0	7	0	2	12	65	5	93	1132	1833	1792
L	0	0	0	0	0	0	0	7	0	0	0	0	0	0	3	3	0	0	0	0	0	0	0	0	0	0	0	0	0	11	11	200	
NL	0	0	16	4	2	6	0	11	6	45	0	0	0	0	0	0	40	0	6	0	3	0	0	0	0	8	27	0	0	11	173	63	
N	0	0	7	0	8	8	0	11	22	20	0	0	0	0	0	0	3	20	10	0	13	2	4	0	0	34	40	2	0	74	255	63	
PL	0	0	7	3	136	8	0	26	213	80	0	43	0	0	18	0	7	0	565	20	13	2	0	0	0	34	32	2	0	77	1330	1250	
P	0	0	0	0	0	0	0	0	0	0	0	0	0	0	0	0	0	0	0	20	0	9	0	0	0	0	0	0	0	29	73	70	
R	0	3	0	30	37	0	0	38	4	20	4	71	0	0	27	0	3	0	38	9	287	2	0	0	0	48	15	115	2	60	797	833	83
E	0	0	2	0	18	0	0	38	4	20	0	0	0	0	2	0	3	0	31	9	0	367	0	0	0	24	15	7	2	111	583	833	
S	0	0	5	0	18	16	8	15	42	35	0	5	0	0	4	0	5	8	31	0	3	0	83	0	0	24	35	7	0	113	472	229	
CH	0	0	0	0	2	0	0	23	3	13	0	0	0	0	47	0	0	0	0	0	0	2	0	14	0	0	5	3	0	17	141	48	
TR	0	0	0	28	5	0	0	3	6	5	20	7	0	0	13	0	0	0	5	0	12	3	0	0	175	17	0	22	0	79	416	417	
SU	3	14	18	69	189	25	50	67	283	190	22	159	0	2	94	3	23	5	386	0	205	10	38	3	175	4536	103	208	3	1061	6901	6750	
UK	0	0	7	0	0	4	0	27	11	21	0	0	0	7	0	0	5	0	2	0	0	0	0	0	0	0	675	0	0	72	847	2133	
YU	3	14	2	32	38	0	0	20	25	22	6	72	0	0	131	0	2	0	21	0	26	7	0	0	0	8	7	557	2	83	1093	1229	

R = Receivers
E = Emitters

Calculated average monthly country-by-country sulphur budget for the selected two-year period. Except for UK, the countries are represented by the official automobile registration abbreviation. The total deposition from all sources is given under SUM for each country. RE signifies remaining area of grid, and UND signifies undecided wet deposition. Average monthly sulphur emission is given under Q. In three cases official corrections to the emissions were received, the new emissions were effected from 1 April, 1980 and are given under Q2.

Source: UNECE EMEP Programme 1983.

4. **CHEMICAL TRANSFORMATION AND DEPOSITION**

4.1 **Introduction**

This section deals with the chemical transformation of acid
pollutants and their deposition or removal from the atmosphere.

In particular it considers the linkages between the major
pollutant emissions of sulphur dioxide, oxides of nitrogen and
ammonia and:

i.   the dry deposition of gaseous and particulate oxidised
        sulphur and nitrogen compounds, and certain photo-
        oxidants formed from NO_x and ammonia, and

ii.   the wet deposition of acidic rainwater and snow
        containing nitrates, sulphates and ammonium.

The principal questions at issue may be generalised as:

o   what are the final oxidation products of sulphur and
        nitrogen when precipitated in dry or wet form?

o   what are the principal determinants of the extent and
        rate of conversion?

o   is there a linear relation between the concentration of
        major acidifying agents precipitated and the emitted
        pollutants from which they were formed?

4.2 **Uncertainty Concerning Mechanisms of Conversion**

Whilst there is some certainty about the rates at which these
transformations take place, there is considerable uncertainty
about the detailed mechanisms involved. This is particularly
true of the products of wet precipitation. It is not difficult
to see why this uncertainty exists. The parent compounds of
rainwater can only be indirectly specified because rainwater
consists of dissolved ions which are not directly associated with
their precursor emission compounds. It is generally thought that
NH_4, Na, Ca, SO_4, NO_3 and Cl form the parent compounds in
rainwater.

There is also a good deal of uncertainty surrounding the
conversion products of nitrogen.

The following sections review the current state of knowledge
concerning chemical transformation and removal of the chemical
products from the atmosphere.

4.3   <u>**Chemical Transformation of SO$_2$ and NO$_x$**</u>

4.3.1   **Reaction phases and influencing factors**

Chemical transformation processes of sulphur and nitrogen oxides broadly takes place in two phase categories:

o   homogeneous gas phase reactions;

o   heterogeneous reactions involving liquid droplets in the form of cloud, fog or rainwater and solid particulates. [1]

It is generally accepted that the rates of these different processes are greatly modified by climatic factors such as temperature, sunlight, and humidity. This is supported by data showing seasonal variations in transformation rates. These rates are also influenced by the concentrations of trace metal catalysts, oxidants and water vapour.

Though both of the processes are said to involve sulphur and nitrogen oxides, to date there is less evidence concerning the latter.

At present, most investigators are of the opinion that liquid phase reactions are of comparable importance to gas phase reactions although much less is known of the liquid phase of chemical transformation.

It is stated by some that true heterogeneous oxidation involving solid particulates is unlikely to take place to any great extent.

4.3.2   **Homogeneous gas phase reactions**

i. The Importance of Oxidants

The gas phase oxidation of sulphur dioxide has probably been studied in more detail than any other atmospheric species. In general terms the types of reaction are also appropriate to NO$_x$. They involve the oxidation of sulphur dioxide and NO$_x$ by free radicals - namely the hydroxyl radical generated by the photolysis of ozone - to form an acid aerosol. In polluted atmospheres where there are larger quantities of NO$_x$ and hydrocarbons generating photo-oxidants, there is evidence to suggest that the aerosols formed will be a mixture of sulphuric and nitric acids. In other words, the conversion process to sulphates and nitrates will take place much more readily when the acid pollutants emitted pass through polluted air (more likely to be over land, than over water).

---

(1) There is some dispute over terminology here as many authors regard the atmospheric oxidation of sulphur compounds in the aqueous phase as a homogeneous process.

ii. The Reaction Process

The stages in the reaction process are believed to be as follows:

$$OH^\cdot + SO_2 \rightarrow HSO_3^\cdot$$

$$HSO_3^\cdot + O_2 \rightarrow HSO_5^\cdot$$

$$HSO_5^\cdot + NO \rightarrow [HSO_4^\cdot + NO_2]$$

$$HSO_4^\cdot + NO_2 \rightarrow \text{hydrolyses to give a mixed } H_2SO_4 + HNO_3$$
aerosol forming a strong acid particle.

Other reaction sequences probably involve:

$$HO_2^\cdot + SO_2 \rightarrow HSO_4^\cdot$$

$$RO_2^\cdot + SO_2 \rightarrow RSO_4^\cdot$$

and $\qquad NO_3 + SO_2 \rightarrow SO_3 + NO_2$

It has been shown that direct photo-oxidation of sulphur dioxide in sunlight is not as important as the oxidation process involving short-lived pollutants photochemically generated.

Although there is limited information on the rates of oxidation, the rate of acid production clearly depends upon SO_2 and NO_2 concentration and also on the OH concentration. OH concentrations tend to be a complex function of sunlight intensity and ambient air composition since precursors to OH are generally supplied by the ambient atmosphere, except in certain areas (e.g. around oil and petrochemical plants) where anthropogenic sources of ozone and other photo-oxidants are more prevalent. There is general agreement therefore that these reactions are dependent upon solar radiation, that their importance decreases significantly in wintertime and at nightfall, and that in sunny, summer, urban conditions, oxidation rates increase considerably.

iii. Relationship between Rate of SO_2 Emitted and of SO_4 Deposited

It is generally accepted that the supply of the oxidants ozone/OH may often be rate-determining rather than the amount of SO_2 emitted, a point of critical importance with respect to understanding the relative role of NO_x and SO_2 as damaging agents or precursors of them. If it is true that the limiting factor to SO_4^{2-} formation at certain levels of SO_2 emissions (and above) is the supply of photo-oxidants, then a reduction in emissions would not necessarily produce an equivalent reduction in SO_4^{2-} deposition. There is a difference of opinion over the relative importance of this effect, some taking the view that its importance has been exaggerated.

This hypothesis is of relevance where the source of atmospheric acidity is wet-deposited sulphate, SO_4^{2-}, rather than dry-deposited SO_2, after allowance has been made for local sources of

SO_2. Such a situation exists in Norway and western Sweden, i.e. where the imported pollutants have been transported over long distances.

iv. Rates of Reaction

Values of 0.5 to 5%/hr have been suggested for oxidation rates of SO_2 in the W European summer, with the lower part of the range likely in clean air.

4.3.3   **Reactions of nitric oxide emissions**

Nitrogen oxides are first largely emitted as nitric oxide (NO), with some nitrous oxide (N_2O).

Nitric oxide is oxidised in the atmosphere to NO_2 and thence to nitric acid and possibly nitrate aerosol; this results ultimately in precipitation as the nitrate ion. The mechanisms of these processes are complex and interdependent as well as being influenced by the degree of availability of other pollutants and natural atmospheric components.

The oxidation of nitric oxide can occur via molecular oxygen or ozone. However, as the reaction is an order of magnitude faster with ozone, oxidation mostly proceeds via this mechanism:

$$NO + O_3 \rightarrow NO_2 + O_2$$

Ozone is therefore once again seen to play a key role in gaseous phase oxidation of air pollutants.

The various stages involved in this mechanism are as follows:

Ozone undergoes photolysis to give excited oxygen atoms

$$O_3 \xrightarrow{h\nu} O_2 + O\cdot$$

The oxygen atoms react with large amounts of water vapour giving rise to hydroxyl radicals:

$$O\cdot + H_2O \rightarrow 2OH\cdot$$

These in turn react with trace gases such as methane and carbon monoxide producing various chemical species such as hydrogen, carbon dioxide formaldehyde and hyperoxyl radicals, e.g.

$$OH\cdot + CO \rightarrow CO_2 + H\cdot$$

$$H\cdot + O_2 \rightarrow HO_2$$

Hyperoxyl radicals can be converted back to hydroxyl radicals by reaction with nitric oxide:

$$HO_2\cdot + NO \rightarrow NO_2 + OH\cdot$$

This step is vitally important in sustaining levels of atmospheric OH· radical concentration, and also provides a route for NO_2 formation from nitric oxide. Oxidation can also take place in the presence of hydrocarbon-free radicals R· via RO_2·.

The formation of ozone from anthropogenic emissions or natural sources of NO_2 is itself a reaction of key importance, given its phytotoxicity at relatively low concentrations.

Nitrogen dioxide is photolysed to give nitric oxide and oxygen atoms

$$NO_2 \xrightarrow{h\nu} NO + O·$$

$$O· + O_2 \to O_3$$

The formation of O· is considerably enhanced in polluted regions where larger hydrocarbon concentrations are themselves photolysed to free radical intermediates, reacting further with oxygen to form O·. Thus under certain conditions ozone is able to accumulate. The process of photo-oxidation has been recognised for some while in areas such as the Los Angeles basin in California, where the combination of long hours of sunlight and stable or inversion air conditions are particularly conducive to O_3 and other photo-oxidant formation, (e.g. peroxyacetyl nitrate - PAN). It is only more recently that the problem has been recognised in Europe. As will be discussed in later sections, ozone concentrations have been measured in significant quantities in parts of continental Europe and in England and have been particularly noticeable after long hot dry spells in summer, such as occurred in 1976.

4.3.4 Heterogeneous phase reactions

There are potentially two possible reactions in this phase. The first, involving the liquid phase oxidation of sulphur and nitrogen species in the atmosphere, in clouds, fogs and rain droplets, has been the subject of numerous investigations.

The second, the absorption of sulphur dioxide on solid particles, has received far less attention, and thus it is difficult to assess its applicability under normal atmospheric conditions, though it is possible that oxidation of this type may in fact occur in special situations such as in the plume of a chimney very close to the source. As research on this particular aspect is at a very early stage, it is difficult to outline with any certainty the mechanisms and processes involved. Several research workers note that given further analysis, this particular reaction could be of importance in the atmosphere at large.

i. Liquid Phase Oxidation

There is a great deal of dispute concerning the actual mechanisms involved in the reactions. For example, a chain reaction which has been catalysed by a metal ion is similar to a chain initiated by a metal ion, especially if the metal radical produced in the initiation of the chain can be reoxidised in the chain itself. To date the most widely accepted chain reaction is the following, although other authors have chosen to modify the reaction depending upon their own findings:

$$SO_3{}^{2-} + M^+ \rightleftharpoons SO_3 {\cdot}{}^- + M{\cdot}$$

$$SO_3 {\cdot}{}^- + O_2 \rightleftharpoons SO_5 {\cdot}^-$$

$$SO_5 {\cdot}{}^- + SO_3{}^{2-} \rightleftharpoons SO_5{}^{2-} + SO_3 {\cdot}^-$$

$$SO_3{}^{2-} + HSO_5{}^- \rightleftharpoons HSO_4{}^- + SO_4{}^{2-}$$

$$SO_3{}^{2-} + SO_5{}^{2-} \rightleftharpoons 2SO_4{}^{2-}$$

$$SO_3 {\cdot}{}^- + SO_5 {\cdot}{}^- \rightleftharpoons S_2O_6{}^{2-} + O_2$$

The various oxidation products are hydrolysed to H_2SO_4.

ii. Reaction Mediums

To date, reactions involving the liquid phase oxidation of sulphur dioxide to form sulphuric acid in clouds and fogs is considered to be the most important process in this phase.

Rain droplets have a very short life in the atmosphere and also a small surface to volume ratio, compared to cloud and fog droplets. The combination of these two circumstances therefore reduces the effectiveness of rain droplets as a reaction medium.

There is a general picture emerging that, on average, clouds have densities of water droplets ten times higher than precipitation, but that the ratios of the reaction components are the same in both clouds and precipitation.

iii. Conditions Required by the Reaction

For the SO_2 oxidation reaction to take place, it is considered essential that the reactants are highly soluble, and that trace metal catalysts or strong oxidising agents are present. The presence of ammonia is helpful but not essential.

The importance of metal catalysts or oxidants can be summarised as follows:

o   at pH levels below 2.0, SO_2 cannot be oxidised without the presence of metal catalysts;

o   most experiments show that unless the pH of droplets is unusually high, excessively long lead times are necessary for the effective oxidation of SO_2 in the absence of catalysts or oxidants.

As a general rule it is thought that metal catalysts are important in the reaction in polluted areas, i.e. urban plumes and fogs, whilst oxidants are important in the less polluted rural areas, or near to oil refinery/petrochemical plants.

Recent re-investigation of catalytic oxidation has shown that manganese rather than iron is probably the only metal which can act as a catalyst in cloud droplets, but the manner in which it may act is not yet fully understood. In contrast, many researchers have not in fact sought to distinguish between the relative importance of iron and manganese but have simply concluded that different trace metals are important as catalysts in liquid phase reaction processes.

The oxidising agents discussed as being important are ozone and hydrogen peroxide, and it is generally thought that rates of oxidation are higher when oxidants rather than metal catalysts are present. At pH 5.8, oxidation rates involving ozone or hydrogen peroxide are equal, at approximately 5 ug/ml/min. As the pH decreases, the hydrogen peroxide rate is sustained whilst the ozone rate falls.

The role of atmospheric ammonia is essential at the very low pH levels, such as below 2.0. In such circumstances ammonia helps to neutralise the reaction by keeping the pH of water droplets sufficiently high to allow oxidation to continue without the presence of metal catalysts. As the solubility of ammonia is highly sensitive to temperature, the oxidation rate is inversely proportional to temperature.

iv. Meteorological Conditions

As with homogeneous gas phase reactions, it is generally accepted that conversion rates in heterogeneous liquid phase reactions are affected by meteorological conditions and other parameters. The mechanism for example is highly dependent upon the concentration of its precursors and therefore is more likely to take place when the precursors are in proximity to each other and in high concentrations.

Unlike the homogeneous reaction, liquid phase reactions are dependent upon the degree of water vapour saturation in the air, i.e. relative humidity rather than absolute humidity. The reactions also tend to be negatively correlated with temperature and it is thought that hydrogen peroxide oxidation is daylight dependent. The time taken to regenerate 1 ppb of hydrogen peroxide is roughly one day, so once the existing supply of hydrogen peroxide has been utilised, this reaction will cease until more oxidant level is produced outside the cloud.

4.3.5 Critical factors yet to be determined

Although there is general agreement on the type and range of atmospheric conditions necessary for chemical transformation, there is considerable uncertainty over the extent to which these factors affect the conversion rates.

In addition, due to inadequate methods for in situ analysis at ambient concentrations, analysis of airborne particles in their various forms has been limited. Even if the aerosols are analysed in detail, changes have been found to occur in aerosol composition when collected by filters as they tend to react with the filter material itself. Therefore, not only is improved identification of sulphate and nitrate speciation reaction mechanisms required, but also improved techniques for in situ analysis to facilitate greater understanding of the quantitative aspects of the atmosphere which play a fundamental role in the long range transport of these pollutants.

There is continuing debate over **which** chemical reactions predominate under various atmospheric conditions, and also how the effects of dispersion of these pollutants combine simultan-eously with the occurring chemical reactions. For example, in the case of power station plumes one needs to take into consideration the effects of rapid dilution and dispersion with the chemical reactions. In some instances the rate-determining step may be dilution and mixing rather than a chemical process.

However, perhaps the most important relationship to be established is whether or not the supply of photo-oxidants is the rate-determining factor for sulphate formation from SO_2, as discussed in 4.3.2(iv), and, if so, at what SO_2 concentrations/ emission levels their supply becomes limiting.

4.4 Deposition of SOx and Nitrates

4.4.1 Alternative processes

Removal of the products of sulphur and nitrogen reactions from the atmosphere takes place by two processes - dry and wet deposition. Their relative importance is difficult to assess, as dry deposition removal processes are not fully understood.

The dry process involves the deposition of particles and gases by sedimentation and subsequently surface adsorption and impaction. It is more important than wet deposition close to the pollutant source (see Section 4.4.5).

Wet deposition - the precipitation of scavenged pollutants from the atmosphere - is considered to be the dominant removal mechanism in regions remote from the pollutant source, especially in regions subject to heavy annual precipitation downwind of major sources in the direction of prevailing rain-bearing winds.

4.4.2 Dry deposition

Dry deposition is the direct transfer of both gases and particles from the atmosphere.

The **gaseous species** of sulphur deposited is SO_2; for nitrogen they are NO_2 and HNO_3 (most N_2O and NO emissions will have been oxidised), and peroxyacetyl nitrates (PAN). HNO_3 may be of particular significance because of its high velocity of deposition. Gaseous species deposited also include ammonia and ozone - see Section 4.5.

Particulate species occur in the form of sulphates and nitrates.

The relative contribution of particulate and gaseous deposition to total dry deposition is not certain, but given the low velocity of particulate deposition, gaseous deposition is considered to be much more important. The velocity of deposition depends upon particle size: for particle diameter .02 microns - .025 cm/sec; for diameter 0.2 microns - 0.6 cm/sec and for diameter 2 microns - 0.1 cm/sec.

Also, as far as vegetation is concerned, gaseous deposition is far more important, as absorption of gases is much faster than intake of particles.

The rate and extent of gaseous deposition vary according to the chemical species, meteorological conditions and the receiving medium. Estimates for sulphur dioxide deposition range from 0.1 cm/sec to 2 cm/sec; for NO_x there are far fewer measurements and estimates range from 0.01 cm/sec to 0.8 cm/sec.

In Figure 4.4(a) overleaf we show a contour map of annual dry deposition of sulphur for 1980 in Europe, as modelled by the UNECE EMEP Task Force.

Because NO_x is oxidised faster to nitrate than SO_2 is to sulphate over long distances, SO_2 increasingly predominates as the major dry acid pollutant deposited.

4.4.3   Wet deposition

i. Species Deposited

For the most part, sulphuric acid and nitric acid dissolve in a water medium and are brought to the ground by precipitation. The dissolved acids consist of sulphate ions (SO_4^{2-}), nitrate ions (NO_3^-) and hydrogen ions (H^+), though some tends to be neutralised by ammonia whereupon ammonium ions (NH_4^+) are formed.

ii. Deposition Processes

Wet deposition is characterised by the following two processes:

o   rainout - whereby atmospheric species are associated with cloud phenomena;

o   washout - where the species are removed by falling precipitation.

The process of rainout is not yet well understood, whereas there is more general understanding concerning the washout process.

FIGURE 4.4(a): **ANNUAL DRY DEPOSITION OF SULPHUR OVER EUROPE FROM MAN-MADE SOURCES IN EUROPE**

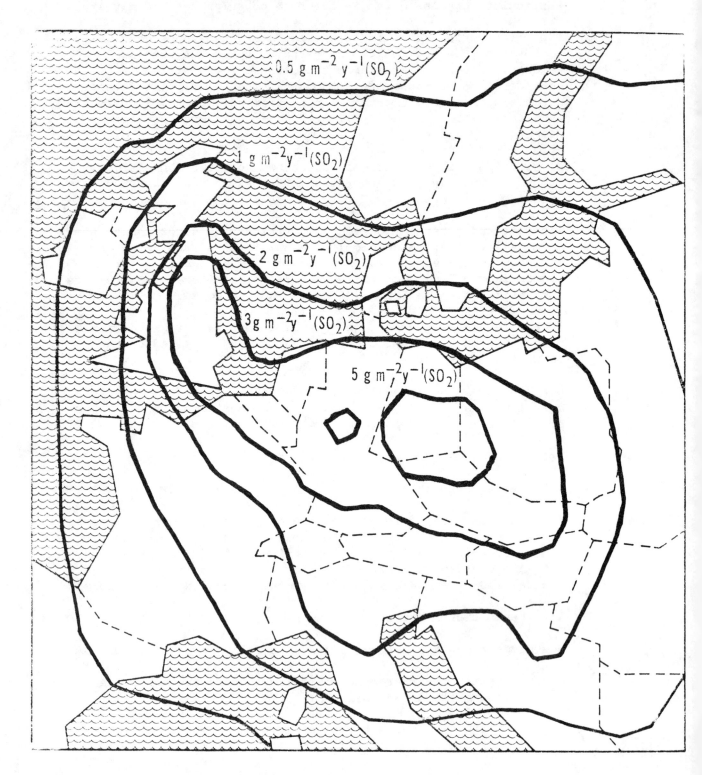

Source: UNECE EMEP Programme (1980) from a paper "Perspectives on Acid Rain" delivered by P.F. Chester, 1983.

iii. Rainout

It is generally accepted that as emissions disperse, sulphur dioxide and nitrogen oxide gases convert to sulphate and nitrate aerosols and at long distances the aerosol phase is dominant rather than the gaseous phase.

It is not known whether sulphur dioxide gas is absorbed into cloud water and then oxidised to sulphate before being removed in rain, or whether the major process is nucleation of cloud droplets on sulphate particles already produced from sulphur dioxide during transport in dry weather conditions.

Many studies indicate that aerosols tend to be more readily scavenged by rainout processes such as condensation than by the washout process, such as capture by falling droplets. Thus sulphate and nitrate aerosols are thought by some to act as cloud condensation nuclei. In addition particulate material containing sulphate and nitrate are captured by cloud droplets via impaction, interception and Brownian diffusion.

iv. Washout

In the washout process, pollutants are removed from the atmosphere by falling precipitation but below cloud level, therefore processes which characterise rainout also occur in the washout process. For example, the washout of particulate material is seen to be achieved by impaction, interception by falling raindrops and Brownian diffusion effects, though the latter process is considered to be of little importance to the washout of sulphate and nitrate aerosols.

It seems that the washout of sulphur dioxide by rain falling through a concentration of sulphur dioxide is influenced by the size of rain droplets, the pH of rain and of course the extent of sulphur dioxide concentrations. For example, large raindrops are less effective at capturing and dissolving atmospheric SO_2 than small rain droplets. Heavy rain, characterised by large drop-lets, will therefore tend to have lower SO_x concentrations than light rain falling through the same atmosphere.

The presence of ammonia is said to enhance the rate of removal of sulphur dioxide as ammonia helps to neutralise the rain medium.

In the case of NO_x very little work has been carried out on the final washout of these species.

v. The Relative Importance of Rainout and Washout

It seems that rainout mechanisms probably account for most of the sulphate found in precipitation in remote areas, as experiments have shown that the washout process is dominant close to the source of pollution. A typical value of sulphate concentration in rain in areas remote from major sources is about 70 meq/l with values as high as 250 meq/l during episodes of high deposition.

Calculations suggest that such levels cannot be reached simply by scavenging of either SO_2 gas or sulphate aerosol by falling rain and therefore point to the likelihood that pollutant materials are already present in cloud water, before precipitation occurs.

4.4.4   Acidity of rain

Traditionally rain with a pH of less than 5.6 has been considered acidic. However, a number of studies show evidence of unpolluted rainfall having a pH in the range 4.5 to 7.4.

Rainfall acidity data for any one sampling station reveals large variations on a monthly basis. Whilst annual averages reduce the variation, nevertheless it is still substantial.

Table 4.4(a) lists past and present annual average precipitation pH data from selected European countries.

Most of the data have been collected at stations forming a network of 160 sites in several West European countries - European Atmospheric Chemistry Network (EACN). The network was set up in the early 1950's. Stations collect both wet and dry deposited material, and measurements include the pH of monthly precipitation samples.

Taken as a whole, and accounting for the high annual variability, W and N Europe shows a core area covering SE England, the Netherlands, Germany and parts of Denmark, that experiences the highest annual average acidity of rainfall.

There have been relatively few analyses of how rainfall pH has changed over the years since EACN began, and none have extended beyond the mid 1970's. The accuracy of these trend analyses must be considered in the context of known sampling and analysis inconsistencies over the 20 year period.

Several analysts in this field take the view that the acidity of precipitation has increased over a substantial area of Western Europe. Both Grannat and Oden show that acidity has intensified and extended spatially over the period 1955-1970. Oden extended his analysis into the early 1970's and concluded that between 1970 and 1973 pH values had stabilised at constant levels in many parts of Europe.

On the other hand Kallend concludes that over the period 1956-1976, only 29 out of 120 stations have shown a significant increase in H^+ concentration, and in the case of some of these a sudden change occurred in the mid 1960's rather than a gradual change over the whole period.

Table 4.4(a)		
THE AVERAGE ACIDITY OF RAINFALL IN WESTERN EUROPE		
Country	Past pH	Present pH
SE England	4.5/5.0 (1956)	4.1-4.4 (1978)
E Scotland		4.2-4.4 (1978-80)
W Wales		4.9 (1981-83)
Netherlands	4.5/5.0 (1956)	
W Germany		3.97 (October 79 to September 80)
Black Forest		4.25 (1972)
S Norway	5.0/5.5 (1956)	4.7 (1977)
N Norway	5.5/6.0 (1959)	
S Sweden	5.5/6.0 (1956)	4.3 (1975)
N Sweden	5.5/6.0 (1959)	4.3 (1972)
N Italy		4.3-5.5 (1981)

Sources: Warren Spring Laboratory, Acidity of Rainfall in the UK, 1982.

S. Oden, The Acidity Problem - an Outline of Concepts, 1976.

Land Institute for Pollution Control, N Rhine-Westphalia Forest Damage in the Federal Republic of Germany, 1982.

R. Mosello & G. Tartari, Effects of Acid Precipitation on Subalpine and Alpine Lakes; Water Quality Bulletin, 8, No 2, 1983.

I. Nicholson & I. Patterson, Aspects of Acid Precipitation in relation to vegetables in UK; Water Quality Bulletin, 8, No 2, 1983.

A. Martin, A survey of the acidity of rainwater over large areas of GB; CEGB, SSD/Mid/N30/78.

A. Martin & F. Barker, Some observations of acidity and sulphur in rainwater from rural sites in Central England and Wales; Atmospheric Environment, 12, 1978.

Private Communication, Welsh Water Authority.

4.4.5   **The relative proportion of dry and wet deposition**

The relative importance of dry versus wet precipitation is
essentially dependent upon the distance from the source at which
acid pollutants are deposited. The closer to the source, the
more likely dry deposition is to take place.

In addition the extent to which wet deposition will predominate
depends upon the volume of rainfall.

i. Sweden

This point is emphasised by calculations which have shown that
the amount of sulphate ions deposited in precipitation is
greatest in SW Sweden. This is because of the proximity of these
areas to pollutant sources abroad and because of the high levels
of rainfall which characterise those areas. In south eastern
Sweden, the dry deposition of sulphur is almost as large as wet
deposition values, whilst further north the significance of the
dry deposition falls rather sharply.

ii. UK

The Warren Spring Laboratory believe that it is not possible to
measure directly the dry deposition of acidity but that to
determine the extent of dry deposition one must measure the
species responsible for acidity. Therefore in order to assess
the annual dry deposition of SO_2, an average deposition of 8 mm S
was used so that 20 $\mu g/m^3$ SO_2 gives a deposition rate of 2.5 g/
m^2/year. Such calculations indicate that the contribution of dry
and wet deposition to total sulphur depositions are approximately
equal over significant areas of the UK and that dry deposition is
relatively more important in central and eastern England, while
wet deposition predominates in the north and west of Scotland.

iii. Norway

In the case of Norway, precipitation is found to be highest along
the SE coast where the annual mean concentrations are approximately 70 μeq SO_4/l and 60-70 μeq H^+/l. Seasonal variations in
wet deposits of sulphate occur due to the following factors:

o   The level of emissions of SO_2 in Europe are known to
           reach a maximum in January, whereas SO_4 concentrations
           in precipitation peak in early spring. This delay can
           be attributed to increased solar radiation and increased
           concentrations of oxidants, which favour SO_4 aerosol
           formations.

o   Precipitation amounts are low between March-May.

o   Maximum deposition of SO_4 is known to occur during
           summer at Norwegian inland stations, and in autumn at
           coastal stations.

iv. Germany

Germany has the highest overall deposition rate among the EEC Member States, and annual average SO_2 concentrations in many parts of rural Germany are found to be in the range 20-50 $\mu g/m^3$. Dry deposition accounts for just over half of the total. One particularly important form of wet deposition in certain areas of Germany is the winter mists.

FR Germany experiences high SO_x precipitation levels partly because of its proximity to E Germany/Czechoslovakia, where SO_2 emissions are high, and partly because of the somewhat adverse climatic conditions which often permit less dispersion of emitted pollutants within the country, compared to most other NW European countries.

v. Netherlands and Belgium

Studies by the ECE estimate that total deposition of sulphates and nitrates in Netherlands is between two and four times as high as in south Sweden. Of these, nitrates and SO_2/sulphates are present in roughly equal proportions with dry deposition being of at least equal importance to wet deposition. It is probable that the experience of Belgium is somewhat similar.

vi. Northern Italy

No systematic study of the relative importance of dry and wet deposition has been undertaken in northern Italy. It is likely, though, that dry deposition is more important in the Po Valley, whereas in the Alpine regions, wet deposition, as recorded in Table 4.4(a), is more important.

4.4.6 The relative importance of nitrates and sulphates in wet precipitation

It is believed that the principal agent causing acidity in wet precipitation in Europe is sulphuric acid (H_2SO_4), with the remainder due to nitric acid (HNO_3); ammonium ion (NH_4^+) also has an important role (see also 4.4.7 below). The 1982 Stockholm Conference concluded that averaged over the whole of Europe, the net combination of nitrate and ammonium **together** contributed between 25% and 33% of the acidity in acid rain. More recently it has been stated that as the conversion rate of NO_x to HNO_3 is faster than the conversion of SO_2 to H_2SO_4, and the deposition velocity of HNO_3 is faster than H_2SO_4, nitric acid deposition is of more significance closer to the pollutant source. The molar ratio of $SO_4:NO_3$ in rain in the Netherlands is estimated as 1:1.5, in S Scandinavia is 2:1 and in N Scandinavia is 5:1.

The contributing role of nitrate is expected to grow as NO_x emissions continue to increase, whereas SO_2 emissions are constant or falling. Also, as sulphates in the atmosphere occur mainly as ammonium sulphate, i.e. neutral, and nitrates occur as HNO_3, i.e. acid, nitrogenous pollutants are likely to have a stronger effect on the acidity of precipitation than do sulphurous pollutants.

4.4.7 Role of ammonium ions

Very little has been documented concerning the role of ammonium except that it is a recognised component of acid precipitation. There is a correlation between the ions SO_4^{2-}, NO_3^- and NH_4^+ in acid precipitation, but the proportions of each will vary according to sulphur and nitrogen budgets and the rate of ammonia released to the atmosphere from biological processes and from fertilizers.

Essentially it has been concluded that in the atmosphere, ammonium acts in a neutralising capacity, i.e. by forming neutral ammonium sulphate and ammonium nitrate aerosols it neutralises acid particles in the atmosphere. Consequently in very acid atmospheres, the concentration of ammonia tends to be very low, often less than 1 ppb, while concentrations up to 20 ppb have been observed in alkaline atmospheres.

Though ammonium is vital in neutralising the acid particles of the atmosphere, particularly nitrate, it appears that it will be increasingly unable to fulfil this role. Studies have shown that the emissions of nitrogen oxides are increasing whilst those of ammonium are remaining relatively stable. Therefore ammonium will be able to neutralise a decreasing proportion of atmospheric nitric acid thus resulting in rain which is progressively more acidic.

Once ammonium comes into contact with the soil, it will be seen that it is an important mechanism mobilising H^+ ions through the nitrification process.

4.4.8 Chloride

Most chloride ions have a marine origin, principally as NaCl. This, and the fact that deposition of chloride declines quickly with distance inland, means that chloride does not make a significant contribution to acidity.

Overall the relative concentrations of the various ions measured in the rain of UK and southern Norway is shown below.

Table 4.4(b)						
TYPICAL CONCENTRATIONS OF MAJOR NON-SEA IONS IN RAIN (μeq/l)						
	H^+	Excess SO_4^{2-}	NH_4^+	NO_3^-	Excess Cl^-	Precipi- tation (mm)
N Britain	40	43	19	17	–	1200
E England	50	108	71	57	11	600
W Wales	20	43	14	17	3	1420
S Norway	50	52	30	30	–	1300

Source: Warren Spring Laboratory, Acidity of Rainfall in the UK, 1982.

4.5   **Ozone**

4.5.1   **Mechanism**

In Section 4.3 it was shown how ozone is important as a photo-oxidant in converting SO_2 and N_2O/NO, either directly or indirectly, to sulphate and NO_2. However, equally important in the context of possible damage caused by gaseous acid pollutants is the role of of NO_x in forming ozone and other photo-chemical oxidants, e.g. peroxyacetyl nitrate (PAN). Ozone is a particularly phytotoxic gaseous pollutant, causing necrosis of plant leaves and interfering with photosynthesis of crops and plants.

Ozone is formed by the naturally occurring photo-oxidation processes

$$NO_2 \quad \xrightarrow[\text{light}]{\text{UV}} \quad NO + O\cdot$$

$$O\cdot + O_2 \quad \longrightarrow \quad O_3$$

But also, the presence of certain hydrocarbons (RH olefins and certain aromatics) are oxidised to form free radicals R. and oxidised compounds RO_2. These in turn react with NO to form NO_2. Thus the balance of O_3 consumption by NO ($NO + O_3 \rightarrow NO_2 + O_2$) is upset so that O_3 and NO_2 concentrations gradually build up, while NO concentrations are depleted.

4.5.2   **Sources of anthropogenic ozone**

The formation of ozone is particularly prevalent in urban areas where vehicles and, if present, gasoline or other hydocarbon storage, provide a source of both reactants, and in summertime when bright sunlight provides UV light. The photo-oxidant problem is particularly acute where inversions prevent the escape of pollutants, as in Los Angeles and Athens, or if there is a particularly large source of hydrocarbons, as is to be found in an oil refining area such as Rotterdam. Large single point emitters of NO_x are nitric acid and certain other chemical plants and power stations burning coal in high temperature furnaces.

4.5.3   **Ambient ozone concentrations**

Natural ambient ground level concentrations of ozone, not influenced by ozone generated from NO_x, are normally around 40-80 $\mu g/m^3$ summer daily average. However, concern over the level of ozone concentrations in Europe has grown since the hot dry summer of 1976 when elevated concentrations of ozone were found. In Table 4.5(a) overleaf we show measured ambient ozone concentrations in five countries in the EEC and in Norway.

It may be seen that, in summertime in many rural areas of Europe, ambient daily average concentrations of ozone regularly reach concentrations more than twice what might be considered natural background levels, i.e. with no anthropogenic sources. Peak hourly concentrations can be ten times higher.

Table 4.5(a)

MEASURED AMBIENT SUMMER OZONE CONCENTRATIONS IN THE EEC IN μg/m³		
	Summer Daily Average	High Daily Average	Peak
Netherlands	55-65(1)	80-130(2)	500 (2)
Germany		100-150(3)	110-180(3) 400-500(2)
United Kingdom		90-165(4)	200-500(2)
Belgium			300 (5)
France		70-120(6)	
Norway			200-300(5)

(1)   Average of national network - 28 stations.
(2)   Frequently recorded in rural areas.
(3)   Black Forest.
(4)   Maximum daily average 1979/80 at 3 sites in S England.
(5)   Belgium at 1 station. Norway at 2-3 stations 1976-79.
(6)   Four stations in France, 1979.

Sources: J. Mooi, Responses of some poplar species to mixtures of SO_2, NO_2 and O_3; Proceedings of 12th International Meeting on air pollution damage in forests, Finland, 1982.

J. Mooi, The influence of ozone on the growth of some poplar species; Research Institute for Plant Protection, Wageningen, 1982.

Land Institute, Forest damage in Federal Republic of Germany; LIS Report 28, Land Institute for Pollution Control of the Land N.Rhine Westphalia, Essen, 1982.

Warren Spring Laboratory, Reports LR397, LR400, LR401.

Ministry of the Environment, La Pollution de l'Air en France en 1979.

M. Ashmore, J. Bell, C. Reilly, C. Dalpra, A survey of ozone levels in the British Isles using indicator plants; Imperial College, Centre for Environmental Technology, Series B, No.4, 1978.

Norwegian Institute for Air Research, Photochemical Oxidants in North Western Europe 1976-79. A Pilot Project. April 1981.

The spatial distribution of these high concentrations in rural areas varies among countries. In the south east of the United Kingdom they have been found [1] up to 100-150 km from London.

As given in Table 4.5(a), high ozone concentrations in Germany have been recorded 300 km from what are considered to be their principal urban/industrial sources. In central Germany at times of summer anticyclones very stable air conditions permit emitted air pollutants to travel a long way before dispersion takes place. This phenomenon illustrates:

i. the relative chemical stability of ozone under certain conditions;

ii. the possibility of trans-frontier ozone pollution on the Continent of Europe.

One other interesting feature noted by Ashmore et al, [2], and to some extent also found in the Netherlands and Germany, was that lower average concentrations of ozone are found in urban areas than in rural areas beyond the 20 km urban limit. A plausible explanation for this, hypothesised by Ashmore and Bell, is that the high urban concentrations of NO, close to the source of NO_x emissions, consume ozone.

$$NO + O_3 \longrightarrow NO_2 + O_2$$

No such readily available ozone sink exists in rural areas.

---

[1] R. Derwent et al; The Occurrence and Significance of Air Pollution by photochemically produced Ozone in the British Isles, 1972-1975; Warren Spring Laboratory, Report LR227, 1976.

[2] M. Ashmore, N. Bell, C. Reily, C. Dalpra, A survey of ozone levels in the British Isles using Indicator Plants; Imperial College Centre for Environmental Technology, Series B, 4, 1978.

5. **BIOLOGICAL AND BIOCHEMICAL MECHANISMS CAUSING CHANGE AND POSSIBLE DAMAGE TO TERRESTRIAL ECOSYSTEMS**

5.1 **The Imporance of Different Pollutants**

5.1.1 There are a number of points that are common in considering the mechanism of acid pollutant damage to trees, crops and other plants. These are outlined below. However, before discussing this mechanism it is useful to review the principal pollutants which lead to direct or indirect damage and their relative importance.

5.1.2 **Acid pollutants**

Until recently, attention concerning acid pollutant damage has focused principally upon compounds of sulphur and nitrogen. As discussed in the previous section, ammonium and to a much lesser extent, chloride, also have a role.

Their relative importance in causing damage to terrestrial ecosystems is of obvious importance for control strategies.

Historically, interest and importance have been particularly centred on sulphur and its compounds. At the present time increasing attention is being paid to nitrogen. However, more important still, NO_x is a precursor of **ozone,** which is known to be the most phytotoxic of air pollutants exercising a direct effect on plants, crops and trees.

The relative importance of these pollutants is a function of their ambient concentration or deposition rate in relation to the vulnerability of receiving ecosystems to each. This latter subject will largely be dealt with in later sections.

5.1.3 **Heavy metals in acid precipitation**

In addition to compounds of sulphur and nitrogen oxides, acid precipitation is known to contain a variety of heavy metals, particularly in the vicinity of metal smelters. The metals such as lead, cadmium, zinc and vanadium are obviously soluble, and in areas experiencing high rainfall are washed out, giving rise to rather higher levels of deposition than in low rainfall areas.

Although heavy metals are generally viewed with concern because of their human and eco-toxicity, in some areas it is known that atmospheric deposition of some of these trace elements help make up for their deficiency in vegetation. Very little documentation is available discussing the role of these airborne elements to vegetation, although inhibition of vegetation growth by the build-up of metals in soils has been studied in relation to the disposal of sewage sludge to land.

5.2   Direct Damage Mechanisms

5.2.1   The term 'direct' damage to plants and trees means damage caused by the direct interaction between gaseous pollutants, in particulate or dissolved aqueous form, and the foliage and other exposed plant matter.

5.2.2   **Influencing factors**

As will be discussed in particular sections dealing with damage to trees, crops and other flora, the extent and form of the damage, i.e. whether acute, chronic or invisible (i.e. growth effects) depend on:

i.   the pollutants themselves and whether they are acting in combination with each other;

ii.   the ambient air concentration of the pollutants;

iii.   the species of the plants;

iv.   age and growth cycle of a particular plant;

v.   climate and soil conditions.

5.2.3   **Degree of damage and mechanisms involved**

i.   **Acute Effects**

The first and fairly obvious point to be made is that acute effects, e.g. plant death, necrosis, collapsed interveinal areas of broad leaves, loss of pine needles, are easiest to detect and therefore more is understood of the mechanisms involved. Most of the established cases of acute SO_2 effects have occurred to trees and other vegetation close to or downwind of high level SO_2 emitters, such as the well known Sudbury smelter in Canada. The incidence of such high atmospheric concentrations in the EEC is relatively limited, but because the damage mechanisms involving high concentrations are more easily studied in laboratory experiments, they have received more research attention.

Acute injury has generally been thought to involve rapid absorption of toxic concentrations of pollutants through the stomata of vegetation over a short period of time. In the case of SO_2, the damage is probably caused after hydrolysis and oxidation of SO_2 to SO_4^{2-}. The sulphate ion is thought to affect carbon fixation and the good functioning of cell membranes. The affected cells collapse and show plasmolysis and, in the case of young trees in particular, dead tissues prohibit normal development. HSO_3^- is particularly toxic, e.g. to sphagnum. The point should be made that acute injury does not necessarily have growth effects associated with it. Nitrogen dioxide is thought to be less important in causing direct acute affects to vegetation in its own right, one reason being that there are few situations where NO_x concentrations reach exceptionally high levels in rural areas. However, as will be discussed later, at lower concentrations the NO_2 contribution may well be significant when acting synergistically with other pollutants, e.g. SO_2 and O_3.

Acute injury may also be induced by sufficiently high concentrations of ozone, possibly in conjunction with other gaseous pollutants.

Increasing attention is now being focused on the possibility of acute damage to trees in central Europe, being caused, at least in part, directly by ozone.

ii.   Chronic and Growth Effects

Direct chronic effects or reduced tree growth or vegetable/crop yields have been seen as being caused by prolonged exposure to low concentrations of pollutants. Again the pollutants considered to be principally involved were SO_2 and NO_x. More recently the growth effects of ozone have been recognised. It is very likely that chronic or growth effects are caused by the combined gases acting synergistically on the vegetation rather than by a single pollutant, and by episodic high concentrations (possibly in critical periods of the growing cycle) rather than prolonged exposure to low average concentrations. However, far less is understood about the mechanisms of direct chronic or growth effects,

   i.   because less research work has been carried out
           involving field experiments,

   ii.   because of the complexity of the biochemical processes
           involved.

It is undoubtedly harder, more time-consuming and generally much more costly, to carry out field experiments, often involving 'open' fumigation chambers, filtered air systems etc., than to perform laboratory experiments. However the emphasis of research work is now changing in this direction.

The second problem concerning assessment of direct growth/yield effects of gaseous pollutants is the difficulty of separating pollutant effects from variations of climate, soil, attack by fungi, pests, etc. Even when pollutant effects have been clearly identified, it is not always obvious how widely applicable the results are.

With regard to the relationship between average and peak concentrations of gaseous pollutants, with SO_2, the short term concentrations may be 3-4 times the annual average level. In the case of ozone, peak concentrations can be 10 times average levels. Usually, however, there is a close relationship between the incidence, duration and size of short-term excursions of high level concentrations and the annual average concentration.

5.2.4   The form of pollutants causing direct damage

Evidence would suggest that acid pollutants, mostly SO_2 and NO_x, cause direct damage principally when deposited in gaseous form. Some damage may also be the result of dry deposition of aerosols.

Particulate sulphates are not thought to be a damaging agent unless hydrolysed to sulphuric acid while lodged on the plant/ tree foliage.

Wet acidic deposits, i.e. rain, mists and snow containing ions of hydrogen, sulphate, nitrate, nitrite, ammonium and chloride, are thought not to cause damage to crops or flora. As will be seen, there is disagreement about its importance in causing tree damage, particularly with respect to the mists of central Germany.

5.3   Form of Acid Pollutants Contributing to Indirect Changes in Ecosystems

Acid pollutants deposited in both wet and dry form can cause changes in soil chemistry and damage terrestrial ecosystems. Acid rain deposits H^+ and associated sulphate and nitrate anions, each of which can play a part in soil acidification effects.

Dry deposits also play a role in affecting the soil and hence, indirectly, ecosystems and vegetation. The dry acid pollutants (SO_2 and particulate sulphates) accumulate as sulphates. Some are reduced anaerobically to sulphides which remain in the soil surface. They are subsequently oxidised back to sulphates when it rains.

However, as will be discussed below, there are other causes of soil acidification besides acid precipitation.

The lifetime of dry-deposited SO_2 is one half to two days, depending on the climatic conditions, giving an average distance travelled of a few hundred kilometres. That of wet-deposited sulphate is three to five days, giving an average distance travelled of 1,000 kilometres. It follows that indirect damage mechanisms can take place at much greater distances from source emissions than direct damage, the latter principally being caused by gaseous pollutants.   There are some measurements for nitrogen; those we have examined indicate a shorter lifetime for both its dry and wet species.

However, where probably indirect damage is taking place at long distances from the sources, the relationship between emissions and effects is subject to many more influencing factors than direct damage mechanisms. The aspect of atmospheric conversion of SO_2 to SO_4^{2-} has already been discussed in Section 4.3.

5.4   **The Causes of Soil Acidification**

5.4.1   The mechanism of soil acidification and soil impoverishment is relatively well understood, and is one that has been naturally operating in several areas of Europe (particularly forest zones) since the last glacial period. Less well understood are the rates at which these acidification processes operate.

> o   With certain trees, acidity of rain is enhanced by passing through tree foliage canopy and by stem flow.

5.4.2   **Natural acidification**

The principal natural causes of soil acidification are:

> o   carbonic acid from precipitation,
>
> o   carbonic acid derived from microbiological and root respiration,
>
> o   acidic decaying products (humic acids), especially from tree litter of spruce, pines and heathland vegetation,
>
> o   podsolisation,
>
> o   nitrification from natural sources of nitrogen,
>
> o   sulphuric acid from the oxidation of iron sulphides.

The relative importance of these sources, and the resulting degree of soil acidification depends upon the bedrock, soil and vegetation circumstances.

5.4.3   **Anthropogenic acidification**

The main anthropogenic causes of soil acidification are:

> o   acid precipitation,
>
> o   nitrification from soil utilisation, particularly nitrogeneous fertilisation of soil; this process results from the oxidation of ammonium ion:

$$NH_4^+ + 2O_2 \longrightarrow 2H^+ + NO_3 + H_2O$$

> o   certain forestry practices, particularly whole tree harvesting (not much employed now), where the cation nutrients taken up from the soil in the tree's lifetime, and exchanged for H^+, are not all returned to the soil.

The role of acid precipitation in causing soil acidification is examined below.

5.4.4 **The relative importance of natural and anthropogenic causes of soil acidification**

The first point to be made is that for most soils in most situations causes of acidification other than acid precipitation are likely to be far more important in determining soil acidity. However, other than acid precipitation, the relative importance of each will depend not only on the geology, soil type and natural vegetation but on the uses to which the soil will be put. This situation was summarised in Figure 4 in paragraph 8 in the report's Findings and Conclusions. The following generalised observations may be made:

o   In most soils, except those under intensive agriculture, the soil pH will be determined principally by the soil chemistry, underlying geology and the vegetation itself.

o   On fertilised agricultural soils, nitrification is by far the most important source of H^+ input.

o   On upland peaty and heathland soils, even those subject to significant acid precipitation, the high acidity of the soil is largely caused by formation of organic acids (humic and fulvic acids) from decaying vegetation. This can also be true for soils of certain forests, as a result of the decomposition of tree litter.

o   The buffering capacity of most soils is sufficient to prevent significant changes in soil acidity (pH) from acid precipitation. The nature of the buffering systems changes according to soil type and as its pH falls.

o   The importance of forestry practices in causing soil acidification depends upon the types of tree, their age, and the manner in which they are harvested.

However, it should at the same time be recognised that certain soils, principally thin siliceous clay or sandy soils, and particularly those overlying granitic bedrock, are susceptible to acid precipitation. Also, there is a distinction to be made between the acidity of natural 'weak' acids (humic, fulvic, carbonic) and 'strong' acids largely from anthropogenic sources. Although weak acids contribute significantly to overall acidity of soil - in terms of the amount of alkali needed to neutralise the acidity in soil solution, this can be as low as pH 4 - they do not dissociate into their respective anions and cations to anything like the same extent as strong acids (H^+, SO_4^{2-} and NO_3^-). The dissociated cations and anions cause particularly important soil acidification effects.

The mechanisms of the various processes mentioned above will now be discussed in more detail below.

5.5   The Mechanisms and Effects of Soil Acidification

5.5.1   Soil phases and pH

It is useful to think of the soil as consisting of essentially two phases - soil solution and soil particles. The term soil acidity is normally taken to mean the condition of both phases collectively, although the acidity may well not be uniform.

Acidity strength is normally expressed as pH which is a function of the activity of hydrogen ions. However, except in the case of dissociated strong acids, it is not the actual concentration of free H^+ ions which is measured when determining acidity strength but a figure derived from the amount of alkali required to neutralise the acid, expressed as if it were free H^+ ions that were being neutralised. With strong acids, the two parameters are the same.

5.5.2   Base cation exchange and leaching

The critical element in determining the rate at which soils acidify is the rate at which basic cations of Ca, Mg, K, Na etc. can be displaced from the exchange sites of the soil particles and replaced by H^+ (and Al^{3+}) ions present in the soil water. This process is shown in Figure 5.5(a) overleaf. As acid precipitation increases the rate of supply of dissociated hydrogen ions to soil water, the rate of cation exchange is also enhanced.

Soils vary widely in their ability to retain cations. Soils with a high clay/humus content have a high cation exchange capacity, because they have an abundance of exchange sites.

Once the Ca, Mg, K and Na cations have been displaced from the soil exchange sites into the soil water, they are available to be leached down, through and out of the soil profile into ground-water etc. This movement requires mobile, i.e. available, anions to act as vehicles for cation transport. Much of the potential impact of acidic atmospheric deposition stems from the fact that it increases the supply of mobile anions, i.e. dissociated anions such as SO_4^{2-}, to the soil. It has been shown that atmospheric H_2SO_4 inputs in some podsolic soils cause perhaps a threefold increase in the natural rate of cation leaching.

5.5.3   Mobilisation of aluminium ions

Aluminium ion Al^{3+}, like Ca^{2+}, Mg^{2+} and K^+ ions, can be mobilised by strong acids, whereby H^+ is exchanged for Al^{3+} at the site, and Al^{3+} becomes dissolved in soil solution with the balancing (or mobilising) free anion - see Figure 5.5(a). Because it can be dissolved by strong acids in a form toxic to plants and fish, this process is extremely important.

FIGURE 5.5(a): KEY ION EXCHANGE PROCESSES BETWEEN BIOMASS, SOIL SOLUTION, SOIL AND CLAY/BEDROCK IN TERRESTRIAL ACIDIFICATION

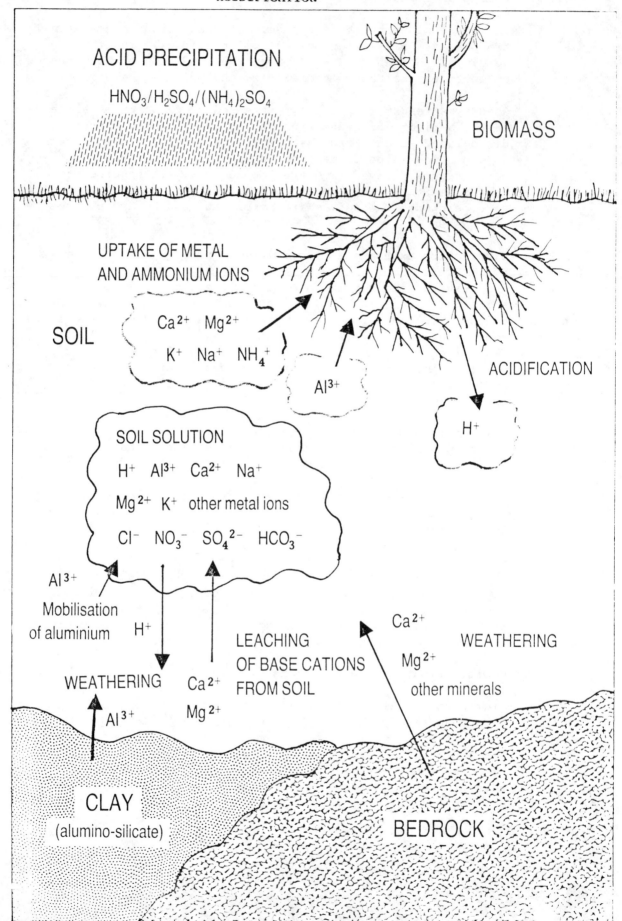

5.5.4   **The relative importance of sulphuric and nitric acids**

Most research would suggest that except in special circumstances sulphate anion is much more important in mobilising cations than nitrate ion. This is because most soils of Europe are nitrogen deficient (particularly in soluble form), and therefore NO_3^- is very quickly taken up by vegetation, roots and the soil.

However, when very rapid precipitation and water run-off occurs, most notably with snow melt, there is a short-lived high release of ions including nitrate ions which do not have time to be taken up by the vegetation/soil system. In this situation nitrate ion probably has a significant cation-mobilising role. It has been suggested that the greater solubility of $Al(NO_3)_3$ over $Al_2(SO_4)_3$ enhances its mobilising capacity but this is considered unlikely to be of significance at the concentrations involved.

5.5.5   **The chelating of metal cations by weak acids**

Although weak organic acids do not mobilise cations from soil in the same way as strong acids, they do remove metal cations from the soil by forming organo-metallic compounds, principally in chelate form. The toxicity of metals to flora and fauna is generally much less in this organic form. Nevertheless, in certain instances, this process is of significance.

5.5.6   **The buffering capacity of soils**

It has already been mentioned that soils vary in their ability to withstand or buffer acidification according to:

o   the type of bedrock,

o   the kind of soil,

o   the use to which land is put.

Bedrock, including clays, influences soil buffering capacity according to its hardness. The more easily weathered a bedrock, the faster is the release of buffering metallic cations, and the stronger its resistance to acidification. Lime-rich rocks such as limestone, marble and marble slates are very easily weathered. Much of Scandinavia, parts of the UK (particularly Scotland) and the eastern part of N America have bedrock which is much more resistant to weathering generally.

Taken overall, most soils have sufficient concentrations of weathered base cations to provide buffering capacity to negate the acidification effects of acid precipitation. It should be recognised that the process of cation exchange takes place very much faster (minutes) than the weathering process (months or years). However, soils are not uniform in their buffering capability. For example deep soils are less vulnerable to acidification than thin soils as they are more likely to contain larger quantities of weatherable minerals and other buffering substances.

The size of soil particles also influences susceptibility to acidification. Sandy soils, with coarse particles and high permeability to water, have few cation exchange sites and are not as vulnerable to acidification as clayey soils. However, as a result, sandy soils also lose their alkali status more quickly.

But perhaps the two most important points to be noted are:

o   Recent work has shown that aluminium, leached out from soils which are more susceptible to acidification, is 'weathered' and replaced more quickly in top soil from alumino-siliceous clays in or underlying the soil, than are base cations, also experiencing leaching.

o   While the rate of soil's ability to replenish leached base cations may considerably exceed the rate of deposition of the leaching strong acids, the soil solution run-off can deplete cations from the upper parts of the soil most in contact with the acid soil solution.

These last two phenomena are important relative to the possible aquatic effects of acid rain. The possibility of gradual long term change in the overall buffering capacity and soil pH is on a time scale of at least 100 years.

5.6   Effects on Soil

The two processes of cation exchange and cation leaching can have the following effects in soils susceptible to acidification:

o   increased acidity, i.e. a soil with an increased concentration of H^+ ions on the surface of soil particles;

o   fewer available plant nutrients such as Ca, Mg, K, Na;

o   a tendency for soil solution and hence soil leachate to become more acidic, and hence also lakes, rivers and groundwater.

5.7   Effects on Soil Biota

The following changes in **soil** biota have been claimed as a result of the acidification effects on soil:

o   a decrease in the number and activity of soil bacteria, which affects nitrogen fixation and internal acidification;

o   a change in fungi numbers;

o   reduced organic matter decomposition and mineralisation. Some studies support this conclusion and a consequent increase in organic matter; others claim the evidence is inconclusive.

5.8   **Heavy Metal Mobilisation**

Cadmium is of particular note, partly because there is more understanding regarding its mobilisation mechanism, but also because of its toxicity and ability to accumulate up the food chain. The mobilisation of cadmium is dependent upon the pH of the soil solution, and unlike other heavy metals, cadmium does not become fixed within the soil structure. Research has shown that the divalent cadmium ion will be displaced by hydrogen ions when the pH is lowered by one unit from pH 5 to 4. Concentrations of up to 1-2 μg/l have been obtained.

Like other heavy metals, cadmium in natural water becomes chelated to dissolved organic substances upon acidification. The organic substances then precipitate out in the soil leaving a high proportion of free heavy metal ions. In such circumstances heavy metals assume higher toxicity.

At low concentrations Mn and Fe are essential nutrient elements to vegetation; but at higher concentrations these metals, and others, can be detrimental. However, even at fairly low concentrations, some metals and particularly Al, can be detrimental. Some believe for example that Al at 10 ppm can cause reduced root growth, although firs in Scotland have been known to tolerate 40 ppm Al soil concentrations.

It is generally agreed that the toxicity of these metals is dependent on other factors. The concentration of calcium, for example, is a critical factor. The state of oxidation of the soil is another factor - the more oxidised the soil, the more detrimental are the metals present.

5.9   **Extent of Soil Acidification caused by Acid Precipitation in Europe and its Significance for Plant and Tree Growth**

Taking Europe as a whole, the areas where significant soil acidification has occurred as a result of acid precipitation is relatively limited and is mostly confined to Scandinavia and parts of the UK and Germany. However, it is also true to say that the actual extent of acidification is not yet that well known.

There is considerable debate and disagreement about the importance of soil acidification by acid rain to plant and tree growth. Certainly there is not yet substantial proof that it has occurred on any significant scale. There is also debate about the manner and degree to which soil acidification from this source has contributed to disappearance of fish and other aquatic organisms. These points will be discussed in the following sections.

6.   DAMAGE TO TREES

6.1   Form and Incidence of Tree Damage in Europe

6.1.1   As summarised in Section 2.2 at the beginning of the report, two kinds of damage have been attributed to the effects of gaseous pollutants:

o   acute or chronic visible injury,

o   growth effects, or invisible damage as it is sometimes referred to.

We shall first discuss the evidence for growth effects.

6.1.2   **Growth effects**

There is no unequivocal evidence supporting reduced (or enhanced) growth of trees having taken place in EEC Member States as a result of dry or wet precipitation of acid or other gaseous pollutants.

For a time it was widely believed that tree growth effects had been observed in Scandinavia. It is now generally accepted that there is no firm evidence for this.

i.   Negative Growth Effects

Gaseous pollutants can cause tree growth effects without any visible injury. Until now, the principal pollutant believed to be the cause of any such effects was sulphur dioxide. Concentrations considered possibly damaging are smaller than was previously thought. But it is by no means certain that SO_2 is necessarily the only pollutant that can be involved.

There are considerable difficulties in establishing a dose-response relationship for such invisible damage, firstly because invisible damage is hard to diagnose, and secondly because it is difficult to isolate pollutant growth effects from climate and other factors. Research has focused particularly on the response of coniferous trees as they are more easily damaged than hard wood trees, due to the longer time of exposure of their needles.

Considerable evidence in Europe, particularly Czechoslovakia, Poland and Finland, suggests that coniferous tree growth is decreased when average annual concentrations of SO_2 reach 25-50 $\mu g/m^3$. However, this evidence has all been martialled from areas in the locality of high emission sources such as sulphuric acid plants and metal smelters, where other factors may have been important, or where episodes of very high pollutant concentrations may have been the cause of damage.

Linzan concluded that average growing season concentrations of 45 μg/m^3 resulted in reduced pine growth in Canada, although such concentrations prevail over large parts of Europe where no adverse tree growth effects have been observed. Reduced growth of red and white spruce have been recorded for some time in New York State. In 1982, the International Union of Forest Research Organisations drew up an SO$_2$ guideline of 25 μg/m^3 to ensure protection of spruce forests in mountain and heath zones.

Fumigation experiments carried out in the UK revealed that with concentrations of 150 μg/m^3 for up to two years, the growth of Scots Pine was reduced by 10-13%. Such average concentrations are not found naturally in rural, and rarely in urban, areas. It is also becoming increasingly accepted that the incidence and level of peak concentrations may be more important in determining growth effects.

In the Netherlands, Posthumus, conducting open air experiments with poplar trees exposed to ozone and SO$_2$/NO$_x$ at concentrations found in the Netherlands, found some loss of dry matter (i.e. yield effects) along with chronic effects such as leaf drop and chlorosis. Similar experience with spruce trees in Westphalia, Germany has been noted by Prinz.

In the USA, ozone has also been found to cause reduced growth in trees with little or no visible injury.

ii.   Positive Growth Effects

The view has also been expressed that acid precipitation is in fact a positive advantage to ecosystems. Nitrates, ammonium and sulphates deposited on soils may help to redress any deficiencies in the ecosystem of N and S elements, and thus act as fertilisers and enhance the productivity of the forest.

However, sulphur-deficient ecosystems are not significant in temperate forests and boreal zones and hence, with respect to sulphates, acid precipitation is no advantage. Inputs of 5 kg/ha/yr appear sufficient to satisfy S requirements in most forest ecosystems. Inputs of S in acid precipitation-affected regions frequently exceed this value.

On the other hand, European forest ecosystems are commonly nitrogen-deficient and nitrates, and ammonium, in most conditions could increase tree growth, especially when supplied in soluble form. However, it is by no means certain that nitrate and ammonium supplied by precipitation is in fact always taken up by trees. In particular, as trees reach 30-40 years of age there is strong evidence to show that coniferous trees become nitrogen saturated.

Also, as discussed in Section 5.2, oxidation of ammonium ions (nitrification) leads to soil acidification with possibly damaging effects through mobilisation of aluminium.

Some also claim that there is evidence to show that nitrogen saturation in ecosystems leads to increased leaching of the nutrient magnesium and hence acid precipitation is particularly disadvantageous in magnesium-deficient soils.

6.1.3   Acute and chronic gaseous visible injury

At its most extreme, pollutants have led to widespread death of trees. The nature of other visible damage is well documented and the effects are seen on leaves or needles, or in the roots. Necrosis, i.e. acute damage, results in a browning or death of needles or leaves. Chlorosis, i.e. chronic damage, takes the form of a yellowing of the leaves or needles and premature senescence.

Until fairly recently, the only firm reported gaseous pollutant damage of this kind was confined to North America and to special situations where particularly high pollutant concentrations were found. The best known example is the extensive downwind damage caused by SO_2 emissions from the Sudbury nickel smelter in Canada; and secondly in the San Bernadino Mountains in California, where 75% loss of 30-year-old ponderosa pine found were extensively damaged by the high ozone and possibly PAN photo-oxidant concentrations of the Los Angeles area.

However, in the last 4-5 years, reports of widespread tree damage in Germany attributed to acid and other gaseous pollutants, mostly in Bavaria, the Black Forest and in Solling, central Germany, have received extensive publicity. More recently evidence is believed to have been found in North Rhine Westphalia. In East Germany, Poland and Czechoslovakia the damage is believed to be widespread.

In the eastern part of Holland, premature senescence of needles of Scots pine and Douglas fir has been found over a wide area, and in May 1983 acute damage to pine trees was discovered in places. Subsequent tests revealed no evidence of attack on the roots by pathogens or by fungi, and acid rain is considered a possible cause. It is also of note that in 1974 damage to pine trees was found near Rouen, France, which exhibited symptoms similar to those found in the Black Forest; and more recently in parts of Italy, air pollution is believed to be a contributory cause of similar stress found with pine trees.

Elsewhere in Europe and N America, no evidence has been found of direct damage resulting from wet deposition.

6.2   Forest Damage in Germany

6.2.1   Context of damage

The extent of tree damage in Germany has already been outlined in the opening sections. In this introductory section, it is worth drawing attention to certain other factors, besides acid pollutants, which are believed by many to be at least contributory causes of the damage.

i.   Geography and History

In many ways, the combination of characteristics in many of the affected areas of Germany, i.e. altitudes over 800-1000 m, acidic soils, and under-thinned trees over 50-60 years old, are not commonly found in the rest of Europe. In other words, many of the ecosystems of central and southern Germany, where extensive damage has been observed, are naturally fragile with respect to their ability to sustain permanent and robust tree growth. One critical question in examining the damage is the time scale over which it has occurred. A recent document drawn up in Germany outlined 200 or so papers which have recorded damage to fir trees in S Germany over a period of many years. Many of these quote damage in the 1850's onwards; others go back even earlier to the 17th or 18th century.

In recent years damage to fir trees has become more severe, and other tree species have started to experience damage, notably spruce, but also beech.

ii.   Forestry Management

In Section 5.4, we drew attention to aspects of forest management which significantly contribute to soil acidification, most notably whole tree harvesting, and the humus deterioration process.

Several research workers in Germany including Ulrich, support the view that particularly spruce forests in Bavaria have degraded soils and hence cause the vegetation they support to decline. However, other areas of Europe with a long history of spruce cultivation do not show the damage being experienced in S Germany, Poland and Czechoslovakia.

Some German papers also discuss fir mortality in relation to age of trees. Meyer, for example, in an historical study of fir stands in Saxony, supports the idea that stands with trees all of the same age lead to a fragile ecology for firs and the likelihood of disease susceptibility. He especially sees problems in mixing firs and spruce of the same age in a timber forest.

Investigations of fir deaths in the Frankenwald support this theory, although other authors have found mixed fir and spruce stands of the same age that are disease free.

Kostler claims that the unhealthy forests in Bavaria are partially explicable by their location in areas experiencing storms and snow and to the use of the forests for grazing.

iii.   Climate

A number of authors in Germany support the view that forest damage could well be linked with climatic factors, particularly drought and wind.

Rehfuess and Leibundgut believe that dry years lead to increased fine root damage and are a major cause of fir mortality. Attention has been drawn by some to the long dry summer of 1976 as being particularly damaging. Leibundgut states: "Weather influences could play a major role, because spruces have extensive root systems which are sensitive to long dry periods, since the fine roots die and there are increased possibilities for pathogens and fungi to attack the root systems. Such effects do not occur immediately, though. These infections can be spread to adjacent trees through root growth."

Ulrich also considers dryness an important factor in his hypothesis of tree damage.

Mülder on the other hand believes that the East Prussian spruce deaths were caused by the winter frost of 1928-29.

Various writers, including Schütt, argue against the climatic theory. He writes that: "...because fir deaths often occur in the centre of plantations, the optimum fir location (e.g. in the Swiss Jura, Black Forest, Carpathians), it hardly seems justifiable to discuss disease as one of the causes of such deaths, as climatic and ecological boundaries do not restrict the mortality observed."

Nevertheless, it is generally accepted that insects and fungi are an important secondary, if not primary, cause of fir deaths.

iv.   Soil Condition and Chemistry

Gross believes that disturbance of the water supply is the principal cause of spruce deaths. According to Kleinschmidt the physiological equilibrium of the soil profile is the main cause.

Hiss and Beer emphasise the importance of the soil condition for firs. Schubert accepts the cause as being calcium deficiency and Nemec the cause as being the disturbance of the potassium supply. Magnesium deficiency has also been cited as a possible reason for damage.

Soil condition is of course influenced by many factors, as discussed in Sections 5.2-5.8, and many of these observations do not discount the possibility of acidification from air pollution as a major contributory cause.

6.2.2   Contribution of acid pollutants to damage

The previous section discusses a number of factors which probably contribute to a greater or lesser extent to forestry damage in Germany. But the manner and apparently widespread increase of damage in recent years would strongly suggest an additional factor has been contributing to tree damage. It seems probable that this factor is air pollution, of which acid pollutant emissions are likely to be the main cause.

This observation is supported by two facts:

i.   Sulphur dioxide concentrations in many rural areas of central and southern Germany are high (20-30 $\mu g/m^3$) in comparison to those pertaining in most rural areas elsewhere in the Community; high ozone levels have also been found.

ii.   This situation is brought about by the high incidence of stable air conditions which allows emissions from the main urban and industrial areas to be transported long distances in air flows without much dispersion.

In the following section we examine the two principal damage mechanisms that have been hypothesised to explain forest damage in Germany.

6.3   Mechanisms of Forest Damage by Air Pollutants

6.3.1   Indirect mechanism

Indirect mechanisms involving effects on trees (and flora and crops too) caused by alteration of the root environment, i.e. the soil, are due to both wet and dry deposition of acid pollution. Because this mechanism of damage is complex, and involves other factors, a whole spectrum of arguments have evolved in linking acid precipitation with forest damage.

In Germany, the main indirect mechanism link between tree damage and acid precipitation has been made by Ulrich. He claims that an acidification pulse is set up in the soil during dry years, and that acid precipitation has increased this acidity. Soil acidity may then lead to the appearance of aluminium ions in the soil solution. (Several studies note that high [1] Al concentrations in soils are related to the presence of nitrate, rather than to sulphate ions.) Al toxicity may cause fine root damage. Bacteria and fungi are then able to enter the tree through the damaged root system and can consequently interrupt the water and nutrient transport in the tree trunks.

Ulrich developed this hypothesis on the basis of his work in Solling, where conditions of soil and altitude are quite different from those in Bavaria.

He then links soil acidity (and hence aluminium) and acid precipitation by stating: "air pollutants considerably increased the soil acidity in Solling between 1966 and 1973."

Rehfuess has subsequently examined Solling soils and claims no relationship between soil pH and acid precipitation.

---

[1] Ulrich found 2-5 mg/litre Al^{3+} concentrations in the soil leachate.

There is little doubt that tree roots in Bavaria are damaged.
Lack of pathological root evidence, however, makes assessment of
damage difficult, although some claim Bavarian root damage bears
little resemblance to aluminium root damage.

Several authors question Ulrich's hypothesis; for example
Rehfuess states that:

> "The calcium/aluminium ratios that are especially
> sensitive to acidification in the root substrate and
> should be reduced by acidification, have not fallen.
> Also, in the experiments referred to with pines, the
> aluminium and manganese contents of the needles did not
> increase between 1969 and 1979. Ulrich found that in
> his experimental areas, in Southern Germany where fir
> deaths occurred, aluminium concentrations in the soil
> leachate were 2-5 mg/l. The extent of the damage has
> not yet been correlated with these aluminium values. In
> fact, under a healthy stand of firs, similar aluminium
> concentrations in the soil leachate of 2-4 mg/l would be
> expected."

Fir mortality, although sometimes less extensive, is also
observed on steep calcareous slopes on soils with a good buffer
capacity which are almost free of soluble aluminium and
manganese. On this basis Rehfuess states that the aluminium
theory is highly improbable.

Others note that spruces, firs, and beeches, etc. have developed
physiologically adaptable mechanisms which allow them to survive
on acid soils and on soils with leachates containing high
concentrations of aluminium, manganese and other heavy metals.
Such adaptable mechanisms are well known.

6.3.2   Direct damage mechanisms

In the last two years or so there has been increasing support,
both inside and outside Germany, for the hypothesis that air
pollutants principally have caused tree damage in Germany (and
possibly elsewhere) by direct mechanisms, i.e. by interaction
between the leaf or pine needle matter and the gaseous
pollutants/acid rain/mist. Certainly there is quite good
circumstantial evidence for this view in the spatial manner that
tree damage has occurred in Solling; most of the trees affected
have been on the windward edge of the forests exposed to the air
stream most likely to carry high pollutant levels. Also damage
has been observed in soil relatively rich in lime where the
aluminium effect would not be strong.

The second point that has emerged from recent work is that ozone
and possibly NO_x are likely to be damaging agents, as well as
SO_2. Indeed, the gases almost certainly have a synergistic
effect, heightening the damage potential of the individual
pollutants, the mechanism of which is not at all well understood.
It is also generally thought that it is incidents of high peak
concentrations which are of consequence rather than long term

exposure to average concentrations, although the level of the latter obviously gives an indication of the former. However, the relative importance of these pollutants and acid rain is by no means yet identified. Observations, based on experimental work, that have been made include:

o   Damage has been observed in areas of Germany where average SO_2 concentrations are below 25 $\mu g/m^3$, set as 'safe' according to the standard set by IURFO; NO_x levels were also found to be low.

o   Ozone levels have been reached in Europe which are above those considered to be potentially damaging to certain trees, based on extensive work in the USA (where ozone has long been recognised as a major phytotoxic pollutant).

o   High ozone concentrations occur at the same time as periods of hot dry weather when tree parasites increase markedly.

o   Ozone concentrations increase with height, implying it may be particularly important in more elevated forest areas, e.g. >500 metres.

o   In the Netherlands, experimental work has suggested that poplars are particularly susceptible to ozone, suffering from premature defoliation, although unequivocal evidence for such ozone damage has not been produced.

o   Most research workers still stress that acid rain and SO_2 are likely to play important, and in some areas primary, roles in causing tree damage. A key symptom of spruce and fir injury is the low calcium/magnesium levels in needles. It is believed that ozone, by attacking the cuticles, may significantly increase the susceptibility of trees to direct injury by acid rain/ mists, which in turn leads to magnesium loss.

o   At rains of < pH 3.5, erosion of the wax layer on the cuticle of fir needles takes place, with intensified leaching of solutes.

o   Ozone may not be able to account for the type of spruce damage found recently in North Rhine, Westphalia.

6.4   Conclusions

It seems very probable that a major contributing cause to the scale and type of the damage to forest in various parts of Germany is acid pollutant emissions, recognising that NO_x also contributes to ozone formation, known to be phytotoxic. It is also probable that the extent of the damage has not yet been fully appreciated. However, geography, soil conditions, climate

and possibly forest management practices are also undoubtedly
important factors, and this aspect, taken together with the
higher than average (for EEC rural areas) gaseous pollutant
precipitation levels found in Germany, could well mean that the
extent of future tree damage found outside Germany may be
relatively limited. However, in the eastern part of the
Netherlands, symptoms of loss of pine needles and their average
lifetime on the tree have been found to be similar to those of
affected forest areas of Germany.

The mechanism of visible damage to trees is by no means
established, although there is increasing evidence to show that:

i.   direct attack by pollutants/acid rain is probably more
         important than indirect mechanisms involving root/soil
         aluminium transfer mechanisms;

ii.   apart from SO_2/SO_4 precipitations, ozone and possibly
         NO_2, are likely in many circumstances to play an
         important contributory (and synergistic) role as
         damaging agents.

7. DAMAGE TO CROPS AND OTHER PLANTS

7.1 Observed Damage

7.1.1   Damage to crops caused by gaseous pollutants, like that of trees, can be acute or have chronic/growth effects. However, unlike trees, there is little evidence for any acute damage. Identification of yield effects, by their very nature, must rely upon constructed experiments, otherwise other factors such as climate, soil or agricultural management mask any possible effects.

7.1.2   Until recently, most of the experiments were glasshouse fumigation experiments, largely examining dose/response relationships of different crops/grasses and vegetables to different average levels of SO_2, and occasionally NO_2. The following points may be made with respect to this previous work:

o   Most of the experiments were concerned with long term exposure to average concentrations of SO_2 and/or NO_2. It is quite likely that when effects are caused, it is by episodic exposure to high concentrations of SO_2/NO_x, possibly at particular times in the growing season.

o   The experiments mostly exposed plants to different average levels of SO_2 concentrations at levels considerably above ($>100 \ \mu g/m^3$) those found in actuality.

o   The experiments did not reflect actual conditions of climate and low concentration mixtures of gaseous pollutants, both of which vary over time. They also introduced unnatural boundary effects from the walls of the glasshouses.

The conclusions that may be drawn from such experiments are therefore rather limited. While they do provide insights into mechanisms of damage/growth effects, they give no guide to dose/response relationships at gaseous concentrations likely to be observed in the field. Certainly, one is not justified in extrapolating glasshouse experiments of dose/response relationships, using average concentrations above $100 \ \mu g/m^3$ in order to deduce possible naturally occurring effects at ambient average concentrations of $15-50 \ \mu g/m^3$.

7.1.3   Preliminary evidence from more recent experimental work suggests growth effects may well occur in the EEC. Experiments conducted in open-topped chambers ventilated with ambient air and with filtered air found that certain crop, grass and vegetable species may experience significantly reduced growth, and also leaf injury when exposed to certain air pollutants at concentrations found in many agricultural areas of EEC Member States. Reference is made to some of these below.

7.2   Direct Effects

7.2.1   Nature of effects

Depending on the level of pollutant concentrations, and the time of exposure, acute visible damage to leaves (necrosis), or chronic effects (chlorosis and premature senescense of leaves) and reduced growth can occur to certain sensitive plant species. Growth effects may occur with or without visible injury.

7.2.2   Sulphur dioxide and nitrogen dioxide

1.   Visible Injury

SO_2, on its own (generally not experienced in rural areas at concentrations high enough to cause effects), can cause visible foliar injury over a period of 3 hours at concentrations above 1000 $\mu g/m^3$. These concentrations are not likely to be experienced in rural areas except close to relatively low point sources with high emissions. Evidence would suggest that NO_2 may synergistically enhance SO_2 effects but even for sensitive crops such as barley, buckwheat and lucerne acute injury could not occur at levels less than 300-500 $\mu g/m^3$ of SO_2 and 300 $\mu g/m^3$ over a period of 1-3 hours. Such concentrations again are only likely to occur episodically near to local emission sources, probably near urban areas.

2.   Yield Effects

Fumigation experiments have indicated that negative growth effects (7-17%) for winter and spring wheat, potatoes, beet, lucerne and clover can occur when exposed to peak SO_2 concentrations of 475-650 $\mu g/m^3$ for periods of 10-23% of the time. Again the presence of NO_2 in concentrations of >50-100 $\mu g/m^3$ lowers this SO_2 yield effect threshold; some have suggested a threshold as low as 130 $\mu g/m^3$, at fairly continuous concentrations. However, it is difficult to draw any firm conclusions on the significance of these experiments for agriculture.

More meaningful open chamber experiments in fields were conducted by Buckenham et al. In the vicinity of brickworks unfiltered ambient air showed decreased grain and straw yields of 25-35% for spring barley, compared to barley exposed to filtered ambient air. The associated ambient downwind average concentration of SO_2, which was halved in the filtered air, was about 50 $\mu g/m^3$ with episodic concentrations of 180-220 $\mu g/m^3$. However, the ambient air also contained fluoride and it was not possible to dissociate SO_2 from fluoride effects on yield.

3.   Mechanisms

The mechanism of synergistic effects of SO_2 and NO_2 is not clearly understood. It is generally thought that SO_2 inhibits the enzyme nitrate reductase from converting nitric acid to ammonia in the crop. This reduces growth and an accumulation of unconverted nitrate is thought to have toxic effects on plants, although the nature of the effects is not known.

7.2.3   Ozone

For over two decades there has been conclusive evidence of the adverse effects of ozone found at ambient summer concentrations in rural areas of many parts of the USA. Such ozone phytotoxic concentrations cause visible damage and inhibit growth of certain crop and plant species. The most sensitive species are potato, tobacco, grape, dwarf bean and radish, many of which can experience visible leaf damage at concentrations as low as 200 $\mu g/m^3$. Growth effects (mostly in the range 5-25%) have been found in a wider variety of crops, including soya bean, winter/spring wheat and clover. It has been estimated by the USA Office of Technology Assessment that if ozone were reduced to 'natural' ambient levels, the value of increased yields of wheat, corn, soya bean and peanut would be $3.1 billion per annum.

More recently, and particularly after the hot dry summer of 1976, it was recognised that phytotoxic concentrations of ozone regularly occur in rural areas of Europe. The concentrations that have been measured are reported in Section 4.5.3. Experimental work in assessing the possible effects of high episodic ozone concentrations found in anticyclonic spring/summer conditions, partly in conjunction with other acid pollutants (SO_2 and NO_x), has only recently begun. No conclusions can yet be formed on the degree of possible growth effects caused by ozone under different climate, soil and other influencing conditions, nor its importance relative to other pollutants. Some preliminary open chamber experiments in the southern part of the UK indicate that in 1980 (a year when ambient concentrations of ozone were in fact relatively low for the time of year), growth rates of two ozone-sensitive species, clover and radish, were significantly reduced (approximately 5-12%). Effects were recorded for one of the grass species, known not to be sensitive.

While the relative importance of individual pollutants in causing adverse growth impacts upon sensitive species is not yet known, it is accepted that ozone does have an important role both in its own right and synergistically with SO_2 and possibly NO_2 (and, in some instances, anti-synergistically). As yet there has not been sufficient spatial and temporal ambient ozone concentration mapping to know the possible extent of any ozone-induced negative growth effects on sensitive crops and other plants. Mention has already been made of the high ambient concentrations that can be found at long distances from urban/industrial areas of Germany. In England, it would appear that phytotoxic concentrations of ozone can be found 100-150 km or more from major urban areas, and high ozone concentrations can be transported over the channel.

7.3   **Indirect Effects on Agriculture of Acid Precipitation**

7.3.1   **Negative growth effects**

In Section 5.4 it was concluded that in intensively cultivated
agricultural areas, the soil acidification effects of N
fertiliser nitrification would considerably outweigh any acidification from acid precipitation. It is also considered unlikely
that, at the pH levels of acid rain found in Europe, acid
precipitation would have a significant leaching effect on agricultural soil nutrients and minerals.

7.3.2   **Positive growth effects**

In theory, acid precipitation provides a beneficial growth effect
for crops by virtue of the fact that it is supplying sulphur and
nitrogen, both essential nutrients for plant growth.

As regards nitrogen, most cultivated soils of Europe have
nitrogen fertiliser added to them. The artificial supply of
nitrogen is so large compared to that supplied by atmospheric
ammonium and nitrate deposition, that the cessation of nitrogen
supply from acid NO_x emissions would have an insignificant effect
on crop growth.

The situation is rather different for sulphur. Relatively little
sulphur is now supplied artificially to European agricultural
soil in the form of sulphates (usually $(NH_4)_2SO_4$ and compound
super-phosphates fertilisers). This is because few soils of the
EEC Member States are sulphur-deficient, and most of the sulphur
deficient areas anyway are not usually suitable for arable
farming. However, there are certain areas, comprising probably
not more than 10-20% of agricultural land in the EEC, which might
be described as 'sulphur marginal'. If SO_2 and sulphate
deposition in these areas was halved, say, it is possible that a
deficiency would have to be made up with a supply of artificial
sulphates. In other words, in these areas, acid precipitation
could be providing a beneficial effect. It is not yet possible
to say whether the value of any such benefit is more or less than
the possibility of loss of yield value caused by the direct
effect of dry SO_2 deposition.

7.3.3   **Uptake of heavy metals**

Certain Swedish scientists have expressed concern over the
enhanced heavy metal concentrations, particularly cadmium, found
in soils signficantly acidified by acid precipitation. It is
thought these might be taken up in the foliage of certain
vegetables with high metal uptake potential, e.g. lettuce and
cabbage.

7.4   Conclusions

A considerable amount of field research still needs to be carried out to establish whether acid pollutants and ozone, independently but more probably together, cause significant loss of yield in certain crops and other plants within the EEC. Nevertheless, preliminary evidence suggests that from time to time, and in certain areas, ambient concentrations of SO_2 and ozone (enhanced by NO_2) can be sufficient to cause significant loss of yield on a number of the more sensitive cereals, grasses, root crops and some vegetables. Ozone is particularly important in this respect, and is also known to enhance SO_2-negative impacts. Indications are that the scale of such effects can be in the range 5-40%. These effects are likely to be most prevalent relatively near to urban and industrial emission sources, although phytotoxic ozone concentrations have been recorded long distances from urban conglomerations.

However, it must be stressed that in most cases the degree of any such adverse yield effects is critically dependent upon soil and meteorological conditions, especially at critical early stages in the growing cycle.

In most years and situations, it is probable that these factors are likely to mask any direct adverse impacts from air pollutants. This does not necessarily mean that pollutant effects are not significant, only that their relative importance is difficult to identify.

It is possible that in certain marginal sulphur soils, some positive agricultural benefit is being gained from SO_2 emissions. However, such areas are not large in Europe and the size of any such possible benefit has not been evaluated.

8. EFFECTS ON AQUATIC ECOSYSTEMS AND FISH

8.1 Acid Deposition

The level of acidity from precipitation in Europe has been discussed earlier in Section 4.4.4, dealing with the acidity of rain. In the following sections we examine how this may be modified in the process of run-off to surface waters by catchments, and also its importance in relation to other sources of acid input. Also, the section examines the extent and mechanisms for damage to fish from acidification of surface waters.

8.2 Evidence of Water Acidification

8.2.1 Surface waters

Data from Norway consistently show that a decrease in pH in freshwaters has occurred in large regions of southern Norway. They indicate that pH levels in rivers have decreased from 5.0-6.5 (the average being 5.8) in 1940 to pH values of 4.6-5.0 in 1976/78. Similarly measurements of pH levels in lakes also show a decline from 5.5 to current levels of 4.7. Figure 8.2(a) shows existing levels of lake acidity in southern Norway.

Similar trends have also been observed in Sweden where acidification has been greatest in the southern and western parts of the country. For example the pH of 15 lakes on the west coast of Sweden was investigated in the 1930's and 1940's; pH levels were recorded in the range 8.0-6.5. A new study in 1971, revealed that the lakes had become acidified quite markedly with pH levels falling to 4.5. The current pattern of acidification in Sweden is shown in Figure 8.2(b).

In Scotland some 22 lakes in the south west (Galloway area) have undergone a significant degree of acidification as a result of acid precipitation. It is almost certain that the acidification process has begun in a number of other Scottish lakes. Evidence of episodic acidification of rivers has also been found in a number of rivers of Scotland and NW England over the last five years or so, although the contribution from acid precipitation is uncertain.

Belgium, the Netherlands and Denmark have also reported surface water acidification in a few areas where the ground is deficient in calcium. A few Danish lakes show a pH decline of up to one unit over a period of 12-25 years.

In Germany, lake acidification has been detected in Thuringer Wald and Erzgebirge with pH values recorded of 3.9. Acidification has also been reported in Eastern European areas.

These trends do not indicate that a pH change across all areas of Europe has been effected, as the rivers and lakes monitored are those likely to have been affected the most.

FIGURE 8.2(a):   ACIDITY OF SURFACE WATERS OF 155 LAKES IN SOUTHERN NORWAY

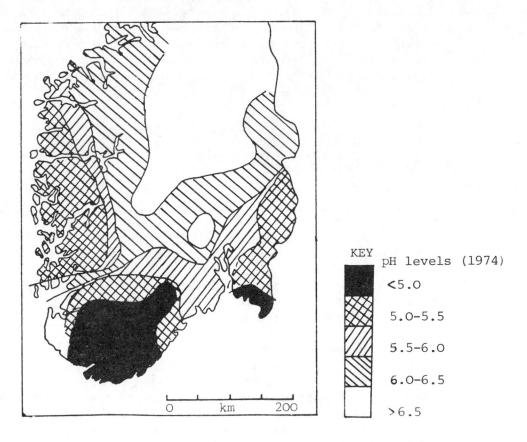

Source: Wright et al, 1977.

In the case of North America, a large decline in pH has occurred in some lakes within one to two decades. Forty lakes in the Adirondacks over the period 1930-1975 showed a dramatic decline in pH, with the mean value shifting from pH 6.7 to 5.1. However, land use changes in certain areas could also have been a cause of the increased acidity.

Several studies have surveyed diatoms, i.e. preserved sediments, on lake bottoms. Although to date we have only read of studies in Scandinavia and Scotland, these show there has been a trend towards increased acidity. Evidence from Scottish lochs indicates a slow acidification rate up to the 1900's, which then increases from the 1940's onwards. Where catchments are forested, the acidification rate is even faster. Evidence from a study of lakes in Sweden shows a gradual pH decline from the earliest sediments analysed in 1949, through to 1964. After 1964, pH declined more rapidly. Figure 8.2(c) shows the decrease in pH found in Lake Gardsjon in S Sweden. Another study of a single lake in Norway showed no reduction in pH over the last two centuries.

FIGURE 8.2(b):   ACIDITY OF LAKES IN SWEDEN

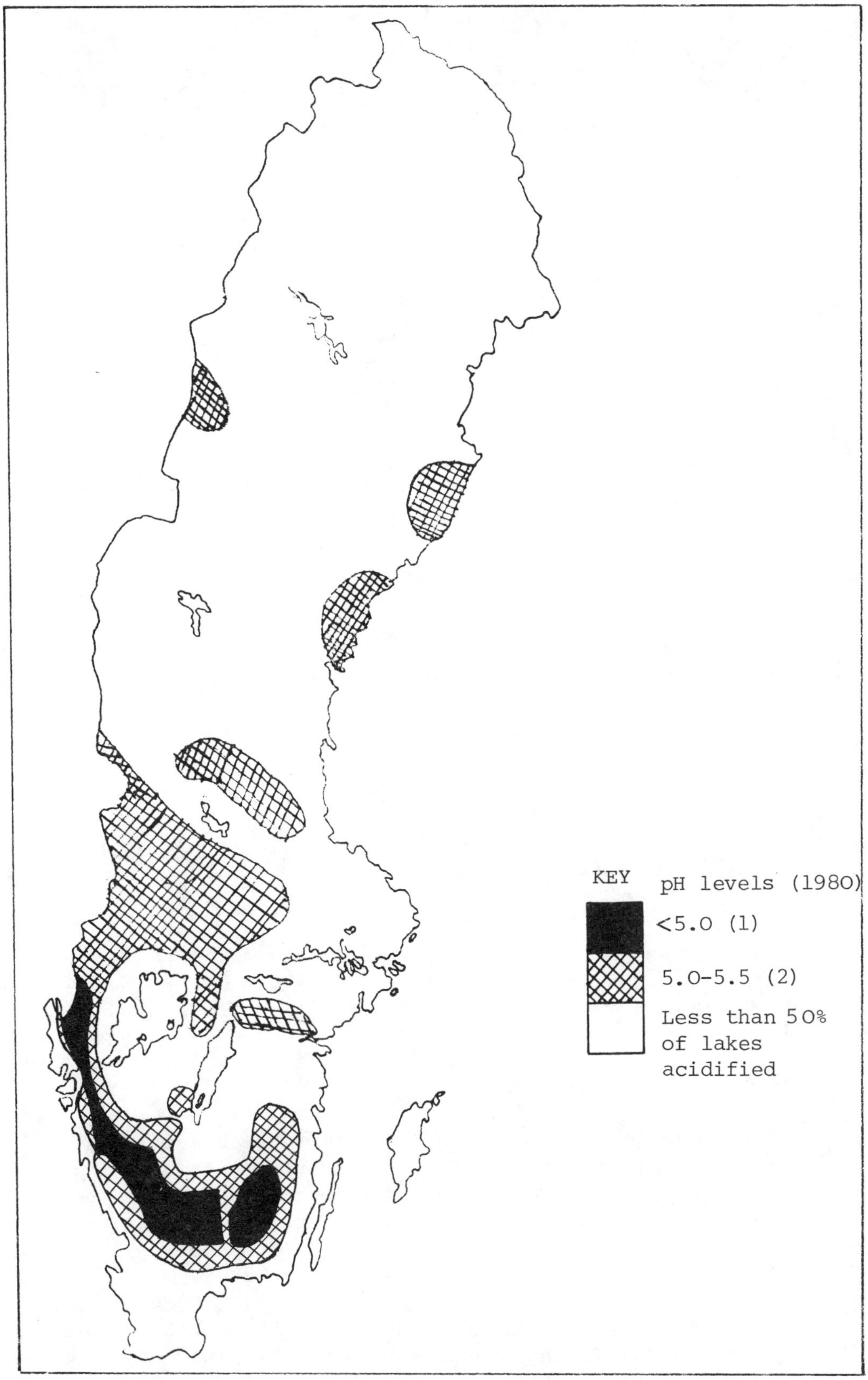

KEY   pH levels (1980)

■   <5.O (1)

▨   5.O-5.5 (2)

□   Less than 5O%
of lakes
acidified

Source: Statens Naturvardsverk, 1981.

Notes: (1)   All year round in at least 33% of lakes.
          (2)   Some time during the year in at least 50% of lakes.

FIGURE 8.2(c): THE pH OF LAKE GARDSJON OVER A TIME SCALE FROM 12,500 BC to 1979 AD

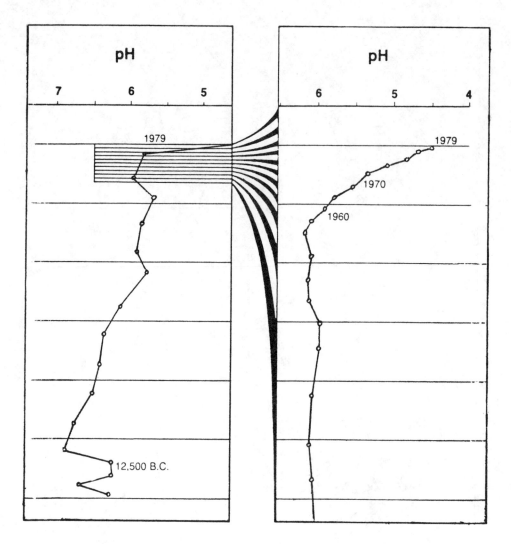

Source: I. Renberg and T. Hedberg, _Ambio 1_, 1982.

8.2.2   Groundwaters

Fewer studies have been carried out on the acidification of groundwaters, and little is known about the changes that have taken place in groundwater pH during the last ten to twenty years. The recent Stockholm conference on acidification reached a general conclusion that the acidity of shallow groundwaters in Europe has increased.

Over Scandinavia as a whole, pH values between 5 and 6 occur in groundwater. In the south western part of Sweden, pH values between 4 and 5 have been recorded in shallow wells with the odd case of a pH below 4. In this area the data show a marked increase in sulphate content and a decrease in alkalinity but it has proved difficult to determine whether the pH values have declined. In some cases obviously, groundwater can be naturally acidic with pH levels as low as 5.

8.2.3   Conclusions

It would seem indisputable that in parts of Europe surface waters have become more acid since 1950, and that in parts of Scandinavia groundwaters probably are too. However, it is more difficult to be clear about the slope of the overall downward trend. This is partly because it is difficult to identify long term trends from what in some instances are relatively short-duration historical pH data. And secondly, methods of pH measurement have changed somewhat in the last 25-30 years, and in any case, pH measurement of low conductivity solutions (i.e. pH above 5.0, were historically probably not more accurate than $^{\pm}0.2$). Also in biologically active lakes (where CO_2 concentration will vary), pH may change substantially from time to time.

The last point to be made, and one which will be discussed later, is that a lake (and possibly a river system) can undergo acidification without a change in pH occurring. This is a function of the acid neutralising capacity of its catchment area. Some scientists have suggested that loss of alkalinity (or increase in Ca/Mg ion concentrations) would be a better measure of the acidification process.

8.3   Acid Inputs to Surface and Ground Water

8.3.1

Surface water acidity depends principally upon acidic input to soil and soil solution in the water catchment area, and the soil chemistry/buffering capacity of the catchment. (As noted in Section 5.5.1, acidity in the context of soil and water acidification is not the same as free H^+ ion concentration, and mobile sulphate anion is critical in this process.) The other relatively minor acid input to lakes comes from direct precipitation onto the surface waters.

As discussed in Section 5.4, acid input to soil/soil solution derives from a number of natural sources and human activities, only one of which is acid precipitation. It is worth considering the relative importance of the SO_4 in relation to surface water acidification.

8.3.2   Acidification from sources other than acid pollutants

1.   Atmospheric Carbonic Acid

The CO_2-pressure with respect to the soil solution, which in the atmosphere is about 0.3 mbar, may initially be more than 100 times greater in the soil due to biological activity. Such high CO_2-pressures in equilibrium with otherwise pure water result in pH values less than 4.7. However, the run-off is not continually in equilibrium with the CO_2 pressure in the soil, but moves towards a lower pressure, similar to that of the atmosphere.

It is, therefore, unlikely that carbonic acid will contribute much to the acidity of surface waters at pH less than 5.5.

It is also unlikely that carbonic acid, which has remained relatively stable in the atmosphere, could lead to a dramatic change in water pH. Increases in atmospheric CO_2 concentration over the last 20 years are not sufficient to make a significant impact.

2.   Organic Acids from Humus Decomposition

Apart from carbonic acid it is generally thought that the most important natural sources of H^+ acting in soil systems are organic acids, produced by the decomposition of organic matter. Ecosystems that produce the highest quantity of organic acids are peatlands - i.e. mull and mor soils. Coniferous forest soils contain little organic matter.

As a natural process that has operated for a long period of time, it is unlikely that the formation of organic acids is the cause of recent water acidification. Nevertheless, their presence is extremely important and can contribute to background acidity as low as pH 5. At < 4.5, the contribution to fully dissociated H^+ ion acidity by organic acids will be small, except in small sphagnum-dominated bogs/ponds, where sphagnum cation exchange ability can maintain a natural pH < 4.5.

3.   Podsolisation

In certain soils subject to high rainfall, the natural action of organic acids formed will slowly remove base cations, as well as other metals and nutrients from the upper layers of the soil. This can reduce the buffering capacity of the soil.

4.   Afforestation, Forestry Practices and Land Use

Land use, most notably afforestation, can be a cause of water acidification, as described in Section 5.4. Streams and lakes in coniferous forest catchment areas are more acid than streams and lakes in adjacent moorland catchments. In central west Scotland the range of pH levels observed in streams draining moorland and forested areas vary between 5.8 and 4.2 respectively. Correlations have also been found between acidity and forest age, e.g. forests with young trees aged 5 years have streams with higher pH levels of 5.2 and 4.8 compared to those catchments flowing through mature forests of 25 years with a pH of 4.7 and 4.2. Changed soil hydrology, leading to reduced interaction of acid run-off with base cation exchange sites, has been suggested as the reason.

Secondly, forest canopies can accumulate dry-deposited acid pollutants (mostly SO_2 and sulphates) which are then washed to the ground. Where the dry deposition is high enough the throughfall can be of significantly lower pH than the falling acid rain.

Thirdly, the manner of tree harvesting has an important bearing on the potential acidity of water run-off. Whole tree harvesting removes 2-3 times the amount of metal and other nutrients that are present in the tree at the end of its life, compared to conventional tree harvesting methods. If part of the tree and roots are left, the subsequent decomposition of the tree allows some of the base cations to return to the soil.

The relative importance of effects will obviously vary according to the soil types and land use and, as will be discussed below, there is considerable debate as to whether these processes are sufficient to have given rise to the more recent falls in pH observed in certain waters, with their associated effects.

8.3.3   Acid precipitation

The principal distinguishing feature of acidity in acid precipitation is that it occurs in the form of strong acids: sulphuric and nitric acids. By their nature, they give rise to lower pH's than the same concentration of organic acids. Also, as noted in Section 5.5.5 strong acids are more effective than inorganic acids at leaching out metal cations from soil, particularly in thin soils. To distinguish water acidity caused by acid precipitation, reference is often made to the concentration of excess sulphate ion. This means the concentration in strong acid derived from SO_2/sulphuric acid precipitation after adjustment for natural (from the sea) sulphate ions in the atmosphere.

Acid precipitation undoubtedly has contributed to considerable reduction of pH in certain lakes, principally in Scandinavia and Scotland over the last 30 years. Measured pH has shown a marked decline in pre-war years and more recently in certain Scottish lochs.

Another important phenomenon associated with acid precipitation is the rapid episodic excursion of low pH. Such episodes occur with snow melt or intense rain following a dry period in summer when accumulated SO_2/H_2SO_4 and HNO_3 are suddenly released. As ion fractionation occurs in deep snow, when the first snow thaws, an especially high release of H^+ ions occurs. Such waters may be three times more acidic than the snow pack as a whole, thus thousands of Scandinavian mountain streams and Canadian shield brooks suffer annually from pH episodes in the spring, unless they are particularly well buffered.

SO_2 precipitated in a long dry period accumulates as S, H_2S and other sulphides in vegetation and the soil. When rain falls, this sulphur in various forms is oxidised and dissolved as sulphuric acid of considerably higher concentration than would normally fall as acid rain. This effect is further enhanced if the surface run-off is rapid, allowing little time for neutralisation by contact with the soil and bedrock. Indeed the general point can be made that the pathway of run-off through the soil is generally critical in influencing the acidity of the resultant surface waters.

8.4   The Process of Water Acidification

8.4.1   Catchment buffering

We have already described in Section 5.5.6 how the soil structure and chemistry, bedrock type, presence of clay etc., determines buffering capacity to inputs of acid precipitation, and also how the leaching out of base cations and other metal ions from soil into soil solution takes place. This process is the main factor influencing the overall buffering capacity of a catchment and the subsequent hydrogen ion and other cation and anion inputs into surface waters.

8.4.2   Susceptibility of surface water to acid inputs

The pH response, i.e. buffering capacity of the water, will also be determined by the amount of dissolved calcium (and magnesium) bicarbonate, i.e. the HCO_3^- concentration. The process of lake acidification by acid precipitation and run-off through the catchment may be considered in three distinct stages, which as Henriksen (1980) has pointed out, is analogous to the titration of a bicarbonate solution with strong mineral acid.

i.   Bicarbonate lakes - Here the dissolved bicarbonate acts as a buffer to increased inputs of strong acids

$$H^+ + HCO_3^- \longrightarrow H_2O + CO_2$$

and pH levels stay generally at the 'natural' pre-acidification levels of 5.5-6.0. Fish populations usually remain normal during the period the lake experiences loss of alkalinity.

ii.   Transition lakes - Here the bicarbonate buffer is lost during longer periods of H^+ input and severe pH fluctuations can occur.

iii.   Acid lakes - The final stage of lake acidification is characterised by severely depressed pH levels, below 5.0, and elevated metal concentrations. If aluminium is predominant in this metal cation leaching into the lake, fish tend to be increasingly absent.

The shape of the pH titration curve over time will depend upon the chemistry of the lake, which in turn will be dependent upon the catchment characteristics. Normally the pH curve over time, i.e. as H^+ is added, will be of the kind shown in Figure 8.4 .

FIGURE 8.4:   ACIDIFICATION 'TITRATION' OF A LAKE

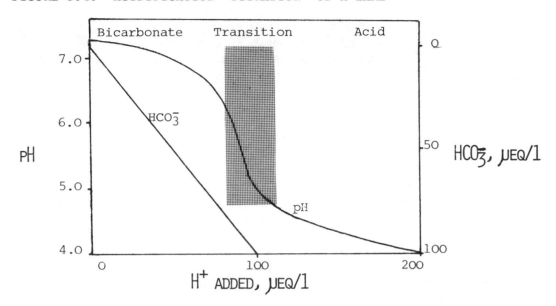

Source: Henriksen, 1980.

As further H^+ is added, pH is buffered by the Al^{3+}/H^+ buffering system,

$$Al(OH)_3 + 3H^+ \longrightarrow Al^{3+} + 3H_2O$$

and pH stabilises around 4.5. Massive changes in aquatic biology occur as a result.

8.4.3   Aluminium ion and base cation release

As will be discussed in Section 8.6, fish are particularly sensitive to the level of dissolved aluminium ion in relation to dissolved base cations, principally calcium. In watersheds with short retention times and where base cations have been leached out from the upper soil horizons through which fast run-off occurs, the aluminium can be leached out faster from the soil than calcium ions, the rate of replacement of the latter (by weathering of bedrock) being a slower process. Thus the critical Al^{3+}/Ca^{2+} ratio in the lake can increase. This situation is most prevalent in upper catchment areas with bedrock, where calcium is relatively unavailable.

By raising the pH level, i.e. reducing the level of acidity in precipitation, it has been hypothesised that lakes can be returned from acid lakes to bicarbonate lakes. But the restoration of the Al/Ca balance, which depends upon the catchment characteristics, may also be an important factor. The response of catchments to reduced inputs of strong acid are hard to predict, although it should be recognised that as pH increases, the toxic form of Al will decline.

8.4.4   Leaching of heavy metals

The solubility of heavy metals normally also increases with
decreasing pH. In acidic groundwater areas concentrations of
metals such as copper, zinc and cadmium are often 10-100 times
higher than in neutral groundwaters. Studies of leaching water
in lysimeters suggest that a pH of about 4.0-4.5 in soil water is
critical, with concentrations of cadmium, zinc and manganese
increasing sharply in more acidic conditions. Surface sediments
in lakes in Switzerland and in north eastern USA have been found
to have enriched metal concentrations.

In one area of northern USA, there has been some concern over
mercury levels accumulating in the food chain in one area subject
to acidification. Leaching of copper and lead from pipes made of
these materials by acid waters (not necessarily strong acids) can
also be a problem.

8.4.5   The vulnerability of catchments to increasing acidity

It is generally accepted that several factors influence the
vulnerability of catchments to increasing acidity:

o   **The ability of the soil to neutralise the acid** is
probably the most important factor. In Sweden a good
correlation has been found between soil conditions and
lake acidity. Lime-poor, weathering resistant soils and
expanses of flat bare rock are mostly associated with
acidified, endangered lakes and watercourses. In
Scotland, the area that is most vulnerable to acid
precipitation is the south west Galloway area, although
other parts of the country have similar geology also.

o   **The extent and volume of surface run-off** is an important
factor. Impermeable ground and heavy rainfall will lead
to large surface run-off and hence little time for water
to penetrate into the ground and be neutralised. The
spring thaw is also a time when little neutralisation of
water can occur.

o   **Short water transfer time, small watercourses.** The
shorter time the water is in contact with buffering
soil, the greater will be the risk of its acidifying. A
small lake contains only a small amount of water and
therefore has little by way of diluting influxes for the
very acidic water.

o   **If the catchment area is small** the acidic input has a
shorter path to the lake and there is less time for it
to be neutralised in the soil layer.

8.5   **The Decline in Fish Populations**

Loss of fish, where circumstantial evidence strongly suggests
that acid precipitation has been a major factor if not the only
cause, has occurred in the following countries.

8.5.1   **Sweden**

Most of the damage to fish stocks has been recorded in south and
central Sweden, in the lakes and streams of Götaland and
Svealand. Salmon, trout, perch, roach, minnow, char, pike and
grayling have been 'damaged' (not defined) in more than 2000
lakes in Götaland and 1000 lakes in Bergslagen. Severely damaged
(undefined) fish, notably those mentioned above, have been
reported in 1500 lakes. Fish stocks have 'suffered' in more than
1000 lakes in Norrland.

8.5.2   **Norway**

In the four southernmost counties more than half of the fish
stocks have been lost during the period 1940-1980.

Lakes in southern Norway covering an area of more than 13,000 km^2
contain no fish, and fish stocks have been reduced in another
20,000 km^2.

The most severely affected species is brown trout, but other fish
have also been recorded.

Fish kills have been reported in certain rivers; believed to be
the result of episodic surges of low pH water.

8.5.3   **Scotland**

Because of its more diverse geology and lower incidence of snow
melt, disappearance of fish from Scottish lakes and rivers is not
as severe as in parts of Scandinavia. Nevertheless a number of
lakes no longer contain trout and other fish, which were
previously known to do so. This has been particularly marked in
the Galloway region in the south west. There have also been in
certain rivers, significant reductions in fish populations,
especially in trout and salmon from catchments flowing through
forested areas.

It has also been reported that fish reared in hatchery water at a
high pH 7, when introduced into acidified lakes and waters, whose
pH can vary between 4.8-5.5, are unable to survive successfully
for long periods. For example, many dead brown trout were found
in an acid loch pH 5.0 in south west Scotland. The fish had been
stocked four days previously from hatcheries at pH 7. It is also
believed that such a reaction to a sudden change in pH might
account for the disappearance of salmon and trout fry introduced
to the Duchray streams in central Scotland in 1976.

Fishless streams have been observed in Scotland. These have been observed in areas where afforestation is a key factor contributing to the high acid input.

8.5.4   England and Wales

In 1980, a major fish kill (trout and salmon) occurred over 14 km of the River Esk in NW England, following heavy rainfall after a dry spell. Investigations have attributed the most likely cause to a surge in acidity level. Even after considerable dilution, pH levels of neary 5.0 were recorded in the middle reaches of the main river. At the same time fish mortalities occurred in an adjacent catchment (Duddon). Preliminary observations of a wider survey of 75 streams in the upper catchment areas of these rivers have revealed a number of streams with low or absent fish populations (which would not have been predictable), and a generally good correlation between pH level and fishlessness - at pH 5.6 (the geometric mean) below, fish were mostly found to be nearly or wholly absent or of odd population structure. Also, in streams of higher alkalinity/Ca levels, fish populations were mostly found to be greater.

In the upper Tywi catchment in West Wales, where rainfall is generally less acidic than the rest of the UK but where episodic excusions of low pH rain (3.8) and surface waters occur, a preliminary survey of 13 streams has indicated low fish and less diverse invertebrate populations, when hardness (Ca + Mg concentrations) is < 8 mg/litre; in afforested areas the threshold was < 10 mg/litre.

8.5.5   Canada

In Nova Scotia, 9 rivers with a pH of 4.7 no longer support salmon or trout reproduction; 11 rivers are in the range pH 4.7-5.0 where some juvenile salmon mortality is occurring; 7 rivers are in the pH range 5.1-5.3 which is considered borderline for Atlantic salmon.

In the La Cloche Mountain area of Ontario, 24% of lakes surveyed have no fish at all. 56% of these fishless lakes are known to have suffered a reduction in fish species composition. Smallmouth bass, walleye, white suckers, norther pike, lake trout, lake herring, perch and rock bass have been affected.

8.5.6   USA

In the Adirondack Mountains, in northern USA, the fish populations in at least 180 lakes (representing 2.5% of the surface area of lakes and ponds) have been lost since the 1950's. Species lost include: lake trout, white sucker and brown bullhead. However, as previously mentioned, some areas have undergone land use and forestry practice changes in this period.

8.5.7 Democratic Republic of Germany

In the Erzgebirge area of Germany, trout stocks have either vanished or suffered marked reduction compared with the state of affairs 30 years ago.

8.5.8 Time scale of decline

If decline in fish is linked to increasingly acid waters it ought to follow broadly a similar time scale to that of water acidification. Hence a fairly rapid decline in fish populations i.e. over the last 30/40 years, is required if the two trends are to be linked.

A rapid change in fish populations may not necessarily indicate a rapid change in pH however. Many lakes in Scandinavia are fairly acidic naturally, around pH 5. Over the particular pH range 4.5-5.5, sudden visible changes in aquatic systems, e.g. fish, flora, fauna, have been recorded. Thus even a slight change in acidification in these particular lakes, as a result of a natural tendency in this direction, could have the effect of suddenly tipping the balance of the system, resulting in quite dramatic visible changes in aquatic ecosystems and in fish populations.

The point has also been made, that although surveys based on the statements of 60 year old fishermen have shown reduced fish stocks in many lakes during the period 1940-1980, there are records which show that catches of salmon and trout in the seven most affected areas in S Norway have been decreasing since records were first analysed in the 1870's. In other words, acid precipitation has not been the only cause of disappearance of fish. Even so, the bulk of the evidence would suggest that acid rain has been a major cause of decline in fish populations in the last 30 years in Scandinavia and in a few parts of the UK.

8.6 Causes of Fish Damage

8.6.1 Physiological mechanisms of damage

It is generally accepted that low pH levels can cause a decline in fish populations. Since this fall has usually been accompanied by an increase in the aluminium concentration, it is now widely believed that aluminium plays a key role but not necessarily the only role in causing fish kills.

Though such a relationship between low pH and aluminium is known to exist, the relative roles, importance and interaction of aluminium and reduced pH on fish physiology and mortality are not generally agreed upon.

The chemistry of aluminium in freshwater is complex and therefore its role is **not** fully understood, i.e. aluminium is able to complex with a variety of different organic compounds which can affect the fish at different pH levels. The most widely held view is that aluminium in soluble inorganic form is the toxic agent.

Aluminium toxicity is known to depend, among other things, upon the level of pH. At pH 5, it is known to have maximum toxicity such that concentrations of 0.2 mg/l are known to be toxic to adult brown trout. Since findings have shown that at pH 5 the species Al^{3+}, $Al(OH)^{2+}$ and $Al(OH)_2^+$ exist in roughly equal proportions, it is possible that the toxic effect of aluminium is primarily related to the concentration of one or more of these species.

Various physiological mechanisms have been hypothesised to explain how fish deaths/disappearance of fish occur. They may all operate to a greater or lesser extent. Salmonid species (trout and salmon) are found to be particularly sensitive to acidification, but other fish such as perch are also known to be affected.

Research has shown that the target organ affected by aluminium is the gills, in both adult and newly hatched fish. This is also the case with increased H^+ concentration. Once the fish has started to breath at the hatching stage, aluminium reduces ion exchange across the membrane. The aluminium precipitates onto the gill filament, causing death. So far it is known that aluminium causes mucus clogging, which in turn disturbs the ion exchange.

Experiments have shown that calcium is of critical importance in controlling sodium losses via its effect on gill permeability. In other words the permeability of the gill to sodium and H^+ is critically dependent upon external calcium concentrations. In addition fish are known to undergo hyper-ventilation and a lowered blood oxygen tension. In such a condition, aluminium is acutely toxic to fish.

The effects of acid waters on fish physiology are similar to those caused by aluminium. For example, fish exposed to acid waters suffer a reduction in blood salts, which could be attributed to an impairment of salt uptake in the gills, and increased sodium use from the brown trout. The salt balance of freshwater fish is maintained by active, energy consuming exchange of ions across the gill membrane and excretion in the urine. Therefore in fish in waters of pH levels between 4.0 and 4.3, particular physiological effects are known to appear in respiration, metabolism and cell volume, and in some cases death can occur.

8.6.2   **Non-recruitment**

Lowering pH, with increasing aluminium concentrations, also affects recruitment levels of fish. A study carried out in Scotland has shown that newly fertilised salmon eggs planted into streams of various pH levels survived for different periods of time. The eggs in the most acid stream (pH 4.1) died within two months of planting whereas those in a slightly less acid stream (pH 4.3) remained alive for three months after planting. Aluminium raises the pH threshold at which salmonid eggs do not survive.

8.6.3 Vulnerability to pH change

An interesting observation concerning fish vulnerability to H^+/Al^{3+} ion concentrations is their ability, particularly among older fish, to adapt to a certain degree to a gradual lowering of pH. However, fast change in pH over the same range can cause death. Fish populations may recover from such episodic effects, caused by snow melt, for example, but repeated episodes can give rise to a permanent decline in fish populations. This phenomenon may be at least as important in causing long term falls in fish populations as gradual pH decline, particularly if such episodic pulses occur at egg spawning/hatching time.

Also fish kills may be caused by several factors other than a sudden change in pH level such as release of a biocide.

Many lakes in Scandinavia are fairly acidic naturally, around pH 5.5-6.0. Mobile sulphate ions (naturally formed or supplied by precipitation) will transfer natural soil acidity to surface waters.

8.7 Damage to Other Aquatic Biota

As the pH of surface waters declines, effects will be noted on biota other than fish. As most organisms have a specific pH tolerance range it will be obvious that an organism will disappear from the system if pH exceeds this range for a substantial time. Beside these direct effects, indirect effects usually occur due to water chemistry changes other than pH or changes in interspecific relationships. The most conspicuous difference between acid aquatic systems and systems having a roughly neutral pH is the greatly reduced diversity of taxa in acid waters.

8.7.1 Effects on micro-organisms

Decomposition of leaf litter has been shown to be decreased in acid waters, while a shift is observed from bacterial to fungal decomposition. However, experimental studies on decomposition in lake sediments are inconclusive. Reduced decomposition may lead to reduced nutrient cycling and consequently to changes in the entire food chain of ecosystems.

8.7.2 Effects on plants

Species diversity of algae is usually reduced in acid waters although some exceptions to this have been observed. There is nc evidence of reduction of primary production, except in those cases where available phosphate is low. Acid lakes are often characterised by increased growth of benthic filamentous algae forming dense mats thus possibly reducing light availability to macrophytes. On the other hand, chrysophytes and diatoms usually decline, and acid lakes are often dominated by dinoflagellates. Diatom assemblages can be used to estimate pH values with reasonable accuracy. In the Netherlands, a number of pools have greatly changed diatom spectra compared with old samples taken around 1920, indicating a change in pH from a wide range of 4 to 6 to a narrow range of 3.7 to 4.6.

Information on the effects on macrophytes is scarce. One paper has reported a suppression of isoetid-dominated vegetation by luxurious sphagnum growth. In other instances the isoetid vegetation is suppressed by Juncus bulbosus. In the Netherlands, isoetid vegetation, usually dominated by Littorella iniflora, is absent or dwindling in 78% of the stands known around 1950, in most cases being replaced by Juncus bulbosus or sphagnum-dominated vegetation. As the mean water pH for Littorella-dominated vegetation is around 6.5 compared to 3.9 for Juncus and 3.8 for sphagnum-dominated systems, this indicates drastic changes in pH for these waters. The capacity of sphagnum to exchange H^+ for other cations will lead to lower pH, calcium, aluminium and iron in the waters.

8.7.3 Effects on aquatic macro-invertebrates

Numerous aquatic macro-invertebrates are known to be susceptible to water acidification.

Evidence indicates that molluscs in general are highly sensitive. According to Okland, no snails are found at pH values below 5.6 and only a few species can tolerate pH levels below 6. A greater correlation of snail species diversity was found with hardness and geology, than with pH, although with the same level of calcium, both number of species and time-catch abundance decrease with decreasing pH.

Crustaceans are absent from acid waters: Gammarus lacustris is not found below pH 6 and Asellus aquaticus becomes very rare below pH 5.2. Freshwater crayfish species are sensitive to low pH while moulting, calcium uptake being inhibited at pH 5.3.

Insects differ greatly in sensitivity. The diversity of the macro-invertebrate community is usually much smaller in acid waters: one study found 46 taxa of benthic invertebrate fauna in a non-acid stream (pH 6.5 to 7.3) and 18 taxa in an acid stream (pH 4.3 to 5.9) with lower conductivity and calcium.

8.7.4 Effects on amphibians

Most amphibians are highly sensitive to acid water, especially with regard to reproduction, although there are substantial differences in the sensitivity of different species. Reduced breeding success and reduced populations of yellow-spotted salamander (Ambystoma mauclatum) have been reported in meltwater pools with pH 6, while another species (Ambystoma jeffersonium) can breed at pH 4.8. One study reported a correlation between H^+ concentration and percentages of dead and moulded egg masses of frogs and toads in the Netherlands. Most species of amphibian breed exclusively in meltwater ponds; these species are threatened with extinction because of the reduced pH of many such ponds.

8.8   The Relationship of Fish Status to Acid Input by Precipitation

8.8.1   Observed patterns

In the preceding sections we have set out the strong circum-stantial evidence supporting the relationship between acidifica-tion, of which acid precipitation is a major cause, and fish populations of lakes, principally in Scandinavia, Scotland and NE America, and also described likely mechanisms by which this process takes place. The question remains as to whether a strong correlation has actually been found between acidification levels and fish populations. This is clearly of importance in assessing the benefits likely to be realised in measures to reduce acidity of precipitation.

The area that has been most closely studied in this respect is the Sorlandet lake area of southernmost Norway. Sorlandet has high rainfall, and some 3,725 lakes which vary a good deal in size and character of catchment area. Many of these lakes have been acidified to < pH 4.7, explicable only by strong acid input; and as Table 8.8(a) and Figure 8.8(a) overleaf show, there has been a strong decline in fish population since 1940. Using the indicator of excess sulphate ion [1] as the measure of strong acid concentration levels, Chester (1982), from a sample of 699 lakes in the region, derived an apparently random relationship (see Figure 8.8(b)) between fish status and sulphate concentra-tions, pointing out that fish status seemed to increase with increasing sulphate. Brown and Sadler (1981) also traced the relationship (Figure 8.8(c)) between acidity of the lake, as measured by H^+ against excess sulphate ion, showing a relatively gentle slope apparently indicating that additional inputs (or reductions) of precipitated strong acid would have relatively little effect on pH and therefore fish status.

This presentation of the facts has been strongly criticised as being misleading by certain scientists (both Norwegian and British). They argue that it fails to take account of the considerable variation of dissolved (neutralising) Ca^{2+} and Mg^{2+} ions, which in turn are a good indication of the buffering capacity of the catchments. Muniz, Seip and Sevaldrud, grouping more or less the same lakes according to conductivity levels (an indication of the total dissolved cations and anions including base cations), found a relatively strong correlation between fish

---

[1] Dissolved SO_4^{2-} concentrations adjusted down to take account of sulphate input from sea salt.

Table 8.8(a): FISH STATUS IN ACIDIFIED AREAS IN FIVE COUNTIES IN SOUTHERNMOST NORWAY

	Number of lakes in affected areas	Good population		Sparse population		All species lost		Never been fish	Incomplete information
		n	%	n	%	n	%	n	n
Østfold	425	214	50	111	26	26	6	4	72
Telemark	594	122	21	110	19	282	47	18	62
Aust-Agder	1034	232	22	214	21	475	46	23	90
Vest-Agder	1021	136	13	223	22	482	47	93	87
Rogaland	651	218	33	160	25	186	29	77	10
TOTAL	3725	922		818		1451		215	321

Note: 'Good population' is used if at least one species is classified in this way,

'Sparse population' implies that no species is classified as good.

Source: Sevaldrud & Muniz, 1980.

FIGURE 8.8(a): BROWN TROUT POPULATION CHANGES

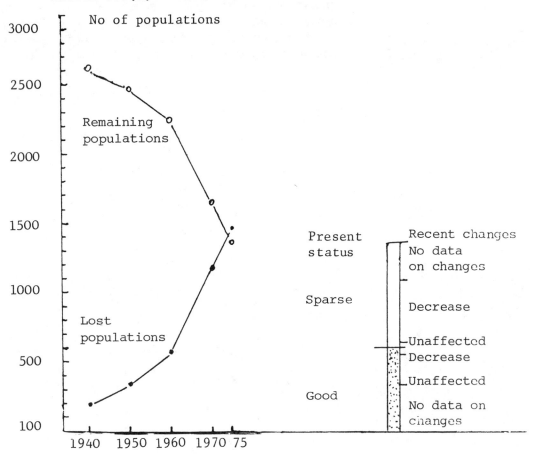

Source: Sevaldrud & Muniz, 1980

FIGURE 8.8(b): PERCENTAGE OF FISHLESS LAKES AS A FUNCTION OF EXCESS SULPHATE CONCENTRATION, µeq/l (20 lake moving average)

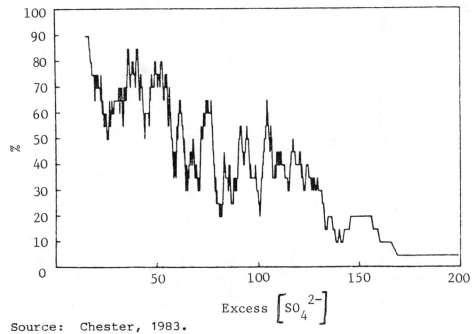

Source: Chester, 1983.

FIGURE 8.8(c): REGRESSION OF STRONG ACID (H$^+$ + Alk) ON NON-MARINE SULPHATE AT CONSTANT (Ca + Mg)*- LEVELS. DATA ARE FROM THE REGIONAL SURVEYS OF SMALL AND LARGE LAKES AND FROM 20 MONITORED RIVERS IN SOUTHERN NORWAY

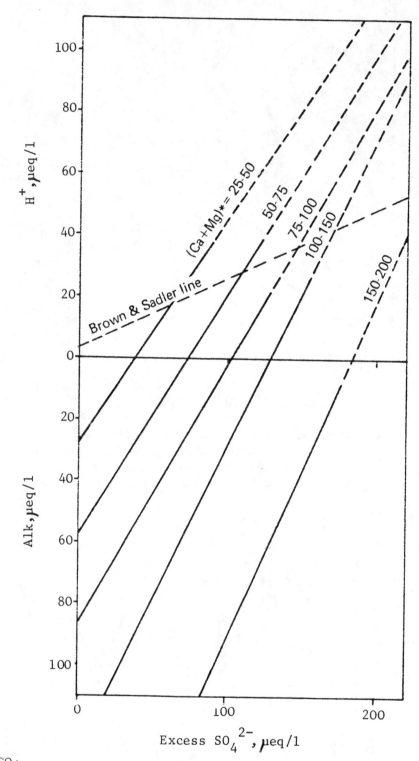

*SO_4 ·

Source: Muniz, Seip and Sevaldrud, 1982.

status and pH within each group - see Figure 8.8(d) overleaf. Seip (1982) has since repeated the exercise with a larger sample of lakes and confirmed the previous findings. What they find is that the upper catchments, which tend also to have smaller lakes, have a relatively high pH and low dissolved sulphate ions compared to those which are lower. This is explainable by the total size of the catchment being relatively smaller and there-fore receiving less acid precipitation/snow melt. However, the thin top soils in the area overlying granite have a low level of available neutralising base cations, so that for a given increase in strong acid input, with accompanying aluminium ion, there is very little dissolved calcium to offset the impact of this on fish. Also, if dissolved sulphate ion is corrected for the dissolved concentration of Ca^{2+} and Mg^{2+} ions, very much steeper slopes are found (see Figure 8.8(c)) to define the acidity/ sulphate ion input relationship. It is argued that the comparison, taking account of catchment characteristics by adjusting for dissolved ion concentrations, shows a more accurate and meaningful relationship between lake acidification and acid precipitation. It has been further argued that by increasing or decreasing the strong acid input, noting that forestry practices can also have a significant impact in this respect, the effect should be to move up and down the fishing status scale within particular catchment categories. The 'dose/ response' slope would depend very much on the buffering capacity of the catchment/lake.

Finally, the point has also been made that measuring fish popula-tion/pH relationships in lakes is much less meaningful than observing what is happening in the streams in the upper catch-ments for these lakes. Several instances have been reported in the UK and in Scandinavia where certain upland streams have become fishless, although the lakes into which they flow still possess fish.

8.8.2 Other aspects of the relationship

While the evidence in the preceding section would suggest a fairly strong correlation between sulphuric acid (with some dry SO_2) precipitation and fisheries status, there are one or two complicating factors that require further understanding before definite conclusions can be drawn on the recovery potential to be realised by a reduction in acid precipitation.

First, there would appear to be an apparent discrepancy in the fact that since 1974 acidity of rain in these areas has not increased (indeed sulphur emissions in Western Europe have fallen), but the trend to loss in fish populations in Scandinavia and Scotland has on the whole continued. This, on the face of it, can be explained by a continued leaching out of base cations and loss of buffering capacity from the top soils through which most of the run-off occurs, and the slow response time of fish populations in lakes to loss of spawning trout in tributory streams. However, at the same time an explanation must also be found for the following:

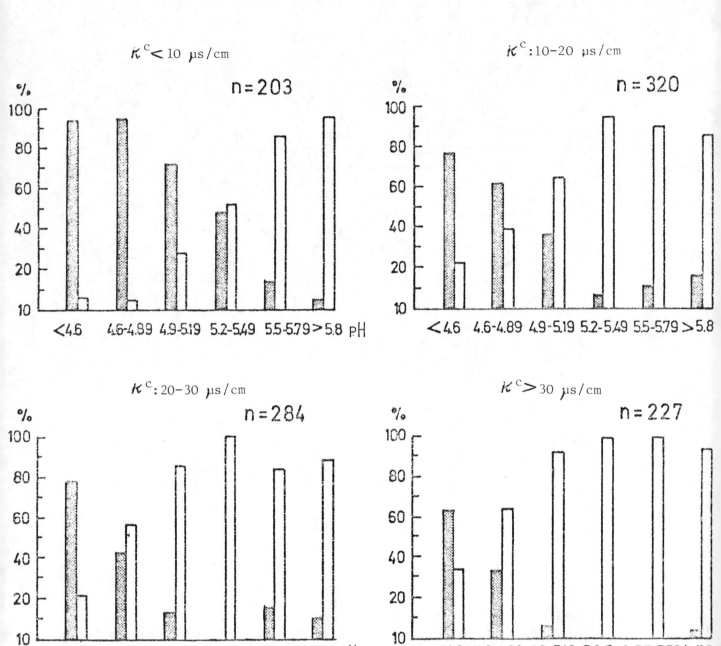

FIGURE 8.8(d): CORRELATION BETWEEN FISH STATUS AND pH IN LAKES OF SIMILAR CONDUCTIVITY

▨ lakes with lost trout populations

▢ lakes with trout populations

Source: Muniz, Seip and Sevaldrud, 1982.

o   If, as seems likely, the principal damaging agent is aluminium, why has not available aluminium also been gradually depleted from the top soil strata through which most run-off occurs?

o   If, to explain this, the hypothesis is put forward that the available aluminium is sufficient and the replenishment to the top soil fast enough for leaching out not to be a significant factor, it is still the case that the concentrations of aluminium in the run-off (especially in snow melt/storm surges in pond input) are unlikely to have increased since 1974 [1].

o   If serious leaching out of top soil calcium has taken place, would a reduction (say 30% for example) on acidic input allow sufficient recovery of buffering capacity such that a satisfactory Al/Ca ratio in the waters would be restored? Some improvement would result simply because a reduced SO_4 input would lead to a reduction in H^+ and Al concentrations in the surface waters.

8.8.3   Conclusions

There may well be satisfactory answers to all of these questions which would give grounds for optimism on the efficacy for fisheries status of lakes of reducing acid deposition [2]. But until further research on catchment chemistry and its responses to inputs of acidity is carried out, it is not yet possible to conclude that lowering the acidity of precipitation will give a positive response in fisheries status with a similar dose/response relationship as increases in acidity have done. There are dangers in using spatial relationships of lakes of different acidity and fisheries status as a guide to how a temporal relationship of acidity/fish status might operate, even for lakes of similar catchment characteristics.

At the same time, there are much stronger grounds for believing that a reduction in acid precipitation would certainly help to prevent further loss of fish populations in lakes already of 'transition' acidity status. Possible remedial measures and their associated cost/benefits are discussed in Section 11.

---

[1] Nitric acid concentrations may have increased but nitrate is mostly likely to be taken up quickly in such soils. During snow melt, it is possible that this effect is less.

[2] One should also be reminded that a reduction in SO_2 emissions does not necessarily give rise to a linear response in deposition of sulphuric acid - see Section 4.3.2.

9. THE MECHANISM OF DAMAGE TO BUILDINGS

9.1 Introduction

It is generally accepted that increased air pollution levels do lead to corrosion of buildings, and there is substantial evidence that sulphur compounds and particularly SO_2 play an important role in this process. However, with respect to this study, the point may be made that this corrosion process is largely caused by pollutant sources within the urban area extending no more than 20-30 km and is therefore a local effect, rather than a regional or international effect.

Acids or acid-forming substances, other than SO_2, deposited by wet or dry deposition on buildings may also be important, but as yet little work has been carried out in this field.

Building materials particularly at risk are thought to be **sandstone** containing calcium carbonate as a binder, **limestone** and **marble**.

Other materials at risk are **metals**, especially steel.

9.2 Agents of Corrosion

9.2.1 Sulphur compounds

It is generally acknowledged that sulphur compounds are the predominant agents of corrosion, of which SO_2 is the most important.

Sulphates in particle form have been shown to cause corrosion in laboratory studies, but not in field studies. This presumably is because polluted air has decidedly lower concentrations of sulphate than SO_2. Moreover, sulphate particles are deposited very much more slowly than SO_2.

The corrosion effect of wet deposits, i.e. sulphuric acid, is difficult to determine. On the one hand, rain has a corrosive effect since it produces a film of moisture on the surface of the receiving medium, which has dissolved in it H^+ ions and SO_4^{2-} ions which stimulate corrosion. On the other hand, rain washes away the sulphates that have been deposited on the surface of the receiving medium during dry periods.

9.2.2 The influence of other pollutants

Little quantitative work has been carried out to determine the role of non-sulphur pollutants such as nitrogen oxides, ozone and chlorides in causing corrosion.

Studies in the USA and Japan have not revealed any significant effect on corrosion due to NO_2.

Chloride attack on metals is thought to be important in coastal areas.

9.3   The Mechanism of Corrosion

9.3.1   Metal corrosion is electrochemical in nature and therefore requires a film of moisture on the surface of the metal.

Damage to sandstone and limestone occurs as the deposited sulphur pollutants react with the calcium cabonate which is converted into readily soluble calcium sulphate (gypsum) which may then be washed away by rainwater. This happens on freely exposed sufaces.

Disintegration of stone may occur at points protected from rain due to an increase in volume that occurs when calcium carbonate is converted to sulphate. The resultant stresses often cause the surface to flake off.

9.3.2   **Factors influencing the rate of corrosion**

Atmospheric corrosion is influenced by a number of meteorological factors of which **humidity** is the most important. This is because the electrochemical corrosion process on metals requires moisture.

Temperature is correlated with corrosion rates in several studies. However, its effect is not straightforward as temperature can increase the rate of reaction but can also dry the surface, thus decreasing the overall rate.

Windspeed can have a dual effect on corrosion rates. With no rain, a high windspeed can have a drying effect and corrosion rates will decrease, and combined with rain it will have a large washing effect again lowering corrosion rates. On the other hand, increasing wind speeds could enhance the rate of supply of SO_2 per unit area.

The intensity, duration and amount of **rainfall** affects corrosion rates. Small amounts and duration will increase corrosion of metals but intensive rainfall will inhibit metal corrosion by washing pollutants from the surface. Metal corrosion is also influenced by the pH of rain.

The levels at which pH influences corrosion are not yet well known. One paper, for instance, stated that if pH dropped to 4.0 then metal corrosion increased. The UNECE report on the Effects of Sulphur Compounds on Materials including Historic & Cultural Monuments, concluded that increased corrosion of carbon steel, zinc and copper occurred at pH values in the range 3-4.

Rates of corrosion also vary according to the material under attack.

In the case of building stones, biological weathering has been proposed as a factor influencing deterioration. Other studies claim that such weathering is negligible.

It is generally accepted in the case of building stone deterioration that physical weathering is a factor influencing the rate of deterioration. Hence buildings subject to frequent temperatures around freezing point will deteriorate more rapidly due to frost action than those in warmer climates.

In summary then, a number of factors appear to influence the corrosion rate of materials. This is an important point when examining dose/response relationships, for the majority simply consider the dose to be SO_2 concentration and humidity.

9.4   Evidence of Corrosion

9.4.1   Metals

Evidence of damage has been substantiated by numerous field surveys and laboratory studies. The work has more or less exclusively dealt with the role of sulphur compounds, largely in the form of dry-deposited SO_2. Field surveys again and again show that for a variety of metals, corrosion is faster in sulphur-polluted than in rural non-polluted atmospheres. Laboratory studies add weight to the evidence, and there are numerous papers showing a linear dose/response relationship, the dose invariably being SO_2 although humidity is recognised by many as an important element to the response.

Zinc and carbon steel are two of the most widely studied metals. Two graphs showing dose/response relationships based on evidence in the USA, UK and Germany are presented in Figures 9.4(a) and 9.4(b).

9.4.2   Building stone

Damage to building stone, particularly to churches, historic buildings and monuments, has been recorded in many European countries. The most infamous examples of such extensive damage reported are to the Acropolis, from pollutant emissions in the Athens/Pireaus area, and to Venice, as a result of emissions from the industrial area some 15 km away. Fewer studies have quantified or examined damage to limestone, sandstone and marble, but they conclude that corrosion is substantially higher in sulphur-polluted than in rural atmospheres. A recent field investigation in W Germany (see Figures 9.4(c) and 9.4(d)) shows a relationship between SO_2 deposition rate and the weight loss of two sensitive stones.

Evidence that air pollutants attack concrete has not yet been sufficiently documented.

FIGURE 9.4(a): RELATIONSHIP BETWEEN CORROSION OF CARBON STEEL AND SO₂ CONTENT OF THE ATMOSPHERE

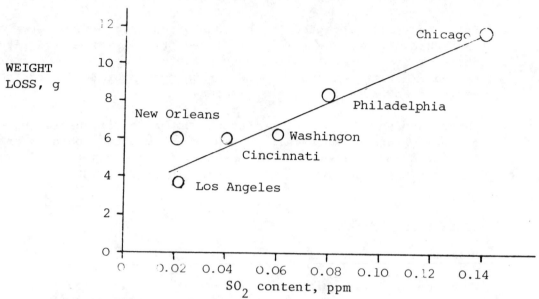

Notes: Corrosion expressed as weight loss of 10 x 15 cm specimens as a function of SO_2 content in the air. The specimens were exposed for 16 months in six American towns.

Source: Upham, 1965.

FIGURE 9.4(b): RELATIONSHIP BETWEEN CORROSION OF ZINC AND DEPOSITION OF SO₂

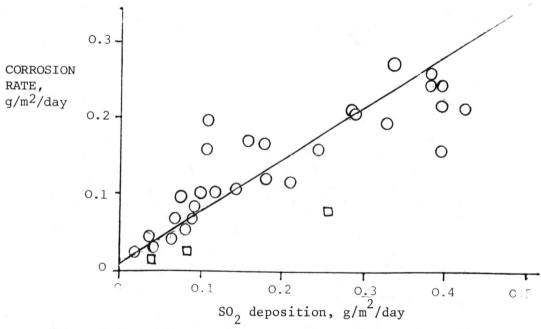

Notes: The corrosion of zinc as a function of SO_2 deposition. The symbols represent readings at 32 stations in the FR Germany and in Great Britain.

Source: Schikorr, 1964.

FIGURE 9.4(c): RELATIONSHIP BETWEEN SO$_2$ CONTENT OF THE ATMOSPHERE AND WEIGHT LOSS OF FREELY EXPOSED SANDSTONE AND LIMESTONE

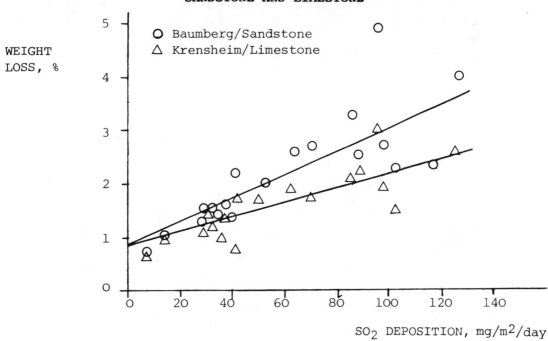

Source: Luckat, 1980.

FIGURE 9.4(d): RELATIONSHIP BETWEEN SO$_2$ CONTENT OF THE ATMOSPHERE AND ABSORPTION OF SO$_2$ IN SPECIMENS PROTECTED FROM RAIN

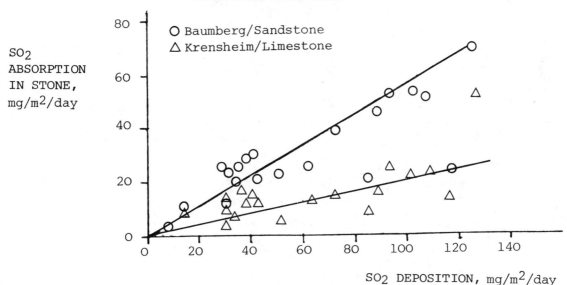

Source: Luckat, 1981.

Notes: In both cases the readings were obtained using the IRMA apparatus and the specimens consisted of 60x60 approx. 3mm plates of Baumberg sandstone and Kresheim limestone.

9.4.3   Threshold level effects

There are some indications that damage to materials has not
occurred at all pollution levels and that there may be threshold
levels above which the rate of material corrosion may increase
sharply. Little attention has been given to this problem and
reports in the literature are inconclusive. Each material
probably has its own threshold level.

9.4.4   Conclusion

There are some who claim that the methodologies employed in
determining dose/response relationships of building materials to
acid pollutants are too simplistic and that inadequate attention
has been paid to factors other than SO_2 and humidity, particularly meteorological factors, influencing corrosion. There is
scope for further research into the mechanism and agents of that
damage in order to establish ambient threshold levels of SO_2
concentrations so as to protect buildings.

10.   THE IMPACT ON HEALTH

10.1   The Potential Threat

Potential threat to human health may occur as a result of:

o   exposure to a higher heavy metal intake from drinking
         water provided in lead or copper plumbing;

o   exposure to a higher heavy metal intake particularly
         mercury and cadmium from the bioaccumulation process in
         the aquatic food chain.

The increased metal concentrations in the food chain and drinking
water are related to increased water acidification. This
relationship has been discussed in Section 5.8.

10.2   Metal Concentrations in Drinking Water

10.2.1   Sweden

In Sweden, there is concern over the leaching by acidified water
of copper from copper pipes. The dissolved content of copper
salts in water has been shown to increase with declining pH below
a critical pH level of 6.0-6.5. This is shown in Figure 10.2(a)
overleaf.

Concentrations as high as 20 mg/l have been recorded in cold
water and 45 mg/l in hot water. The WHO recommended maximum
permissible concentration is 1.5 mg/l.

10.2.2   United Kingdom

Concern over plumbosolvency in drinking water has grown in
several parts of the UK where water sources are naturally acidic.
Concern has been particularly concentrated in Glasgow in
Scotland, and Manchester in the north west of England.

Studies have shown that concentrations of heavy metals exceed WHO
drinking water guidelines in some EEC countries. Where drinking
water is treated these elements are mostly precipitated out and
therefore do not constitute a hazard.

10.2.2   United States and Canada

Drinking water analyses in the Adirondack region of New York
State and in Canada, revealed copper concentrations of 2-7 μg/l.

FIGURE 10.2(a):   COPPER CONTENTS IN TAP WATER IN WESTERN SWEDEN

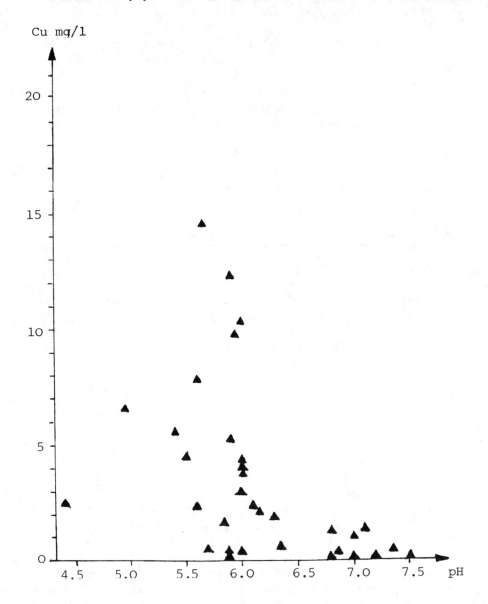

Notes: High copper contents are liable to be found in tap water
          that has remained overnight in copper pipes. This is
          particularly noticeable in the hot water. The
          concentration of dissolved copper salts increases with
          declining pH in the water below a certain critical pH
          value.

Source: Public Health Committee of Lilla Edet.

10.3   **Evidence of Health Effects**

10.3.1   There have been reports of diarrhoea in infants in Sweden that
             are suspected to have been caused or prolonged by the presence of
             copper in water.

             Whilst enhanced concentrations of other heavy metals have been
             recorded in Sweden, such as zinc, lead and cadmium, the only
             other claim of a metal causing health damage has concerned
             aluminium. Some claim it has caused fatalities in dialysis
             treatment.

10.3.2   Health effects related to bioaccumulation of metals in the
             aquatic food chain deriving from acidification of surface waters
             have not been recorded, except in the case of the Cree Indians in
             NW Quebec, where mild effects of methyl mercury poisoning in both
             children and adults have been found. Fish and fish products are
             the only significant source of methyl mercury to humans. In NW
             Quebec, mercury levels in fish may be affected by both industrial
             release and the indirect action of acidic deposition. It remains
             to be determined to what extent acidic deposition has contributed
             to these health effects.

11. **COSTS AND BENEFITS OF ACID EMISSION CONTROL STRATEGIES**

11.1 **The Application of Cost/Benefit Analysis**

11.1.1 **The rationale**

Any programme to reduce emissions of acid pollutants SO_2 and NO_x to mitigate the effects of acid precipitation and of other associated photo-oxidant pollutants should be based on a consideration of the value of the likely benefits of various control strategies in relation to their costs. The political process will, of course, also determine priorities and the level of acceptable expenditure in relation to benefits realised. Society may even decide that an overall net economic benefit is not necessary to justify expenditure control. However it is reasonable that in making such decisions it should be aware of:

- who is benefiting from controls and who is paying for the costs of controls, or the distribution effect, as economists would put it;

- the relative magnitude of current damage costs of different types and to what extent these costs may be reduced, i.e. the realisable benefit if emissions are reduced in relation to the costs of different levels of controls;

- the uncertainties involved in realising the benefits.

Cost/benefit analysis can also help guide where priorities in research effort should take place. Perhaps even more important-ly, it can indicate when it might be justified in delaying control expenditure in order to narrow down the uncertainty of the benefits to be realised. In other words if the value of the range of uncertainty of benefits is very large compared to the costs of control, then there may be justification in carrying out further research. However, if the cost of that research taken together with the most likely accumulating damage costs is similar to the control costs, there would seem no justification for delaying control action so as to reduce the uncertainty.

11.1.2 **The problems**

It will be apparent that while there would seem a strong case for carrying out a cost/benefit analysis of acid precipitation control strategies as a guide to the framing of emission control policies, the difficulties of carrying the analysis out are considerable.

The most obvious of these difficulties is the uncertainty involved in placing values on the benefits of control, even where economic values can be attached to the resources being impacted. The uncertainties can arise in most of the components A to E of a cost/benefit model shown in Figure 11(a) overleaf, although often the most uncertainty resides in the dose/response model (D).

FIGURE 11(a): COMPONENTS OF A COST/BENEFIT MODEL

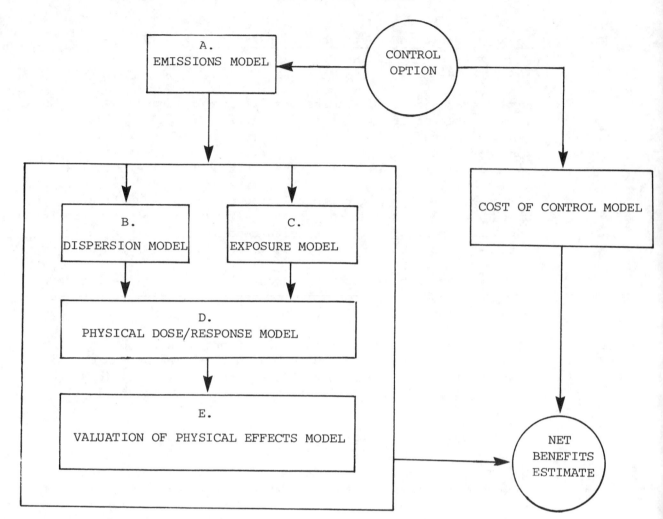

Source: Adapted from UNECE Expert Group Paper "An Example of a
Probabilistic Approach to Cost/Benefit Analysis of
Different SO_x Control Scenarios 1982".

But also, there are some types of environmental damage attributable to acid pollutant emissions for which no direct or easily
applicable surrogate value can be attached. These include:

i.   Historic buildings - It is not sufficient (nor a simple
matter anyway) to assess these in terms of the apparent
value of tourist trade generated by their presence.

ii.   Ecology - For example what value is to be placed upon
having healthy forests, fish in lakes, diversity of
species within them, and so on?

iii.   Unpolluted and clearer air.

Economists would say that the values of these can be determined by an expression of what society is prepared to pay to have them. In theory (and in practice in the USA), questionnaires can be devised on a suitable sampling basis to give an indication of how much society does value such assets. But there are notorious difficulties with such a questionnaire approach, the form of the question having a strong influence on the answer. Political referenda offer a way out of these problems but there are disadvantages to this approach also. Even so, it has to be recognised that the political process will play a major role in deciding whether a given level of emissions control is acceptable or not to society.

In spite of these difficulties in applying cost/benefit analysis to the problem of acid rain and control strategies, there are strong arguments for pursuing it. These are well set out in the UNECE expert report [1] and supporting papers on cost/benefit analysis of sulphur emissions in the ECE region. In particular, it demonstrates the value of adopting a probabilistic approach to dealing with uncertainties. Not only does this show which uncertainties are important, and those which are not critical to decisions, but it also demonstrates how simply comparing ranges of possible benefits based on upper and lower limits of probable (90%) dose/response relationships to costs of control can give misleading conclusions. The conclusions of such probabilistic analysis can be presented to decision makers in helpful ways, even when there is much uncertainty. For example, this might be in terms of the probability of realising at least $x million net benefits of different control strategies, rather than a statement of the calculated net benefits, with the probability multipliers already built in. If the associated control costs are high, governments may choose to require that the probability be at least 0.65 (on a scale of 0 to 1) of the net benefit being realised before committing itself to a control strategy.

11.1.3   The approach taken

Quite obviously a detailed probabilistic cost/benefit analysis of control strategies on acid pollutants is beyond the scope of this study, even if sufficient data were available. However, we believe there is some merit in determining or referring to some very broad orders of magnitude of costs associated with the result of possible environmental damage from acid precipitation (and associated photo-oxidants), and then analysing these costs in relation to each other and the costs of control.

Secondly, in the analysis below, we point out what would seem the appropriate geographical scope on which to conduct cost/benefit analysis of control strategies for dealing with particular eco-

---

[1]   (a) Cost/Benefit Analysis of Alternative Programmes for Sulphur Emissions Control in the ECE Region: Methodological Approach and Data Requirements; UNECE Report by Experts to the Interim Exec. Body for the Convention on Long Range Transboundary Air Pollution; (b) An Example of a Probabilistic Approach to a Cost/Benefit Analysis of Different SO_x Control Scenarios.

system acid rain impacts within the Community. It is also hoped
that this broad analysis will point to where further scientific
research would seem most justified.

11.2   Damage Costs and Potential Benefits of Control

11.2.1   Scope of damage costs

Possible damage and effects which have been claimed to be caused
by acid precipitation, and to which direct costs can in theory be
determined, fall in the following categories:

   i.   tree damage and possible tree growth effects,

   ii.   crop growth and soil damage,

   iii.   disappearance and death of fish,

   iv.   building materials,

   v.   human health.

We will now consider each of these in turn. It will be apparent
that some of these are relevant to all Member States and some
effects applicable to only one or two. Aquatic effects of course
also cover Scandinavia, being a net importer of EEC Member
States' emissions.

11.2.2   Effects on forests

In the last ten years or so, it is believed that 8% of FR
Germany's forests have sustained damage from air pollution;
notably in Bavaria, Baden-Wurttenberg and the Black Forest.
Most-affected species are spruce and fir.

The potential damage cost function for acid precipitation on
forests in theory could derive from:

   i.   tree deaths or damage, or

   ii.   reduced (or increased) forest productivity and yield.

To some extent the delineation between tree death or visible
damage and reduced growth is somewhat arbitrary. Nevertheless,
it is quite helpful in considering the potential cost of any
damage.

So far tree deaths in Western Europe which have been claimed as
being caused by acid precipitation are largely confined to parts
of Germany and possibly Belgium. In Eastern Europe large areas
of East Germany, Czechoslovakia and Poland have been affected.
In the case of some of the Eastern European damage, there is a
strong belief that in many cases the principal cause of the
damage is local high emission sources of SO_2.

The total value of the trees lost in southern Germany to date has been reported by the Bavarian Agricultural Ministry to be 3000 million DM, or about 1.2×10^9. A 5% per annum loss in output to Germany's forestry industry, which is about what the equivalent damage so far expressed on an annual basis over 10 years, is worth 0.2×10^9/year.

The total value of annual spruce and fir forestry production in the EEC is 5.3×10^9/year. In Section 6 it was shown that the geographical soil climatic circumstances of central and southern Germany meant they would be particularly susceptible to pollutant emissions of central Europe. There is some evidence that damage caused by SO_2/ozone may also be taking place in the eastern part of the Netherlands, although the forested area is relatively small. Hypothetically one can note that if a further 20% of EEC pine forests became affected and experienced 10% per annum drop in output as a result, the cost would be 0.1×10^9/year.

The economic benefits of any reduction in impact can be fairly directly measured in terms of the output value of future forestry saved. It is improbable that the loss could be offset more cheaply by other measures, e.g. fertilisation. However, it should be remembered that the economic value of any future loss of forestry output will need to be discounted to give a present value comparable with the costs of any current control action.

With regard to the reduction in emissions necessary to achieve a sufficient fall in ambient SO_2 and ozone concentrations to prevent future tree damage, the following points may be made:

i.   The source of ambient dry SO_2 affecting forestry regions of Germany is about 60-70% within the Federal Republic, the other principal sources being France (15%), East Germany (15%) and Czechoslovakia (5%). It is estimated that if all coal/lignite power station and chemical plant emissions were removed in FR Germany, ambient SO_2 levels in central and southern Germany might fall by approximately 20-30%. If acid rain is a factor, the relative contribution of unimported acid precipitation increases somewhat.

ii.   The principal sources of episodic high ozone concentrations in affected forest areas are likely to be found within FR Germany, and to some extent the GDR.

11.2.3   Crop growth

It is not yet possible to say:

i.   what are the dose/response relationships of various crops and vegetables to associate with exposure to ozone and SO_2/NO_2 concentrations during 'average' summertime climatic conditions; nor,

ii.   how large an area of EEC agriculture could be affected
       on 'average'.

However, certain observations may be made:

o   For France, Italy, Belgium, Denmark and the UK,
       agricultural/horticultural areas exposed to possibly
       phytotoxic ozone concentrations lie within 25-200 km of
       large urban agglomerations. Because of the stable air
       conditions experienced in central Germany, it is
       probable that all areas of the country could be
       affected. The same is true of Holland, partly because
       of its small size and partly because Rotterdam is a
       particularly high source of photo-oxidants.

o   Episodic and potentially phytotoxic concentrations of
       SO_2, sufficient to cause yield effects in certain crops/
       vegetables are only likely in most parts of the EEC
       within 30 km downwind of urban area sources or from high
       output single point sources.

o   From experience in the USA and from very preliminary
       indications gained from experimental work in Europe,
       ozone and/or SO_2 sensitive species grown in Europe are
       likely to include winter wheat, possibly barley, clover,
       soyabean, grape, lettuce and root crops (potatoes and
       radishes). Yield effects might be between 5-25%,
       depending on conditions.

To give an order of magnitude idea of the possible yield loss
value resulting from a combination of ozone/SO_2/NO_2 effects, we
have assumed that:

-      on average 40% of the Community's agricultural/
       horticultural areas are affected by phytotoxic
       ozone/SO_2/NO_2 concentrations;

-      an average 10% yield loss occurs as a result to winter
       wheat, barley, grapes and root crops.

The annual loss value so-computed on 1981 EEC harvest output of
winter wheat, barley and potatoes is worth some $0.9-1.1 \times 10^9$
per annum. Again, it is unlikely that the yield loss could be
cheaply offset by increased fertilisation, since arable farmers
in EEC Member States already apply a high level of fertiliser to
most of these crops. There would therefore be a relatively low
and costly dose/response relationship to further inputs of
nitrogen fertilisers.

We have no idea what reduction in SO_2 and NO_2 emissions would be
necessary to bring about sufficient reductions in ambient high
level episodic ozone, SO_2 and NO_2 concentrations to avoid any
crop yield effects. It is unlikely that the necessary reduction
would be less than 30% in SO_2 emissions from all (i.e. not only
large tall stack) sources, and less than 40-50% reduction in NO_x

emissions from both stationary and vehicle sources. Dry SO_2 and ozone emissions are mostly deposited within 200 km of urban areas/high emitters. With the exception of the Netherlands, Belgium and to some extent Germany, the source of these gaseous pollutants deposited in areas causing possible damage would mostly come from within each Member State.

In other words, it is probable that any damage to agricultural output is mostly caused by emissions within the country suffering the damage. It is probable that all Member States, with the possible exception of Ireland, experience crop yield effects, and so these observations have relatively wide application across the Community. However, quite obviously, the degree to which different Member States are affected will vary considerably and so will the ratio of costs of emissions control to agricultural benefits derived from control strategies.

11.2.4   Damage to aquatic ecosystems

The direct economic costs associated with damage caused by acidi-fication of lakes, rivers and streams include:

  i.   loss of fish formerly caught in affected lakes;

  ii.   loss of salmonid fisheries from rivers and estuaries, i.e. those formerly spawning upstream in certain rivers;

  iii.   value of income loss from sport fishing and tourism.

The OECD (1980) estimated the loss of fish production from lakes susceptible to acidification in Scandinavia. On average assump-tions of fish catch from all lakes, they estimated the loss of production from acidified lakes to be $28 million/year. No assessment of the loss of fisheries value from acidified Scottish lakes has been made, but given the area affected, it is unlikely so far to be more than $0.5 million/year.

No assessment has been made of loss of salmonid fisheries yield from the seven southern rivers of Norway where acidification is attributed to acid precipitation, nor of the periodic fish kills believed to result from snow melt pulses of low pH water. Such estimates would, in any case, be based on rather insubstantial evidence. However, for the sake of this exercise, and given the size of the area affected, it might be expected that the loss in value of such rivers fishing would at maximum be of the order of $0.5 million/year.

Estimates of loss of tourism value from lake acidification are extremely difficult to make and possibly should be ignored overall. The argument against taking loss of tourist expenditure into account is that tourists will spend their money elsewhere. Thus, the loss of the resource, while possibly of significant impact to the local economy for which there is a case for compen-sation (a distribution effect), has no overall permanent impact.

As discussed in Section 8.8, the estimated economic benefit to be gained from reducing emissions in all OECD countries (most notably UK, Sweden and Germany) which could be causing acidification of surface waters in Scandinavia and the UK cannot be equated with the value of total annual loss of fisheries, assuming this could be assessed with reasonable accuracy. It is a matter of considerable speculation as to how many of the most acidified lakes would recover, even with liming of the catchment. On the assumption that all the rivers' and 50% of the lakes' fisheries are recoverable, this would imply a total maximum potential benefit of around $15 million/year. Because of possible non-linearity between SO_2 emissions and sulphuric acid deposition, and the presence of Eastern European and other unaccounted for sources of acidic deposition in Scandinavia, it may also be the case that a 50% reduction, say, in emissions in the countries mentioned might realise only a 30% recovery in pH and of the potential fisheries loss, that is of the order of $2-3 million/year. Indeed, it is highly arguable whether a small reduction in emissions (say < 25%) would produce any benefit in terms of resource gain, and certainly not in the short term. A 16% fall in EEC SO_2 emissions since 1973 has certainly produced no observable improvement. In other words, if any measurable economic benefit in terms of recovery of aquatic systems is to be achieved, it is probable that very major action would be required to reduce SO_2 and NO_x emissions.

11.2.5   Buildings

Damage cost to buildings falls into the two categories:

   i.   corrosion of certain materials leading to their early replacement;

   ii.   reversible and irreversible damage to historic buildings.

The first category can be dealt with by straightforward reference to the economic costs of repair, although the actual calculation is by no means straightforward as dose/response relationships depend upon the depth of corrosion that has taken place, climate, local building materials, construction methods, etc. Nevertheless attempts to estimate building damage costs have been made.

These have been based on either dose(SO_2 and humidity)/response relationships or the regional differentiation method, which estimates differences in deterioration costs between clean and unpolluted areas.

A Swedish study in 1971 estimated that damage to materials in Sweden by sulphur was $4.30 per person per year.

The OECD study of 1981, on the costs and benefits of sulphur oxides control, estimated damage for 12 OECD European countries to galvanised steel and its paint coatings in 1974. These included:

	$ million US p.a.
Belgium and Luxembourg	805
Denmark	462
France	316
Netherlands	873
UK	4,331
W Germany	7,042

A 1980 Dutch study estimated that damage by SO_2 to monuments, libraries and archives in the Netherlands is costing $10-15 million per annum.

A recent document by the UNECE, summarises the position:

- "A number of national and international studies have shown that economic losses due to atmospheric corrosion caused by sulphur compounds are considerable. In these studies such losses have been estimated to range between $US 2-10 per capita per annum."

For the Community as a whole, this would suggest that the annual damage to buildings attributable to sulphur compounds is of the order of $540-2700 million/year.

We make no attempt to assign an annual cost of SO_2 damage to historic buildings. It is considered that the benefits to be gained from emissions control are likely to be often large in relation to the size of the local economy and the cost of local emissions control, but small in relation to overall building damage costs, and certainly within the error of their calculation.

The source of SO_2 causing damage to buildings is largely local and probably arises as much from the emissions of a large number of relatively low-level industrial, and to some extent residential/commercial, source emitters, than to a few large high stack emitters.

11.2.6 Health

Long range transport of acid pollutants is unlikely to lead to any respiratory effects on human health. The latter derive from local, often low-level emissions (as does a considerable proportion of building damage). Attempts have been made to link health care costs to morbidity that may be caused through exposure to SO_x in ambient air quality. However, because of the absence of any reliable epidemiological evidence in this field, or sufficient medical research establishing a dose/response relationship linking ambient sulphate/fine particulate concentrations to health effects, we do not consider that a meaningful damage-cost function for health effect can be calculated. In any case, SO_2 at the concentations now found in cities of Western Europe, is thought unlikely by itself to contribute significantly to morbidity/health damage. The presence of other air pollutants, especially particulates, is thought critical to the potential SO_2 effects.

The capital and operating costs associated with water treatment to correct for low pH in areas where Cu and Pb solvency from piping systems is considered a potential problem (this has not yet been shown to be firmly linked to acid precipitation) are relatively small - annualised costs are less than $20 million per annum.

11.3   Emission Control Costs

11.3.1 SO_2

Emissions of SO_2 may be controlled by one or a combination of three means:

i.   use of lower sulphur fuel oils and coal;

ii.   removal of sulphur in the combustion chamber of solid fuels through establishment of Fluidised Bed Combustion Systems using lime as the bed;

iii.   removal of SO_2 emissions in the flue, adopting Flue Gas Desulphurisation technologies.

i.   Lower Sulphur Fuels

1.   Oil Fuels

Reduction in **gas oil/diesel** sulphur levels from their average today of around 0.4% S.wt. would be achieved by further desulphurisation of distillates costing about $14-18/tonne of feed [1].   Reduction to an average pool sulphur level of 0.3% S.wt. could be relatively cost-effective as it would involve desulphurising only a certain proportion of the total gas oil produced in EEC refineries, i.e. the higher sulphur fractions for which desulphurisation would achieve a reasonable amount of sulphur removal.   The cost of reducing the average sulphur level from 0.4% to 0.3% S.wt. would be of the order of $4-5/tonne over all gas oil produced.   To cut average gas oil sulphur levels by half, i.e. to 0.2% S.wt. would result in a very much higher unit cost - estimated to be around $10-12/tonne averaged across all gas oil consumed.

Fuel oil burnt in industry and power stations within the Community varies in sulphur content from 1% to 3.5% sulphur by weight.   The average sulphur level is 2.5% S.wt.[1].   If only up

---

[1]   This estimate accords with that produced in a CONCAWE paper: "The Effect of Changing Patterns of Petroleum Product Demand on the Emission of Sulphur in Western Europe", J.F.G. Ellis and W.C. Hopper.   Third Seminar on Desulphurisation of Fuels and Combustion Gases.   UNECE.   Salzburg, 1981.   ENV/SEM13/COM41.

to 30% reduction in average sulphur content was required, i.e.
down to 1.75% S.wt, this could probably be achieved by refining a
higher proportion of lower sulphur crude oils and increased
desulphurisation of the light fraction (vacuum gas oil) of
residual fuel oil in oil refineries. The overall cost of this
would be of the order of $4-7/tonne of fuel oil.

To achieve further reduction in fuel oil sulphur levels would
require residual desulphurisation. This is a technically
difficult (the catalyst can be poisoned by metals present in
residual fuel oils) and very expensive process. Currently only
one such unit is operating outside Japan, where there are three
or four. The cost depends on the crude oil type and whether or
not atmospheric or vacuum residual is being desulphurised. The
total cost of desulphurisation from around 3.4% S.wt. to 1% S.wt.
of atmospheric residual is around $40-50/tonne, up to $80-90/
tonne for vacuum residual. It is therefore highly questionable
whether it would be economically feasible. For large fuel oil
consumers, e.g. >25 MW (thermal), flue gas desulphurisation would
almost certainly be the cheaper option for the consumer. For
smaller consumers, blending in lower sulphur (0.4%) gas oil might
well be the more economic option of providing, say, 1% sulphur
from a 1.75% sulphur residual pool. This also would be costly -
of the order of $50-70/tonne of average 1% sulphur fuel oil
produced (blending from 1.75% fuel oil valued currently at
$210/tonne and gas oil value of $300/tonne).

2.   Coal

The average sulphur content of indigenously produced and consumed
Community coal, after it has undergone the currently adopted
level of washing/preparation, is around 1.6% by weight. Imported
coal varies from 0.6% S.wt. to 3.0% S.wt., with the average
around 1.5%. The only economically realisable means of significantly reducing the sulphur level of coal burnt in the Community
would be to substitute low-sulphur imported coal for indigenous
coal, a move which would have serious social, economic and
strategic consequences.

Other means for controlling sulphur emissions concern consumer
technologies.

ii.   **Fluidised Bed Combustion**

While a proven technology, fluidised bed combustion is not yet a
fully commercialised technology - some 30-40 FBC boilers are in
use in Germany, the UK and USA; many of them were installed with
funding assistance from government. Currently FBC boilers are
limited in capacity up to about 20 MW (thermal) [1].

---

[1]   There are two demonstration projects in FR Germany of around
200 MW (thermal), but FBC technology at this rating cannot yet be
considered technically and operationally proven.

Such technology cannot be introduced to existing coal users in industry unless a complete boiler replacement takes place. Because of their high capital cost, normally industrial companies only replace water tube boilers at the end of their useful life, so that a faster introduction of FBC lime-bedded technology would only take place if:

o SO_2 emission control regulations were imposed on industry, and 1% sulphur coal was unavailable at economic cost;

o   capital grants (at 25-50%) were provided by government to encourage this change.

Coal fired boilers in the 5-25 MW range cost around $125-175/kW, i.e. about $2.5 million for a 20 MW FBC boiler. The annualised cost can be computed as approximately $0.2 million, assuming a 25 year life time and 8% interest. Additional operating costs for disposing of calcium sulphate would amount to around $25 million/year.

The additional annual cost of installing FBC lime-bedded boilers (instead of conventional water/tube boilers) for boilers in the 5-25 MW range would be, according to the High and Low Economic Growth cases (see Section 3.1):

Table 11.3(a)		
COST OF INSTALLING FLUIDISED BED BOILER TO SMALL/MEDIUM SIZED INDUSTRIAL COAL USERS IN EEC		
	Additional Cost $ x 10^9	Annualised Cost (by 2000)
New installations	0.3-0.9	0.03-0.1
Retrofitting FBC in 50% existing boilers	7.0-8.7	0.6-0.7

FBC also has the advantage of producing lower (by 15-35%) NO_x emissions than conventional coal-fired boilers.

iii. Flue Gas Desulphurisation

On large coal fired boilers >25 MW, flue gas desulphurisation is necessary to control SO_2 emissions. Removal efficiencies are in the 80-90% range. FGD is now a fully commercialised technology with some 25,000 MW of capacity installed in Japan and the USA.

There are various technologies available but it seems that in Europe dry or wet regenerable systems would most likely be installed, thus avoiding the environmental and costly problem of having to dispose of large quantities of thixotropic sludges, principally composed of calcium sulphite. There are a wide range of regenerable processes designed to produce at a final stage sulphur, sulphuric acid or ammonium sulphate. The most advanced of these systems is probably the Wellman-Lord process using sodium salts.

The capital cost of FGD in new coal fired plant is about $130-150/kW. This represents 15-20% of total capital cost of the plant. Additional operating costs are of the order of $3-5/tonne. Retro-fitting onto existing plant, which may not always be possible in certain industrial locations, can increase the cost by a further 30-50%. Overall the installation of FGD can increase the cost of electricity <u>generated</u> [1] by coal fired power stations by 10-20%.

In a scenario, where only <u>new</u> coal fired power stations were required to install FGD over the 1982-2000 period, the additional total capital cost of installing and operating FGD in new coal and lignite fired power stations and industrial boilers >25 MW added in the High and Low Economic Growth cases would be:

Table 11.3(b)			
TOTAL COST TO COMMUNITY OF INSTALLING FGD IN NEW COAL AND LIGNITE FIRED POWER BOILERS >25 MW FOR 1980-2000 PERIOD			
	Additional coal/lignite consumed mtce(1)	$ \times 10^9$(1982 prices)	
		Total Cost(2)	Annualised(3) Cost (by 2000)
High Case	140	7.3-8.7(4)	0.6-0.7
Low Case	35(4)	1.8-2.1(4)	0.2

(1)   Million tonnes coal equivalent.
(2)   Assumes 65% average load factor for coal input/plant capacity.
(3)   Assumes capital cost recovery at 7.5% over 25 years.
(4)   Assumes a further 20 MW of new coal fired capacity is built to replace retired old capacity.

It should be noted that these figures do not include new FGD investment in new power stations in the Netherlands and Germany, since it was assumed in calculating sulphur emissions that these countries will, as part of existing policy, introduce such investment, [2] i.e. costs in Table 11.3(b) related to new controls. Overall, it is estimated that this investment would reduce total Community SO_2 emissions approximately 5-12%.

---

[1]   Note that the increase in cost of <u>delivered</u> electricity generated only by coal/lignite would be 5-8%. In Member States not dependent upon coal for all the primary energy input for electricity generation, the actual increase in delivered electricity cost would of course be less still.

[2]   The cost of introducing FDG on new coal and lignite fired power stations in these two countries over 1980-2000 is estimated to be $2.6-3.0 \times 10^9$ in the High Case and around $0.6-0.7 \times 10^9$ in the Low Case.

Fitting of FGD to new and 70% of existing coal fired boilers and furnaces >25 MW size, estimated to amount to some 140 GW, (assuming a 50% load factor) would have the following estimated total costs:

Table 11.3(c)		
TOTAL COST BY 2000 TO COMMUNITY OF RETROFITTING FGD IN 70% OF ALL EXISTING COAL AND LIGNITE FIRED BOILERS >25 MW		
Coal/Lignite Consumption in 70% of Large Existing Plant	$ x 10^9 (1982 prices)	
	Total Capital	Annualised Cost (by 2000)
250 mtce	30-40	2.7-3.6

Such investment would reduce EEC emissions by a further 35-40%. It will be noted that proportionately the investment cost in retrofitted FGD increases by more than the additional reduction in emissions, since the load factor (coal/lignite throughput) on existing plant is on average less (assumed as 45%) than that on new plant, and retrofitting FGD is 25-60% more expensive than installation in new plant.

iv. Summary of SO_2 Emission Control Costs

In Table 11.3(d) overleaf we summarise the approximate annualised cost (1982 prices) of reducing sulphur emissions over the 1980-2000 period, in relation to the sulphur emission reductions achieved.

Table 11.3(d)			
COST AND RELATED BENEFIT OF FURTHER (1) SULPHUR EMISSIONS REDUCTION FOR TOTAL EEC OVER 1980-2000 PERIOD			
Action	Annualised Cost $^{(2)}$ x 10^9/year by 2000	SO$_2$ Emission Decrease on Total EEC 2000 levels	
		mn. tonnes/year	%
Gas Oil: 0.4-0.3% S.	0.7-1.0	0.4	2
Fuel Oil: 2.5-1.75% S.	0.4-0.6	1.0	5-6
Industrial Coal - FBC (lime bed) < 25 MW			
- for new boilers	0.03-0.1(3)	0.6-1.3	4-7
- for 50% existing	0.6 -0.7	0.4	3
FGD for Large (>25 MW) Coal & Lignite Boiler			
- new plant	0.2-0.7	0.9-3.8	6-20
- for 70% existing plant	2.7-3.6	6.2	33-39
TOTAL - includes oil & new coal plant	1.3-2.4	2.8-6.5	17-34
- includes oil & new & existing coal plant	4.6-6.7	8.4-13.1	56-67(4)

(1)   Does not include cost of FGD in new coal/lignite power stations in Germany and Netherlands since this assumed to be part of existing policy (see p.135).
(2)   1982 prices.
(3)   Assumes 30% (capital and operating) additional cost over conventional boilers.
(4)   Rounded.

11.3.2   NO$_x$ emissions

i. Vehicles

Reduction in NO$_x$ emissions in reciprocating piston engines of vehicles can be achieved most cost-effectively through control of combustion conditions in the cylinder so that the availability of excess air (O$_2$ and N$_2$) to the engine is minimised. The current programme (based on combustion chamber design and engine tuning) in Europe is expected to achieve a further 15-30% reduction in new cars by 1985. In practice taking account of the increase in vehicle population, which will offset further improvements in engine efficiency, this programme is unlikely to reduce NO$_x$ vehicle emissions in 2000 by more than 5-10%.

Further reduction in NO_x emissions would have to be realised through fitting of exhaust catalytic converters. The cost of this measure is not known.

ii. Stationary Emissions

NO_x emissions for various fossil fuels vary according to the type of fuel and the size/conditions of combustion. Typical emission factors are shown below.

Table 11.3(e)	
NOx EMISSION FACTORS	g/GJ of fuel
Large Pulverised Coal Boilers	260-380
Industrial Coal Stoker Boilers	117-240
Power Plant Fuel Oil Boilers	114-190
Industrial/Commercial Fuel Oil Boilers	172
Gas Oil Boilers	70
Natural Gas Boilers	50-100

It may be seen that the shift to using more coal in the electricity generation and industrial sectors leads to increased NO_x emissions.

On medium to large sized boilers, reduction in NO_x emissions can be achieved by one of the following means:

a.   modification of furnace design;

b.   low excess air firing;

c.   flue gas recirculation;

d.   lowering air preheat temperatures;

e.   two stage firing.

For new boilers a, b, c and e are all technically feasible and of reasonable cost, and in combustion can be expected to reduce NO_x emissions by 40-70%.

For existing boilers the appropriateness and cost of each step will vary according to size and type of boiler, fuel quality, firing method and boiler design. Of the means identified b, c and d are likely to offer the most cost-effective means of NO_x reduction by 25-40%.

However, little experience has so far been gained using these various methods, and operating factors, such as the loading pattern of the boiler, can limit the realizable emission reductions. It should be recognised that there is a direct conflict between the goal of achieving improved energy combustion efficiency (promoting energy conservation of major Commission objectives) and lower NO_x emissions. This comment applies to both static and vehicle emissions. Losses of combustion efficiency can occur if over-ambitious NO_x reduction is attempted, which can quickly raise the cost of NO_x reductions.

Very approximately it is estimated that some 30-50% reduction in NO_x emissions from new boilers and 70% of existing boilers in the EEC can be achieved at total annual average costs between \$0.1-0.4 x 10^9 per annum by the year 2000. This level of NO_x emissions control on static emitters would reduce total availability of NO_x in the atmosphere by some 9-12%. In urban and industrial areas, the reduction in local ambient NO_x concentrations would probably be substantially more, perhaps 15-25%, assuming vehicle NO_x emissions were also reduced in line with the current programme. Fitting flue gas scrubbers to control SO_2 emissions would also reduce NO_x emissions substantially (70-80% removal), so that the two sets of costs should not be considered additive.

11.4   Lime Addition to Lakes

Addition of limestone or dolomite has been carried out on a number of acidified lakes in Norway and Sweden. Almost always lime-dosing has to be repeated if the increase in pH is to be maintained. Some success in re-establishing fishing populations has been achieved by this method but there are potential difficulties and dangers:

i.   it is very difficult to determine in advance what the pH response of acidified waters will be to lime addition;

ii.   there is some concern over the relationship between pH and aluminium toxicity; although increasing the Ca/Al concentration ratio would normally be expected to reduce the toxicity of dissolved aluminium;

iii. other side reaction mechanisms in the aquatic ecology are not properly understood and could have an adverse impact;

iv.   because of the nature of the catchment area, liming of the surrounding area is likely to be necessary if the pH is to be effectively raised since the water turnover in the lake can be a matter of days.

It has been estimated by the OECD that the total cost of liming affected lakes in Norway and Sweden would amount to \$60-100 million per annum. However, further experience may show that such methods are only cost-effective on a certain proportion of the lakes.

11.5   Comparison of Costs of Control and Economic Benefits of Control
Strategies

The principal points arising from this evaluation of costs and
possible direct economic benefits of alternative control
strategies are:

i.   It is impossible as yet to determine with any precision
the average annual damage costs which might be
attributable to acid precipitation. However, it seems
probable that in total they would be in the range $0.5-
3.5 billion (10^9). Of this cost, building damage is
likely to be the most significant share. The cost of
potential reduced forestry output is estimated at $0.1-
0.3 billion/year. Crop yield effects could range
anywhere from $0-1.5 billion/year.

ii.   The value of annual fish loss in acidified lakes is
relatively small, up to $30 million/year, although for
southern Norway (the most affected area), loss of
fisheries is not insignificant in the context of the
local economy.

iii. As regards damage caused by direct mechanisms involving
gaseous pollutants, i.e. to buildings, agriculture and
probably to forestry (although indirect soil mechanisms
may also play a part here), it is probable that a
reduction in emissions would be expected to produce a
benefit similar to the annual damage costs. Such a
benefit response is very unlikely in the case of
fisheries, since not all of the value of lost fisheries
would be recovered by improvements in lower acidity
rain, and improvements would be over an extended time-
scale. The chief expected benefit would therefore be
prevention of further loss of fisheries in lakes.

iv.   Further control of sulphur emissions is expensive. A
10-27% reduction in 2000 emission levels could be
achieved over the next 17 years by introduction of lime-
bedded FBC and FGD boilers in new coal fired plant at a
cost of $1.5-5.1 billion/year (the range largely
reflecting the span of possible future coal consumption
growth, and, as already noted, does not include the cost
of FGD in new coal/lignite power plants in Germany and
the Netherlands). Halving emissions from oil combustion
through some desulphurisation and use of lower sulphur
crude oils would reduce total emissions by 7-8% at a
cost of some $1.4 billion/year. A further 36-42%
reduction could be achieved by retro-fitting flue-gas
desulphurisation plant to existing coal fired power
stations and large industrial plant, and fluidised bed
boilers to 50% of smaller industrial/commercial coal-
fired boilers. This would have an annualised cost of $7
billion. Aggregating these costs, a 56-67% reduction in
EEC emissions by 2000 could be achieved at an annualised
cost of $8.4-13.1 billion/year.

v.   Control of NO_x emissions by currently known technology is less expensive. However, in relation to the overall deposition of NO_2 and nitrates, such control strategies are likely to have limited effect on overall NO_x concentrations - a maximum reduction of 10-15%.

However, these broad Community level cost/benefit comparisons obscure the fact that the relative costs of emissions control strategies in relation to the value of possible benefits are likely to vary a great deal among Member States. It can be pointed out that:

o   The 'value' of the environment potentially at risk from acid precipitation varies considerably among Member States. So also does the level of existing pollutant emissions and the form of, and most effective, control strategies for limiting those emissions.

o   Some Member States, most notably the Netherlands, will depend upon a control action in neighbouring countries if a significant reduction in acid pollutant and ozone deposition levels is to be achieved.

      Long range trans-frontier transport of acid pollutants among Member States is also significant for France, FR Germany, Belgium and Luxembourg.

o   Any pollution damage of forests in FR Germany is probably caused to a considerable degree in certain areas by emissions arising from German DR and Czechoslovakia, as well as those from inside FR Germany. It should also be recognised that attention to SO_2 emissions only, without addressing the question of ozone concentrations, may not prevent further damage.

o   Measures to reduce any potential agricultural damage caused by SO_2/ozone/NO_x would require action on NO_x emissions, taking account of all urban and industrial sources within 200 kilometres of major agricultural areas, in other words in most parts of the Community. Large reductions in NO_x emissions in the many low level stationary and vehicle sources are likely to be difficult and costly to achieve. Measures to lower ambient SO_2 concentrations in agricultural areas would need to tackle many low level urban and industrial emitters of SO_2 as well as high level/tall stack emitters. This would also be necessary if building damage is to be limited. Recognition should also be given to the possibility that in a few areas which are marginal in terms of the natural sulphur nutrient availability of the soil, there may be benefit from <u>not</u> limiting local sulphur emissions.

o   Within the EEC, only the UK, and to a much lesser extent
        FR Germany are significant contributors to total acid
        precipitation in Norway and Sweden. In Sweden the EEC
        contribution to total wet and dry acid precipitation is
        estimated by the UNECE/EMEP programme at no more than 23
        $\pm$ 11%. In southern Norway, the figure could be as high
        as 60 $\pm$ 30%. The maximum potential benefit to be
        realised in improved fishing catch in the areas affected
        by acid rain is not sufficient to justify major SO_2
        emissions control investment in the UK and FR Germany.
        Justification would therefore have to be found either as
        a marginal spin-off benefit of an SO_2/NO_x emissions
        control programme aimed at limiting impacts on
        agriculture, and in FR Germany, on forestry; or, by
        society invoking a high enough value to the
        conservation/ restoration of the aquatic ecology of
        these areas for its own sake.

o   On the face of it, compensation for liming costs would
        probably be a more cost-effective method of limiting
        further impact of acid precipitaiton on the aquatic
        ecology. However, there are practical limits to this
        method and potential unknown adverse impacts.

o   Acid precipitation and ozone levels, if uncontrolled,
        will almost certainly cause as yet unknown ecological
        damage in the future. The scale and timing of this
        damage is quite impossible to predict at present. It is
        quite possible that the cost in present value terms of
        the measurable future damage would be small relative to
        control costs. However, it is evident that society does
        place an 'indirect' value on its terrestrial and aquatic
        ecosystems and decision-makers and politicians will need
        to address the question of how large is this 'indirect'
        value in making decisions about SO_2/NO_x controls.

11.6   Future Research and Control Action

11.6.1   Research

From the analysis in the report, the following research
priorities are suggested:

i.   Building damage

The potentially large size of direct SO_2 damage but also the high
cost of limiting emissions from low level emitters would suggest
strongly the need for both improved understanding of SO_2/humidity
dose/response relationships and reliable techniques of cost/
benefit analysis of control options, taking account of local
climate, fuel and building materials.

ii. Agriculture

There is an urgent need for more open top chamber/filtered air and other field experiments to be carried out on the susceptibility of certain crops and vegetables to ambient levels of ozone and to SO_2/NO_x concentrations. This work should be carried out in the principal growing areas of all parts of the Community so as to replicate local soil and climatic circumstances.

There is a need for ozone concentration mapping in rural crop-growing areas of Member States.

iii. Forestry

Further understanding is needed of the relative importance of direct ozone and direct SO_2 effects in relation to possible indirect soil/root impacts of acid precipitation of affected forest areas.

It is thought that in view of the work now also being pursued in the USA, a large effort in these areas could significantly improve the knowledge of the relative importance of different air pollutants and other influencing factors, and also better-define the size of the dose/response relationships.

iv. Aquatic ecosystems

There is an undoubted need to understand the soil/catchment area influences on acid precipitation in acidified areas in order to appreciate better:

a.   the potential for recovery of acidified/fishless lakes;

b.   the necessary degree to which pH must be raised to realise recovery of lakes, streams and rivers;

c.   the cost-effective scope for and practical approach to liming methods;

d.   the susceptibility of lakes/streams not yet acidified.

However, this work would not yield quick results, but since immediate drastic action to reduce SO_2 emissions is also economically unjustified in the context of the fisheries benefits likely to be realised, such research would seem well worth pursuing.

11.6.2   Control action

The following broad suggestions are made:

o   It is clear that a great deal more attention needs to be focused on future NO_x emissions from both vehicles and stationary sources in view of:

-   the fact that they are still increasing;

-   their role as ozone precursors and the increasing
    evidence of the importance of this pollutant in
    causing agricultural forest damage.

o   A reduction in permitted ambient urban SO_2 levels, or
    possibly of large SO_2 emitters in the vicinity of the
    urban area, would seem likely to yield direct economic
    benefits by reducing building damage. Control
    strategies will need to take account of the relative
    contribution of large high level emitters in relation to
    the many low level emitters.

o   Control strategies appropriate to large high level
    emitters of SO_2/NO_x should be set in the context of
    their contribution to local and national ambient levels
    of these pollutants in urban and agriculturally
    sensitive areas. Even so, account should be taken of
    the fact that controls on new industrial and power
    plants are considerably more cost-effective than retro-
    fitting such controls to existing plants.

REFERENCES

REFERENCES

SECTION 2: APPARENT EFFECTS

D. Drablos & A. Tollan, Ecological Impact of Acid Precipitation; Proceedings of an International Conference, Sandefjord, Norway 1980, SNSF, 1980.

IERE, Effects of SO_2 and its Derivatives on Health and Ecology; International Electric Research Exchange, Vols.1 and 2, 1981.

National Swedish Environmental Protection Board, Ecological Effects of Acid Deposition; Report and Background papers, Stockholm Conference on Acidification of the Environment, 1982.

L. Overrein et al, Acid Precipitation - Effects on Forest and Fish; Final Report of the SNSF Project 1972-1980, SNSF - Project FR 19/80, Norwegian Inst. Water Research, 1980.

Swedish Ministry of Agriculture, Acidification Today and Tomorrow - a Swedish study prepared for the 1982 Stockholm Conference on the Acidification of the Environment; Stockholm 1982.

UNECE, Draft Report on the Effects of Sulphur Compounds on Materials, including historic and cultural monuments; Working Group on Effects of Sulphur Compounds on the Environment, ENV/IEB/WG.1/R.3, 1982.

UNECE, Report on Effects of Sulphur Compounds on Aquatic Ecosystems; Working Group on Effects of Sulphur Compounds on the Environment, ENV/IEB/WG.1/R.4, 1982.

UNECE, Draft Report on Effects of Sulphur Compounds on Soil, Groundwater and Vegetation; Working Group on Effects of Sulphur Compounds on the Environment, ENV/IEB/WG.1/R.5, 1982.

SECTION 3: EMISSIONS AND PHYSICAL TRANSPORT

A. Apling, Air Pollution from Oxides of Nitrogen, Carbon and Hydrocarbons; Warren Spring Report, WSP LR 306, 1981.

R. Belasco, Weather, 3, 1948.

M. Benarie, The influence of the Emission Height on the Meso-scale and Long-range Transport of Reactive Pollutants, Science of the Total Environment, 23, 1982.

CEC, The Outlook for Coal Production and Use in the Community; CON(80)117, Commission of the European Communities, 1980.

CEC, Review of Member States' Energy Policy Programmes and Progress Towards 1990 Objectives; Con (82) 326 Final, Commission of the European Communities, 1982.

Concawe, SO_2 Emission Trends and Control Options in W Europe; Report 1/82.

EMEP, Summary Report of the Western Meteorological Synthesising Centre for the First Phase of EMEP; Norwegian Meteorological Institute, Oslo, 1981.

EMEP, Annex to the Fourth Routine Technical Report from the Western Meteorological Synthesising Centre; EMEP/MSC-W Report 1/81.

Environmental Resources Ltd., The Environmental Impact of Future Coal Production and Use in the EEC; Graham & Trotman for Commission of the European Communities, 1983.

B. Fisher, Acid Rain - the Long Range Transport of Air Pollutants; Weather, 36, 1981.

H.H. Lamb, Quarterly Journal of the Royal Meteorological Society, 76, 1950.

Ministry of Health and Environmental Protection, SO_2 Policy Framework Plan; Netherlands, 1979.

OECD, Measurements and Findings of the OECD Programme on Long Range Transport of Air Pollutants; OECD, Paris 1979.

OECD, The Costs and Benefits of Sulphur Dioxide Control; a Methodological Study, OECD, Paris, 1981.

J. Schjoldager et al, Photochemical Oxidants in North-Western Europe 1976-79, A Pilot Project; Norwegian Institute for Air Research, V, 1981

Swedish Ministry of Agriculture, Proceedings of the Conference on Acidification of the Environment, Stockholm, 1982.

UNECE, EMEP Programme, 1983.

D. Whelpdale, Atmospheric Pathways of Sulphur Compounds, MARC report 7, 1978.

B. Zoeteman & L. van Beckhoven, NO_x-abatement Policy in the Netherlands; NO_x Symposium, Maastricht, 1982.

S. Zwerver, An Air Quality Management System as a Tool for Establishing an NO_x Policy; NO_x Symposium, Maastricht, 1982.

SECTION 4:   CHEMICAL TRANSFORMATION AND DEPOSITION

M. Ashmore, J. Bell, C. Reilly & C. Dalpra, A Survey of Ozone Levels in the British Isles using Indicator Plants; Imperial College Centre for Environmental Technology, Series B, 4, 1978.

S. Beilke & G. Gravenhorst, Heterogeneous SO_2 Oxidation in the Droplet Phase; Atmospheric Environment, 12, 1978.

S. Beilke, Acid deposition - a Draft Paper; Proceedings of Conference on Acidification of the Environment, Stockholm, 1982.

149.

J.G. Calvert, F. Su, J. Bottenheim & O. Stransz, Mechanism of the Homogeneous Oxididation of Sulphur Dioxide; Atmospheric Environment, 12, 1978.

P. Cawse, Deposition of Trace Elements from the Atmosphere in the UK; in Inorganic Pollution and Agriculture, Ministry of Agriculture Reference Book 326, 1980.

R. Charlson & H. Rodhe, Factors Controlling the Acidity of Natural Rainwater, Nature, 295, 1982.

P. Chester, Perspectives on Acid Rain; delivered at the Royal Society, 1983.

A. Cocks & I. Fletcher, Possible Effect of Dispersion on the Gas Phase Chemistry of Power Plant Effluents; Atmospheric Environment, 16, 4, 1982

Concawe, Atmospheric Sulphates, Occurrence, Formation, Fate & Measurement – a Critical Review; Concawe Report 7/78.

R. Derwent et al, The Occurrence and Significance of Air Pollution by Photochemically Produced Ozone in the British Isles, 1972-1975; Warren Spring Laboratory, Report LR227, 1978.

R.G. Derwent, The Sources and Fates of Atmospheric Sulphur Compounds in the UK; AERE-R 10567, 1982.

A. Eggleton & R. Cox, Homogeneous Oxidation of Sulphur Compounds in the Atmosphere, Atmospheric Environment, 12, 1978.

E. Ellis & T. Novakov, Application of Thermal Analyis to the Characterisation of Organic Aerosol Particles; 15th International Colloquium, UNESO, Paris, 1982, pub. in Science of the Total Environment, 23, 1982.

B. Fisher, The Statistics of Precipitation Scavenging during Long Range Transport; in Air Pollution Modelling and its Application I, Plenum, 1981.

B. Fisher, Deposition of Sulphur and the Acidity of precipitation over Ireland; Atmospheric Environment, 16, 11, 1982.

D. Fowler, Wet and Dry Deposition of Sulphur and Nitrogen Compounds from the Atmosphere; Nato Conference on effects of acid precipitation on vegetation and soils, Toronto, 1978.

J. Garland, Dry and Wet Removal of Sulphur from the Atmosphere; Atmospheric Environment, 12, 1978.

G. Glover, A. Kallend, A. Manch & A. Webb, Ion Relationships in Acid Precipitation and Stream Chemistry; Nato Conference on effects of acid precipitation on vegetation and soils, Toronto, 1978.

L. Granat, Deposition of Sulphate and Acid with Precipitation over Northern Europe; Institute of Meteorology, Stockholm, 1972.

L. Granat, Sulphate in Precipitation as Observed by the European Atmospheric Chemistry Network; Atmospheric Environment, 12, 1977.

G. Gravenhorst, S. Beilke, M. Betz & W. Georgii, Sulfur Dioxide Absorbed in Rain Water; Nato Conference on Effects of Acid Precipitation on Vegetation and Soils, Toronto, 1978.

J. Hales, Wet Removal of Sulphur Compounds from the Atmosphere; Atmospheric Environment, 12, 1978.

D. Hansen & G. Hidy, Review of Questions regarding Rain Acidity Data; Atmospheric Environment, 16, No 9, 1982.

J. Hanssen, J. Rambaek, J. Semb & E. Steinnes, Atmospheric Deposition of Trace Elements in Norway; International Conference on Ecological Impact of Acid Precipitation, Sandefjord, 1980.

E. Joranger, J. Schaug & A. Semb, Deposition of Air Pollutants in Norway; International Conference on Ecological Impact of Acid Precipitation, Sardefjord, 1980.

A. Kallend, Chemical Transformation in the Atmosphere; Conference at the National Society for Clean Air, Brighton, 1981.

A. Kallend, Chemical Pathways from Stack Emissions to Surface Water; International Conference on Coal Fired Power Plant and the Aquatic Environment, Copenhagen, 1982.

A. Kallend et al, Acidity of Rain in Europe; Atmospheric Environment, 17, No 1, 1983.

Land Institute for Pollution Control N Rhine-Westphalia, Forest Damage in the Federal Republic of Germany, LOS Report 28, Essen, 1982.

A. Martin, A Survey of the Activity of Rainwater over Large Areas of GB; CEGB, SSD/MID/N30/78, 1978.

A. Martin & F. Barker, Some Observations of Acidity and Sulphur in Rainwater from Rural Sites in Central England and Wales; Atmospheric Environment, 12, 1978.

A. Mason, Sulphur and Nitrogen Contributions to the Acidity of Rain; Atmospheric Environment, 12, 1978.

Ministry of the Environment, La Pollution de l'Air en France en 1979.

J. Mooi, Responses of Some Poplar Species to Mixtures of SO_2, NO_2 and O_3; Proceedings of 12th International Meeting on Air Pollution Damage in Forests, Finland, 1982.

J. Mooi, The Influence of Ozone on the Growth of some Poplar Species; Research Institute for Plant Protection, Wageningen, 1982.

R. Mosello & G. Tartari, Effects of Acid Precipitation on Subalpine and Alpine Lakes; Water Quality Bulletin, 8, No 2, 1983.

G. Neumann-Hauf & G. Halbritter, Site and Season-specific Variations of the Atmospheric Pollutant Transport and Deposition on the Local and Regional Scale; 15th International Colloquium, UNESO, Paris, 1982, pub. in Science of the Total Environment, 23, 1982.

I. Nicholson & S. Paterson, Aspects of Acid Precipitation in Relation to Vegetation in UK; Water Quality Bulletin, 8, No 2, 1983.

Norwegian Institute for Air Research, Photochemical Oxidants in North Western Europe 1976-79, A Pilot Project; April 1981.

S. Oden, The Acidity Problem - An Outline of Concepts; Water, Air and Soil Pollution, 6, 1976.

S. Penkett, Chemical Changes in the Air; International Symposium on Sulphur Emissions and the Environment, London, 1979.

C. Seigneur, P. Saxena & A. Belle Mudischewkyj, Formation and Evolution of Sulphate and Nitrate Aerosols in Plumes; 15th International Colloquium, UNESCO, Paris, 1982, pub. in Science of the Total Environment, 23, 1982.

P.W. Summers, A Global Perspective on Acid Deposition, its Sources and Atmospheric Transport; Water Quality Bulletin, 8, No 2, 1983.

Swedish Ministry of Agriculture, Acidification Today and Tomorrow - a Swedish study prepared for the 1982 Stockholm Conference on the acidification of the environment; Stockholm, 1982.

Swedish Ministry of Agriculture, Proceedings of the Conference on Acidification of the Environment, Stockholm, 1982.

UK Review Group on Acid Rain, Acidity of rainfall in UK - a Preliminary Report; Warren Spring Laboratory, 1982.

UNECE, Effects of Sulphur Compounds on Aquatic Ecosystems - Draft Report; UNECE report ENV/IEB/WG.1/R.4, 1982.

UNECE, Report on Effects of Sulphur Compounds in Aquatic Ecosystems; Working Group on Effects of Sulphur Compounds on the Environment, ENV/IEB/WG.1/R.4, 1982.

J. Warburton, The Chemistry of Precipitation in Relation to Precipitation Type; 15th International Colloquium, UNESCO, Paris, 1982, pub. in Science of the Total Environment, 23, 1982.

Warren Spring Laboratory, Acidity of Rainfall in the UK, 1982.

Warren Spring Laboratory, Report LR397, 1982.

Warren Spring Laboratory, Report LR400 1982

Warren Spring Laboratory, Report LR401 1982.

Welsh Water Authority, Private Communication.

D. Whelpdale, Atmospheric Pathways of Sulphur Compounds; Marc Report, 7, 1978.

S. Zwerver, An Air Quality Management System as a Tool for establishing a NO_x Policy; NO_x Symposium, Maastricht, 1982.

SECTION 5: BIOLOGICAL AND BIOCHEMICAL MECHANISMS OF CAUSING CHANGE AND POSSIBLE DAMAGE TO TERRESTRIAL ECOSYSTEMS

M. Ashmore, N. Bell et al, A Survey of Ozone Levels in the British Isles using Indicator Plants; Imperial College Centre for Environmental Technology, Series B, No 4, 1978.

P. Brimblecombe & D. Stedman, Historical Evidence for a Dramatic Increase in the Nitrate Component of Acid Rain; Nature, 298, No 5873, 1982.

K. Brown, Sulphur in the Environment; Environmental Pollution, 3, 1982.

D. Bruce, A Review of the Environmental Implications of Nitrogen Oxides; Central Electricity Research Laboratories, 1979.

P. Cawse, Deposition of Trace Elements from the Atmosphere in the UK; Inorganic Pollution and Agriculture, Ministry of Agriculture, Fisheries and Food, HMSO, London, 1980.

P. Chester, A. Clarke et al, The Effect on the Environment of producing Electricity from Coal; 11th World Energy Conference, Technical Papers, Division 3, Energy and Environment, Munich 1980.

D. Fowler et al, Rainfall Acidity in Northern Britain; Nature, 297, 1982.

T. Hutchinson & M. Havas, The Effects of Acid Precipiation on Terrestrial Ecosystems; Proceedings of Nato Conference, Toronto, 1976, Plenum. 1980.

IERE, Effect of SO_2 on Ecology; International Electric Research Exchange, Vol.2, 1981.

F. Last & I. Nicholson, Acid Rain; Biologist, 29(5), 1982.

F. Last, Effects of Atmospheric Sulphur Compounds on Natural and Man-made Terrestrial and Aquatic Ecosystems; Agriculture and Environment, 7, 1982.

W. McFee et al, Acid Precipitation Effects on Soil pH and Base Saturation of Exchange Sites; Water, Air and Soil Pollution, 7, 1977.

N. Malmer, Acid Precipitation: chemical changes in the soil; Ambio, 5, 1976.

N. Malmer, On the Effects on Water, Soil and Vegetation of an increasing Atmospheric Supply of Sulphur; National Swedish Environmental Protection Board, 1974.

A. Marsh, Sulphur and Nitrogen Contributions to the Acidity of Rain; Atmospheric Environment, 12, No 1-3, 1978.

H.G. Miller & P. Nilsson, Forest Growth as a Possible Cause of Soil and Water Acidification: An examination of the concepts; <u>Oikos</u> Dnr 2057-6480.

National Swedish Environmental Protection Board, Ecological Effects of Acid Deposition; Report and background papers, Stockholm Conference on the Acidification of the Environment, 1982.

L. Overrein et al, Acid Precipitation - Effects on Forest and Fish; Final Report of the SNSF project 1972-1980, SNSF project FR 19/80, Norwegian Institute Water Research, 1980.

The Society of Chemical Industry, Sulphur Emissions and the Environment; International Symposium, London, 1979.

Swedish Ministry of Agriculture, Acidification Today and Tomorrow - a Swedish study prepared for the 1982 Stockholm Confrence on the Acidification of the Environment; Stockholm, 1982.

UNECE, Draft Report on Effects of Sulphur Compounds on Soil, Groundwater and Vegetation; Working Group on Effects of Sulphur Compounds in the Environment, ENV/IEB/WG.1/R.5, 1982.

B. Ulrich, R. Mayer & P. Khanne, Chemical Changes due to Acid Precipitation in a Loess-derived Soil in Central Europe; <u>Soil Science</u>, 130, 1980.

N. van Breemen et al, Soil Acidification from Atmospheric Ammonium Sulphate in Forest Canopy Throughfall; <u>Nature</u>, 299, 1982.

SECTION 6: DAMAGE TO TREES

U. Arndt et al, The Contribution of Ozone to the Silver Fir Disease Complex - a Hypothesis worth examining; <u>Luft</u>, 42, No 6, 1982.

B. Boullard & G. Loocher, Les Consequences de la Pollution Atmospheric sur le Nassif Forestier de Rommare; <u>R.F.F. XXXVI-5-1974.</u>

R. Harriman & B. Morrison, Forestry, Fisheries and Acid Rain in Scotland; <u>Scottish Forestry</u>, 35, 1981.

T. Hutchinson & M. Havas, The Effects of Acid Precipitation on Terrestrial Ecosystems; Proceedings of Nato Conference, Toronto 1976, Plenum, 1980.

IERE, Effects of SO_2 on Ecology; International Electric Research Exchange, 2, 1981.

F. Last, Effects of Atmospheric Sulphur Compounds on Natural and Man-made Terrestrial and Aquatic Ecosystems; <u>Agriculture and Environment</u>, 7, 1982.

F. Last, P. Mason, J. Wilson & J. Deacon, Fine Roots and Sheathing Mycorrhizzas: their Forestation, Function and Dynamics; <u>Plant and Soil</u>, 1983, in press.

H. Miller, Forest Fertilization: Some Guiding Concepts; <u>Forestry</u>, 54, No 2, 1981.

H. Miller, Studies of Proton Flux in Forests and Heaths in Scotland; in Effects of Accumulation of Air Pollutants in Forest Ecosystems, ed. Ulrich & Pankrath, Reidel, Holland, 1983.

J. Mooi, Influence of Ozone and Sulphur Dioxide on Defoliation and Growth of Poplars; Research Institute for Plant Protection, Wageningen, 1981.

J. Mooi, Responses of Some Poplar Species to Mixtures of SO_2, NO_2 and O_3; Proceedings of 12th International meeting for specialists in Air Pollution Damage in Forests, IUFRO, Finland 1982.

J. Mooi, The Influence of Ozone on the Growth of Some Poplar Species; Research Institute for Plant Protection, Wageningen, 1982.

National Swedish Environmental Protection Board, Ecological Effects of Acid Deposition; report and background papers, Stockholm Conference on Acidification of the Environment, 1982.

I. Nicholson, S. Paterson & F. Last, Methods for Studying Acid Precipitation in Forest Ecosystems; Proceedings of a Workshop, ITE, Edinburgh, 1977.

B. Nihlgard, Plant Biomass, Primary Production and Distribution of Elements of a Beech and Planted Spruce Forest ecosystem in S Sweden; Oikos, 23, 1972.

L. Overrein et al, Acid Precipitation - Effects on Forest and Fish; Final Report of the SNSF-project 1972-80, SNSF-Project FR 19/80, Norwegian Institute for Water Research, 1980.

B. Prinz, G. Krause & H. Stratnann, Forest Damage in the Federal Republic of Germany; Land Institute for Pollution Control of the Land North-Rhine Westphalia, LIS Report 28, 1982.

Saurer Regen und Forstschaden, Eine Dokumentation, Teill; Gesamtverband des Deutschen Steinkohlenbergbaus, Essen 1982.

Swedish Ministry of Agriculture, Acidification Today and Tomorrow - a Swedish study prepared for the Stockholm Conference on the Acidification of the Environment, Stockholm, 1982.

B. Ulrich, R. Mayer & P. Khanne, Deposition von Luftverunreinigungen und Ihre Auswirkungen auf die Waldökosysteme im Solling; 1979.

B. Ulrich, Die Walder in Mitteleuropa; Messergebuisses ihrer Unweltbelastung, Theorie ihrer Gefahrdung, Prognose ihrer Eutwicklung; 1980.

B. Ulrich, Bodenchemische und Umwelt - Aspekte der Stabilität von Waldökosystemen, 1981.

UNECE, Draft Report on Effects of Sulphur Compounds on Soil, Groundwater and Vegetation; Working Group on Effects of Sulphur Compounds on the Environment, ENV/IEB/WG.1/R.5, 1982.

SECTION 7:   DAMAGE TO CROPS AND OTHER PLANTS

M. Ashmore, N. Bell et al, The Distribution and Effects on Plants of Ozone in SE England: A Report of Field Studies during Summer 1980; Imperial College Centre for Environmental Technology Series B, No 1, 1982.

C. Baker, M. Unsworth & P. Greenwood, Leaf Injury on Wheat Plants exposed in the Field in Winter to SO_2; Nature, 299, 1982.

D. Bruce, A Review of the Environmental Implications of Nitrogen Oxides; Central Electricity Research Laboratories, 1979.

A. Buckenham et al, Effects of Aerial Pollutants on the Growth and Yield of Spring Barley; Annals of Applied Biology, 100, 1982.

D. Fowler & J. Cape, Air Pollutants in Agriculture and Horticulture; Institute of Terrestrial Ecology, Penicuik.

W. Heck et al, Assessment of Crop Loss from Ozone; APCA Journal, 32, No 4, 1982.

T. Hutchingson & M. Havas, The Effect of Acid Precipitation in Terrestrial Ecosystems; Proceedings of Nato Conference, Toronto 1976, Plenum, 1980.

IERE, Effects of SO_2 on Ecology; International Electric Research Exchange, Vol.2, 1981.

F. Last, Effects of Atmospheric Sulphur Compounds on Natural and Man-made Terrestrial and Aquatic Ecosystems; Agriculture and Environment, 7, 1982.

T. Mansfield & P. Freer-Smith, Effects of Urban Air Pollution on Plant Growth; Biological Reviews, 56, 1981.

T. Mansfield et al, Effects of Nitrogen Oxides on Plants: two Case Studies; in Air Pollution by Nitrogen Oxides, ed. T. Schreider & L. Grant, Elsevier, 1982.

National Swedish Environmental Protection Board, Ecological Effects of Acid Deposition; report and background papers, Stockholm Conference on Acidification of the Environment, 1982.

Office of Technology Assessment, Interim Draft Report on The Regional Implications of Transported Air Pollutants: an Assessment of Acidic Deposition and Ozone; Washington, 1982.

A. Posthumus, Study on the Up-dating of Scientific Data on SO_2 Effects on Flora and Fauna and the Suggestion of an Approach Allowing for their Protection within the EEC; Commission of the European Communities, 1980.

B. Prinz & C. Brandt, Study on the Impact of the Principal Atmospheric Pollutants on Vegetation; Commission of the European Communities, Report EUR 6644, 1980.

F. Spielings, Influence of Fumigations with NO_2 on Growth and Yield of Tomato Plants; Netherlands Journal of Plant Pathology, 77, 1971.

Swedish Ministry of Agriculture, Acidification Today and Tomorrow - a Swedish Study prepared for the 1982 Stockholm Conference on the Acidification of the Environment, Stockholm, 1982.

UNECE, Draft Report on Effects of Sulphur Compounds on Soil, Groundwater and Vegetation; Working Group on Effects of Sulphur Compounds on the Environment, ENV/IEB/WG.1/R.5, 1982.

M. Unsworth & D. Ormond, Effects of Gaseous Air Pollution in Agriculture and Horticulture; Butterworth, 1982.

M. Whitmore & P. Freer-Smith, Growth Effects of SO_2 and/or NO_2 on Woody Plants and Grasses during Spring and Summer; Nature, 300, No 5887, 1982.

SECTION 8: EFFECTS ON AQUATIC ECOSYSTEMS AND FISH

R. Battarbee & R. Flower, Acidification of Galloway Lakes: Evidence from Diatoms; University College London, 1982.

D. Brown & K. Sadler, The Chemistry and Fishery Status of Acid lakes in Norway and their Relationship to European Sulphur Emissions; Journal of Applied Ecology, 18, 1981.

T. Carrick, Effect of Acid Water on the Hatching of Salmonid Eggs; Journal of Fish Biology, 14, 1979.

P. Chester, Acid Rain, Catchment Characteristics and Fishery Status; Central Electricity Research Laboratories, 1982.

P. Chester, Perspectives on Acid Rain; delivered at the Royal Society, 1983.

R. Clymo, Control of Cation Concentrations and in particular of pH, in Sphagnum dominated communities; Proceedings of IBP Symposium, Amsterdam, 1966.

W. Dickson, Some Effects of the Acidification of Swedish Lakes; Verh. Int.Verein Limnol. 20, 1978.

W. Dickson, Water Acidification - Effects and Counter Measures; National Swedish Environment Protection Board, 1982.

D. Drablos & A. Tollan, Ecological Impact of Acid Precipitation, Proceedings of an International Conference, Sandefjord, Norway 1980, SNSF Project, 1980.

A. Hagen & A. Langeland, Polluted Snow in Southern Norway and the Effect of the Meltwater on Freshwater and Aquatic Organisms; Environmental Pollution, 5, 1973.

R. Harriman & B. Morrison, Forestry, Fisheries and Acid Rain in Scotland; Freshwater Fisheries Laboratory, Pitlochry, 1981.

R. Harriman & B. Morrison, Ecology of Streams draining Forested and Non-forested Catchments in an area of Central Scotland subject to Acid Precipitation; Hydrobiologia, 88, 1982.

A. Henriksen, Acidification of Freshwater - a Large Scale Titration, in Ecological Impact of Acid Precipitation, eds. D. Drabløs & A. Tollan, pp. 68-74, SNSF-Project, 1980.

A. Henriksen & L. Kirkhusmo, Acidification of Groundwater in Norway; Nordic Hydrology, 13, 1982.

A. Henriksen, Changes in Base Cation Concentrations due to Freshwater Acidification; Norwegian Institute for Water Research, Report 1/1982.

A. Henriksen, Susceptibility of Surface Waters to Acidification; Proceedings of Acid Rain/Fisheries Symposium, American Fisheries Society, Bethesda, in press.

IERE, Effects of SO_2 on Ecology; International Electric Research Exchange, 2, 1981.

F. Last, Effects of Atmospheric Sulphur Compounds on Natural and Man-made Terrestrial and Aquatic Ecosystems; Agriculture and Environment, 7, 1982.

P. McWilliams, A Comparison of Physiological Characteristics in Normal and Acid exposed Populations of the Brown Trout Salmo Trutta; Comparative Biochemistry and Physiology, 72A, No 3, 1982.

P. McWilliams, The Effects of Calcium on Sodium Fluxes in the Brown Trout, Salmo Trutta, in Neutral and Acid Water; Journal of Experimental Biology, 96, 1982.

I. Muniz, H. Seip & I. Sevaldrud, Acidification of Lakes and Loss of Fish Populations: Relationship between Fish Status and pH for Lakes in Southernmost Norway; Directorate for Wildlife and Feshwater Fish, Norway, 1982.

National Swedish Environmental Protection Board, Ecological Effects of Acid Deposition; report and background papers, Stockholm Conference on Acidification of the Environment, 1982.

J. Nilssen, Acidification of a small Watershed in Southern Norway and some Characteristics of Acidic Aquatic Environments; Int.Revueges Hydrobiol. 65, 2, 1980.

S. Nilsson, H. Miller & J. Miller, Forest Growth as a possible cause of Soil's Water Acidification: an Examination of the Concepts; Oikos, 39, 1982.

North West Water Authority, Juvenile Salmonid Population and Biological Quality of Upland Streams in Cumbria with particular reference to Low pH Effects; BN 77-2-83.

L. Overrein et al, Acid Precipitation - Effects on Forests and Fish; Final Report of the SNSF-Project 1972-1980, SNSF project FR19/80, Norwegian Institute Water Research, 1980.

I. Renberg & T. Hedberg, Ambio, 1, 1982.

Report from the International Conference on the Effects of Acid Precipitation, Norway 1976, Ambio, 5, No 5-6, 1976.

H. Seip & S. Rustad, Variations in Surface Water pH with Changes in Sulphur Deposition, Central Institute for Industrial Research, Norway, 1982.

I. Sevaldrud & I. Muniz, Acid Lakes and Inland Fisheries in Norway. Reports of Interview Surveys 1974-1979; SNSF Project IR 77/880, Norwegian Institute for Water Research, Oslo, 1980.

Statens Naturvardsverk, Forsurning av Mark och vatten; Monitor 1981, Solna, Sweden.

Swedish Ministry of Agriculture, Acidification Today and Tomorrow - a Swedish study prepared for the 1982 Stockholm Conference on the Acidification of the Environment, Stockholm 1982.

UK Review Group on Acid Rain, Acidity of Rainfall in UK - a Preliminary Report; Warren Spring Laboratory, 1982.

UNECE, Draft Report on Effects of Sulphur Compounds on Soil, Groundwater and Vegetation; Working Group on Effects of Sulphur Compounds on the Environment, ENV/IEB/WG.1/R.5, 1982.

UNECE, Report on Effects of Sulphur Compounds on Aquatic Ecosystems; Working Group on Effects of Sulphur Compounds on the Environment, ENV/IEB/WG.1/R.4, 1982.

Welsh Water Authority, The Effects of Acid Precipitation and Land Use on Water Quality and Ecology in the Upper Tywi Catchment in West Wales, 1983.

R. Wright et al, Regional Surveys of small Norwegian Lakes October 1974, March 1975, March 1976 and March 1977; SNSF Project, IR 33/77, Oslo, 1977.

R. Wright, Acidification of Freshwater in Europe; Norwegian Institute for Water Research, 1983.

SECTION 9: DAMAGE TO BUILDINGS

J. Arntzen, Economic Evaluation of Damage to Materials due to Air Pollution; Report EVR 6641, EN, Commission of the European Communities, 1980.

B. Fassina, A Survey on Air Pollution and Deterioration of Stone Work in Venice; Atmospheric Environment, 12, No 11, 1978.

S. Luckat, Staub-Reinhaltung des Luft, 41, 440, 1981.

S. Luckat, Umweltsforschungsplan des Bundesministerium des Innern; Report 10608003/02, Zollern Institut beim Deutschen Bergbau-Museum, Dortmund, 1981.

OECD, The Costs and Benefits of Sulphur Oxide Control - A Methodological Study; Paris, 1981.

Pollutant Effects on Stone Monuments, Environmental Science and Technology, April 1981.

G. Schikorr, <u>Werkstoff und Korrosion</u>, 15, 1964.

Swedish Ministry of Agriculture, Acidification Today and Tomorrow - a Swedish study prepared for the 1982 Stockholm Conference on the Acidification of the Environment, Stockholm 1982.

J. Upham, <u>Journal of Air Pollution Control Association</u>, 15, 1965.

UNECE, Draft Report on Effects of Sulphur Compounds in Materials including Historic and Cultural Monomuments; Working Group on Effects of Sulphur Compounds on the Environment, ENV/IEB/WG.1/R.3, 1982.

SECTION 10: THE IMPACT OF HEALTH

IERE, Effect of SO_2 and its Derivatives on Health; International Electric Research Exchange, Vol.1, 1981.

Swedish Ministry of Agriculture, Acidification Today and Tomorrow - a Swedish study prepared for the 1982 Stockholm Conference on the Acidification of the Environment, Stockholm, 1982.

UNECE, Draft Report on Effects of Sulphur Compounds on Soil, Groundwater and Vegetation; Working Group on Effects of Sulphur Compounds on the Environment, ENV/IEB/WG.1/R.5, 1982.

SECTION 11: COSTS AND BENEFITS OF ACID EMISSIONS CONTROL STRATEGIES

Concawe, SO_2 Emission Trends and Control Options in W Europe, Report 1/82.

N. Heck et al, Assessment of Crop Loss from Ozone; <u>APCA Journal</u>, 32, No 4, 1982.

National Swedish Environmental Protection Board, Strategies and Methods to Control Emissions of Sulphur and Nitrogen Oxides; report & background papers, Stockholm Conference on Acidification of the Environment, 1982.

SO_2 Policy Framework Plan; Ministry of Health and Environmental Protection, Netherlands, 1979.

UNECE, Report on Cost-Benefit Analysis of Alternative Progammes for Sulphur Emission Control in the ECE Region, presented at the meeting on Cost-Benefit Analysis of SO_x Control, Geneva, 1982.

UNECE, Third Seminar on Desulphurisation of Fuels and Combustion Gases, Salzburg, 1981.

US/Canada Work Group 3B on Emissions, Costs and Engineering Assessment; Final Report, 1982.